Digital Logic and Computer Operations

Digital Logic and Computer Operations

Robert C. Baron

Albert T. Piccirilli

**MEMBERS OF THE TECHNICAL STAFF
HONEYWELL, INC., COMPUTER CONTROL DIVISION**

**M c G R A W - H I L L
B O O K   C O M P A N Y**

New York   San Francisco   Toronto   London   Sydney

Preface

Few aspects of modern life are not being influenced by the digital computer. At the end of 1966, more than 35,000 computers were installed and operating in the United States. It is estimated that by 1970, as many as 85,000 computers will be operational.

The computer, an information-processing device, has found wide application in industry, government, schools, hospitals, and many other fields. Computers are being used to calculate payrolls, tax deductions, and inventory levels. Computers are predicting rocket trajectories, election returns, and future product sales. Computers are controlling machines, railroad cars, and manufacturing processes. The list of applications of the computer could extend through most of this book.

The computer consists of hardware, i.e., the logic and circuits used in making the computer, and software, i.e., the series of instructions and translating means used to command the computer. The usefulness of the computer is dependent on the capabilities designed into the computer and on the ability of the user to understand and take advantage of these capabilities in meeting his specific requirements. Thus, it is of great value to understand the basic operation of the computer.

This book is intended as an introductory text in the computer field and should serve as a basis for further study of a specific computer, computer programming, and computer systems or of the application of computers to specific problems. Although the design of computer equipment and the programming languages are in a constant state of flux, the underlying principles of the computer, which have evolved over a period of many years, are basically similar for all computers. This book describes these fundamental design concepts.

The natural inclination in writing such a book is to describe a specific computer and illustrate all concepts in terms of this computer. We have refrained from doing this since we felt that such an approach tends to make the reader believe that one particular way of organizing a computer is the only way or the best one. Thus we have tried to be as universal as possible in most of our descriptions in order to show what is being accomplished and why it is necessary. We have, in some cases, oversimplified a series of decisions in order to illustrate the underlying principles. We hope the more sophisticated readers will overlook this.

This book is not specific to any one computer. However, we have introduced in several places particular demonstrations to show the various ways logic concepts can be implemented. We have also included, at the end of each chapter, a number of exercises which should further increase the reader's knowledge of the specific subject matter.

The book is organized into 12 chapters, with three additional sections forming an Appendix and with a Bibliography. The first chapters of the book are concerned with the basic concepts and building blocks used in the computer, while the last chapters discuss the organization of these building blocks into the various elements of the computer.

Chapter 1 is a general introduction to the subject of digital computers. Chapter 2 describes the decimal, octal, and binary number systems. Chapter 3 provides a description of computer logic and the various methods of handling logic expressions. The successful development of modern electronic computers is highly dependent on the extensive application of the binary number system, Boolean algebra, and symbolic logic.

In Chap. 4, the flip-flop is introduced and then logically interconnected to form counters and registers. Chapter 5 provides a description of the various codes, other than binary, which are used in digital systems. Chapter 8 discusses word organization and defines the considerations involved in the selection of word length and format, i.e., the special codes used within the computer.

The various elements of the computer are described in the later chapters, using the building blocks defined in the early chapters. Chapter 6 shows how the computer can be designed to perform simple arithmetic. In Chap. 7, the computer memory is described. In Chap. 9, the basic timing and control logic·is shown, and Chap. 10 describes how data are entered into and received from the computer through a wide variety of peripheral equipment.

Chapter 11 is intended to tie the entire book together by showing how a specific computer can be organized for either batch-processing or time-sharing applications. It is hoped that, at this time, the reader will be able to review any specific computer and relate its logic, word format, and specific characteristics and organization to the elements described in this book.

Although the book is not intended as a programming text, we felt that it was necessary to introduce the fundamentals of how the computer is used. Chapter 12 is intended to serve as a bridge between this book and any introductory book on programming.

Three sections are included at the end of the book. The first defines the symbols used throughout the text. The second section is a glossary which defines the most commonly used computer terms. The third section gives examples of electronic circuits that can be used to implement the logic shown in the text, including some of the most widely used integrated circuits.

This book arose out of a series of courses taught by the authors to fellow engineers, scientists, and other technical personnel, to high school mathematics and science teachers, and to high school students from the greater Boston area. Recognizing the diverse educational backgrounds and experiences of such a wide variety of students, we attempted to present the material in a form suitable for introductory courses in industry, as well as in the college and secondary school level. A major objective has been to minimize the need for any background in electronics or advanced mathematics.

Many people have assisted us in our work. We are grateful to our friends and colleagues at Honeywell, Computer Control Division, for their support. This book is an expanded and revised version of our earlier work, "Concepts of Digital Logic and Computer Operation," copyrighted 1964 by Computer Control Division. Special acknowledgment is therefore owed to Donald L. Wallace and Richard L. Ward, who helped in the preparation of the original text. Jesse Richardson, of the Massachusetts Department of Education, supported us in the original teaching assignments. To both Bill O'Neill of Honeywell and Bill Neal of MIT, we are grateful for assistance in the chapter on programming. Finally, special appreciation to our wives, Faye and Lorraine, who managed to find time to prepare the illustrations, type the manuscript and encourage us in this work.

Robert C. Baron
Albert T. Piccirilli

Contents

Digital Logic and Computer Operations

ONE

Introduction to Digital Computers

1-1 *History and Development*

One of the outstanding aspects of the technological revolution has been the development and continued improvement of computing machines. Computers allow one man to do what previously required the time and effort of dozens. They have enabled both technical men and businessmen to devote less time to monotonous, time-consuming, repetitive tasks and more time to new problems and new challenges. Furthermore, computers permit men to attack problems and perform calculations which previously, because of their complexity, were impossible to solve.

The foundations of computer technology were laid when the first man learned to count on his fingers the number of saber-toothed tigers he had killed or to use scratch marks on the ground to tally up the number of times the sun rose between full moons. These attempts marked man's first experience with the concept of quantities. Although early man could not calculate with quantities, he was able to evaluate or count them.

From this primitive beginning, man has become continuously more sophisticated in using techniques of counting and calculating. By 2000 B.C., the Chinese were using a computing machine. This mechanical device—still in use—is the familiar abacus. The abacus represents one of the first attempts at mechanized calculation and reflects an early refinement in man's approach to the concepts of counting and arithmetic.

Western civilization, on the other hand, struggled along with relatively crude methods of calculation until about the thirteenth or fourteenth centuries. The Roman system of calculation, which had been in use in the Western world, was so complex that only the scholar could understand it, and even he was able to perform only the simplest calculations. However, during the Crusades the Arabic system was brought into Europe. As the Renaissance began, this powerful calculating system was available to aid the European merchants and scholars.

In the seventeenth century, two great European thinkers, Pascal and Leibnitz, enlarged upon some of the basic concepts of mathematics and were able to develop more advanced calculating machines. Pascal, with an improved understanding of the carrying and borrowing operations in arithmetic, invented a semiautomatic adding machine that included ratchet wheels capable of transmitting a carry from wheel to wheel after each full rotation.   Later, Leibnitz incorporated the concept of a shifting multiplier into Pascal's design.   Where Pascal's machine had multiplied by repeated addition, Leibnitz' machine could multiply directly.

Another 200 years passed before Babbage—early in the nineteenth century—conceived a fully automatic calculating machine.   Babbage's machine (or *analytical engine,* as he called it) was similar to Leibnitz' as far as calculation was concerned.   However, the need for an operator to select the operations to be performed and the times to perform them was eliminated.   Babbage's design provided for punched cards to feed both raw data and instructions to the machine. and was, in fact, strikingly similar to modern computers.   The machine was too complex, however, for mechanics of that day to build parts with enough precision to perform the required operations, and Babbage's truly brilliant scheme never got off the drawing board.   Several of Babbage's component systems were constructed, but despite the financial backing of the British government, a complete working model of the machine was never finished.

While Babbage's idea waited for the more precise metalworking techniques that could make it a reality, a fellow Englishman applied his mind to the basic concepts of mathematical calculation.   In the middle of the nineteenth century, George Boole reasoned that arithmetic and, in fact, all mathematical calculations were not really ends unto themselves but were special cases of a wider logical scheme.   Boole was able to develop an entire formal algebra that stated the rules for this logical scheme. He then showed that arithmetic and other algebras could be derived from this logic algebra.   Boole's insight was later to provide a powerful tool to designers of computing machinery.

Babbage and Boole were only two contributors from a vast army of scientific investigators of this period.   At the time Babbage was working on his "analytical engine," Michael Faraday was constructing the first electric motor and the first generator.   After the invention of the motor, much scientific attention was focused on electricity.   In the latter part of the nineteenth century, James Maxwell produced his celebrated field equations, which brought problems of electrical circuits completely within the scope of rigid mathematical analysis.   Such knowledge enabled curious inventors to seek out new uses for electricity.   To mention only a few, Marconi, Edison, Morse, Bell, and De Forest all made familiar contributions toward applying electricity to man's needs.   Lee De Forest's contribution, which occurred after the turn of the century, bears special mention because it relates strongly to computer technology.   This was the invention of the audion tube, the forbear of all vacuum tubes, and it marked the birth of electronics.

At the same time, technology in other fields made great strides.   Whole new areas of physics, chemistry, and mathematics opened up.   Problems and calculations became increasingly complex and time-consuming. Although adding machines and desk calculators had been developed and consistently improved, both science and business began to dream of an automatic machine that could go beyond the desk calculator and handle larger, more complex problems.

At the end of World War II, under the pressure of an urgent need to solve gigantic scientific problems, some of the best mathematical minds in the nation combined their efforts to construct machines that could solve problems logically.   Their machines incorporated the insight of George Boole with Babbage's earlier design.   Furthermore, they made full use of the recent advances in technology.   Two such machines constructed were Harvard's Mark I and the University of Pennsylvania's Eniac.   These machines were the forbears of modern computers.

Early computers used a large number of vacuum tubes in their construction; the Eniac alone contained 18,000 tubes.   Since the average life of a vacuum tube is rather limited, this placed a practical limit on the size of a computer from a maintenance point of view.   Therefore, vacuum-tube machines more elaborate than the Eniac were difficult to keep operational.

Then, in 1948, John Bardeen and Walter Brattain, working in the Bell Laboratories, discovered the principle of the transistor.   The markedly increased reliability and theoretically unlimited life of the transistor paved the way for increasingly larger and more complex computers.

Although the principles of computer operation have, by and large, remained unchanged since the time of the Eniac and the Mark I, striking improvements have been made in computer reliability, speed, and capacity.   Future advances in electronics and in technology in general will result in continued improvements and more extensive computers.   Furthermore, as these machines become available, wider and wider applications for computers will be found.

1-2 Digital and Analog Computers

Modern computers fall into two broad categories: analog and digital. An analog computer processes analog signals, and a digital computer, digital signals.

An analog signal is continuous.   It can take on any one of an infinite number of possible values.   Temperature, being a continuously variable quantity, provides a good example of an analog value.   A thermometer reading of $+85°F$ is really only an approximation of the temperature. If sufficiently precise measurement were possible, the temperature might turn out to be $+85.136284°F$.   There are an infinite number of possible temperatures between $+85$ and $+86°F$, the only limitation being the accuracy with which they can be measured.

In contrast to the analog signal, a digital signal has a discrete, discontinuous, numerical value.   The amount of money in a coin purse is an example of a digital quantity.   It can be expressed exactly by a number. If the cent is the smallest available coin, there are only 99 possible values between \$3 and \$4.   Counting could reveal that there is exactly \$3.27 in the purse.

An analog computer is interested in the value of a signal.   It wants to know how large or how small the signal is.   A digital computer, on the other hand, is interested only in the presence or absence of a signal.   The digital computer cares nothing about how much something has changed. It wants to know only whether or not there has been a change.   A digital computer notices only whether something is there or not there; whether something is true or false; whether or not there is a hole in a punched card. In other words, an analog system, transmitting physical quantity regardless of its value, is a continuous system; a digital system, transmitting only discrete or *step* changes in a physical system, is discontinuous.

As an example of a digital system, consider an ordinary hand counter. The counting lever must be pushed all the way down to register a count. If the lever is not pushed all the way down, no count will register.   Either the counter registers a count or it does not; there is no middle ground. An analog counter does not work this way.   It counts continuously as the lever is depressed.   If the lever is pushed halfway down, the register shows a value of $\frac{1}{2}$; if the lever is pushed nine-tenths of the way down, the register shows a value of $\frac{9}{10}$, and so forth.

Both analog and digital computers have advantages in different applications.   Analog computers are used when problems require fast, limited-accuracy solutions; when problems involve analog inputs and outputs; or when large numbers of repetitive calculations are required with slight variations of parameters.   A digital computer is used when the data are in digital form; when high-accuracy, memory, decision-making, and control capabilities are required; or when a large general-purpose machine is needed.   Business problems, for example, are almost always handled on digital equipment.

Since most computers are digital or predominantly digital, the remainder of this book is concerned only with digital computers.

1-3 *Digital-computer Applications*

Digital-computing machinery, operating on logical principles, can perform many useful tasks for science and industry.   First and most obvious, digital computers can do long series of mathematical calculations at extremely high speeds, e.g., making up payrolls for 10,000 employees or solving a number of intricate scientific equations.   Digital computers are frequently used to store vast quantities of data and retrieve specific portions on demand, e.g., systems for filing and maintaining customer accounts or for recording data from space probes for future analysis. Computers are also used to control machinery, so that portions of a factory can operate with a minimum of human attendance.   On receiving information from the operating machinery, a digital computer can logically interpret the information and prepare further instructions.   Tape-controlled machine tools, such as automobile-engine-block machines, have found wide application since the mid-1950s.

Perhaps a less familiar use of computers is in simulating real-life situations under controlled conditions.   To do this, computers are fed information describing how things have behaved in the past or how they should behave theoretically.   Then one or two conditions are changed and set at new values.   The computer can determine what the effect of this change will be on the other variables.   For example, a manufacturer may wish to change his inventory policy to cut costs but is apprehensive about running out of stock and losing sales.   Customer buying patterns or behavior can be fed into a computer in conjunction with information on the new inventory policy.   The computer will apply the known buying patterns to the new policy and tell the manufacturer whether he will run out of stock.   The manufacturer is simulating the real world on his computer.

Computers can also synthesize or analyze mathematical relationships. In other words, on receiving huge tables of numbers, they can determine whether or not functional relationships exist among the numbers; conversely, they can digest mathematical relationships and prepare mathematical tables.   One of the more promising applications is in medicine, where techniques are rapidly developing for using a wide range of digital- and analog-computer equipment for both storing and correlating vast amounts of information for ready reference.   These are a few major uses of computers; there are many others.   Work is being done at present on the use of the computer in the diagnosis of disease, in the translation of languages, and in the composition of music.   All income taxes will be processed by computers within a few years.   Air traffic into all large airports will soon be monitored by computers.   Guidance and control of both aircraft and spacecraft depend on computers, and new programs are constantly being worked out in these areas.

With all these accomplishments and such potentials, however, computers can only do what they are told.   They must receive information in language they understand.   They are limited by the ability of their human masters to form proper instructions in the computer language, to design sufficient capabilities into the machine, and to interpret the results of computer operations.

1-4 *Basic Elements of the Digital Computer*

To perform the varied tasks assigned to them, computers are designed in various ways. A computer designed for machine control would not make a very good filing system. Nevertheless, there are several basic elements common to all computers. The five basic elements of a computer are pictured in the block diagram in Fig. 1-1.

The *input system* translates the input information prepared by the operator into a form to which the machine can respond. Among the major sources of computer input information are punched cards, punched or magnetic tape, a special typewriter, or another computer. Frequently, the input is in analog form and is converted to digital format by an analog-to-digital converter. The input system converts this information into a series of signals. Each signal is merely the presence or absence of a voltage or electric current. A signal is either there or not there at any particular time. Just as the 26 symbols of the English alphabet can be combined into many different words to convey information, so the two symbols of the computer alphabet (signal and no signal) can be combined to form "words," "phrases," and "sentences" in computer language. When the information is put into this form, the computer is able to work with the information and process it through a series of logic operations.

The information, now in the form of signals, is next sent to the computer *memory*, or storage. This element stores information until it is needed. Just as people store in their memories multiplication tables, phone numbers, addresses, schedules of what they plan to do, etc., the computer memory stores information for future reference. The memory element is, in a sense, passive in that it merely receives data, stores them, and gives them up on demand. Devices used as memory elements include magnetic cores, magnetic drums, magnetic tape, and electronic circuits.

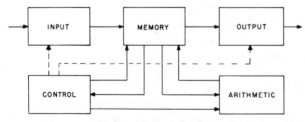

Fig. 1-1 Elements of a digital computer.

The next element, the *control unit*, is an active element. It selects information from the memory in the proper sequence and sends the information to other elements. In addition, the control unit sends along commands so that proper operations will be performed on the information when it arrives. Thus the control element makes decisions. This fact will be discussed in more detail later in the book.

The *arithmetic unit* receives the information and commands from the control unit. Here the information, still in the form of symbolic "words," is analyzed, broken down, combined, and rearranged in accordance with both the basic rules of logic designed into the machine and the commands received from the control unit. A variety of arithmetic operations may be performed at this time.

The astonishing thing here is that there are so few rules of logic designed into the machine. The power of the digital computer is that it can perform complex operations rapidly by breaking them down into a few simple operations that are repeated many, many times. By performing these few simple operations over and over again in many different combinations, immense problems can be solved in simple steps but at fantastic speeds.

When the signals have passed all the way through the arithmetic unit, they are no longer in the form of a problem but are now in the form of an answer. The answer is then passed through the memory unit and to an *output element*. The output element does the reverse of what the input element did, converting the new train of signals back into a form that can be understood by the operator or by other machines and presenting a permanent record or a visual display of the solution.

Basically, that is what goes on in all computers, regardless of their size. Of course, there are numerous differences in computer speed, capacity, variety of input-output devices, and logic organization. Before getting into the details of the rules of logic and how they are designed into the various elements, the language of computers must be understood. The language that most computers use is called the *binary number system*. This system is described in Chap. 2.

TWO

Number Systems
and the Digital Computer

2-1 Numbers and Counting

Numbers have become so familiar that the average person gives them little thought. They are used hundreds of times each day to count money, to tell time, to measure weights and distances, and to do many other everyday tasks. Few persons stop to think that without numbers there could be no quantitative measurement of any kind and no means of calculation. There could be no monetary systems, no weights and measures, and no scientific analysis.

The earliest number system probably resulted from man's desire to distinguish between one and many and to know "how many." How many members are there in the family? One day is, in many respects, like all other days, but how many days are there between full moons? One stone is much like another stone, but how many stones are used to build a wall?

To answer these questions, early man constructed a number system which, today, is called the *tally* or *unitary* system. The tally system uses only one symbol, the scratch mark or tally. One tally is used for each thing being counted—one day, one mark; two days, two marks; three days, three marks; and so on. By recognizing the similarity between a number of tally marks and an equal number of stones, the Stone Age man first conceived of a quantity of things. In a rough way, he knew "how many."

2-2 Historical Development of Numbers

While the tally system does provide a means of measuring simple quantities, it obviously is extremely limited. The system is unwieldy for even moderately large numbers. In the tally system, the number of days in a month is recorded as 11111111111111111111111111111111. As men became more advanced, larger numbers came into use. Men wanted to count the days in the year and the number of men in an entire army. To write these numbers in the tally system would be impractical.

To make the task of recording large numbers easier, the Romans developed a new numbering system. They recognized that a number system, to be manageable and useful, must contain additional symbols. Mere repetition of tally marks was completely unsatisfactory for recording the large numbers used by the Romans.

To provide the additional symbols, the Romans supplied the V to stand for 11111 and the X to stand for VV, or 1111111111. When even larger numbers became necessary, they used L to signify XXXXX, the C for LL, and the D to signify CCCCC. The number of days in a month was recorded in the Roman system as XXX; the number of days in a year as CCCLXV. This system was an obvious improvement over the tally system.

In addition to new symbols, the Romans used one other technique to make their system more compact. They used the positions of symbols to help determine the values of numbers. A symbol placed in front of an unlike symbol signified that much less. A symbol placed behind an unlike symbol signified that much more. Thus the number IV is 1 less than V, the number VI is 1 more than V, and the number XL is X less than L.

The development of the Roman system marked an important improvement in the method of counting; with it, men could think in terms of large quantities. However, the Roman system, too, had serious drawbacks.

Although the Romans did invent new symbols and a more compact number system, they did not really solve the problem of writing large numbers. Had the Roman system continued in use, more and more symbols would have been needed. The Romans themselves continued all the way to M, which signified DD, or CCCCCCCCCC. It would be difficult to record the population of New York City in Roman numerals. The Roman system would be as inadequate today as the tally system was for the Romans. Inventing new symbols was simply not enough. A system was needed that used a fixed number of symbols over and over again. Furthermore, the Romans' use of the positions of symbols was arbitrary. There was no logical reason why III could not be represented as IIV or IX by VIIII.

Since the Roman system had no definite number of symbols and since the construction of the system was arbitrary, calculations were quite complicated. The ability to add, subtract, multiply, and divide gave a Roman citizen the status of a mathematical scholar. In terms of the manipulation of quantities, the Roman system offered little improvement over the tally system.

The Hindus, about the end of the fifth century, developed a positional notation for the decimal system and used the symbols 1 to 9 as known today. This system was adopted by the Arabs in the ninth century. Later, the Arabs, showing more insight into mathematics, devised a symbol to stand for nothing at all. This symbol was, of course, 0 (zero).

The Arabic system used the common stroke, or tally, to represent a single unit. Then, instead of using additional strokes to represent additional units, a new symbol was derived for each unit increase. The result was the numerals 2, 3, 4, 5, 6, 7, 8, and 9, where each symbol represents a number one unit larger than the previous symbol. If the Arabs had continued merely to derive new symbols for each unit increase, their system would have been even more unwieldy than the stroke system or the Roman system. However, they realized this difficulty and simply started over again, using the same symbols but adding the significance of position. For the value of 9 plus the next additional unit, instead of inventing a new symbol, they placed the unit stroke in the second position. To establish the fact that the stroke was in the second position, a 0 was placed in the first position. After all, 0 adds nothing at all to the number, so it was used to show a one-place shift to the left. Such a shift is difficult, however, without that important 0. The number 10 was thus derived. Each numeral in the second position represented a certain number of 10s, just as each numeral in the first position represented a certain number of units. This process could go on indefinitely, using the same symbols again and again; no new symbols were required. Numbers in the third position represented 10s of 10s, or 100s. Numbers in the fourth position represented 10s of 10s of 10s, or 1,000s, etc. For example,

$$3{,}642 = 3 \times 10 \times 10 \times 10 = 3{,}000$$
$$+6 \times 10 \times 10 \qquad +600$$
$$+4 \times 10 \qquad\qquad + 40$$
$$+2 \times 1 \qquad\qquad\ \ + 2$$
$$= 3{,}642$$

The construction of this Arabic system was in no way arbitrary; there was one and only one way in which the system could be constructed. In this consistency lies the power of the system. By constructing this logical, consistent system, the Arabs could perform widely varying calculations by the use of 10 single coefficients and a few simple rules.

The important thing that the Arabs gave to mathematics was the logical, consistent construction of a number system. The number of symbols used and the shape of these symbols are completely arbitrary. The Arabs probably used 10 symbols because it was at 10 that they ran out of fingers. They could just as well have built a system using 8, 12, 16, or some other number of symbols.

The Mesopotamians, before 1700 B.C., devised a positional system using 60 symbols. Although the system requires a very large quantity of different numerals, it has many advantages. Sixty is divisible by enough numerals to make arithmetic simple in many cases. The system had positional notation, with a symbol for zero, and was used extensively for almost 2,000 years. Although the base 60 has not been used for many centuries, its influence is still seen. An hour is divided into 60 minutes, a minute into 60 seconds, and a circle into 360°.

Influences of the base 20 can be seen in the French method of counting (*quatre-vingts* for 80) and in the British monetary system. In short, any base can be used to form a numbering system, and many have been used.

Since 10 symbols are used in constructing the Arabic number system, it is given the special name *decimal*, from the Latin word for ten (*decem*). Although the decimal system is only one of many possible methods, it is the system in principal use throughout the world and, therefore, deserves special attention.

2-3   *The Decimal System*

The decimal number system runs through a cycle of 10 symbols before any symbols are repeated. For this reason, the decimal system is said to have a *base*, or *radix*, of 10. Any decimal number can be broken down into a certain number of 10s, a certain number of 10s of 10s, or 100s, and so on. Therefore, tens, hundreds, thousands, etc., can be expressed as powers of 10. The number 10 is exactly the same as 10^1; 100 (or 10×10) is the same as 10^2; 1,000 (or $10 \times 10 \times 10$) is 10^3; and so on. Table 2-1 lists a few of the more common powers of 10.

TABLE 2-1   *Powers of 10*

$$
\begin{aligned}
10^6 &= 1,000,000 = 10 \times 10 \times 10 \times 10 \times 10 \times 10 \\
10^5 &= 100,000 = 10 \times 10 \times 10 \times 10 \times 10 \\
10^4 &= 10,000 = 10 \times 10 \times 10 \times 10 \\
10^3 &= 1,000 = 10 \times 10 \times 10 \\
10^2 &= 100 = 10 \times 10 \\
10^1 &= 10 = 10 \\
10^0 &= 1 = 1
\end{aligned}
$$

In Table 2-1, note that 10^0 is equal to 1. A general rule in all number systems is that any number taken to the 0 power is equal to 1.

As an example of the use of powers of 10, take the decimal number 3,642 again:

$$3,000 = 3 \times 10^3$$
$$600 = 6 \times 10^2$$
$$40 = 4 \times 10^1$$
$$2 = 2 \times 10^0$$

This same translation process can be done with any decimal number.

2-4 *Numerals, Digits, and Orders*

The decimal number 3,642 is said to be a *four-digit* number; that is, it contains four different powers of 10.   This is the same as saying that the number has four places or four positions.   Furthermore, each digit or place in a number is occupied by a single numeral.   In the number 3,642, the numerals 3, 6, 4, and 2 occupy the four digits, or places, of the number. Since the digit on the far right stands for a certain number of units (or 10^0s) and since that digit is occupied by the numeral 2, it follows that the 2 on the far right stands for two units (or 2×10^0).   Similarly, the 4 in the second position stands for 4×10^1, the 6 stands for 6×10^2, and the 3 stands for 3×10^3.

Each digit in a number represents a different power of 10, and these powers of 10 are always arranged so that the highest power is on the far left and the lowest, or zeroth power, is on the far right.   The digits in a number are, therefore, named for the powers of 10 they represent.   The far-right digit, representing the zeroth power of 10 (10^0), is called the zeroth-order digit.   The next digit to the left, representing the first power of 10 (10^1), is called the first-order digit.   This scheme is continued for higher and higher orders:

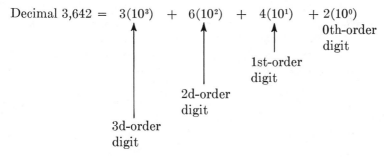

Decimal $3,642 = 3(10^3) + 6(10^2) + 4(10^1) + 2(10^0)$

0th-order digit

1st-order digit

2d-order digit

3d-order digit

To review briefly:

1. A numeral is a symbol representing an elementary quantity.

2. A number is one or more numerals arranged together to represent a larger quantity.

3. A digit in a decimal number is a place representing one, and only one, power of 10.

4. An order is the name given to a particular digit.

Positional notation also allows decimal fractions to be expressed by the use of a decimal point. Digits to the left of the decimal point are multiplied by a power of 10, while digits to the right of the decimal point are divided by a power of 10. Thus the number 476.839 is equivalent to

$$
\begin{aligned}
4 \times 10^2 &= 4 \times 10 \times 10 &&= 400 \\
7 \times 10^1 &= 7 \times 10 &&= 70 \\
6 \times 10^0 &= 6 \times 1 &&= 6 \\
8 \times 10^{-1} &= 8\!\!/_{10} &&= 0.8 \\
3 \times 10^{-2} &= 3/(10 \times 10) &&= 0.03 \\
9 \times 10^{-3} &= 9/(10 \times 10 \times 10) &&= \underline{0.009} \\
&&&= 476.839
\end{aligned}
$$

2-5 The Octal System

Although the construction of the decimal system is logical and consistent, the choice of the base 10 is completely arbitrary. Any number can be chosen as the base for a complete number system.

Had the Arabs been blessed with only eight fingers, they might have devised an octal system, one with a base of 8. In an octal system, only eight symbols are required. The symbols 0, 1, 2, 3, 4, 5, 6, and 7 are all that are necessary for an octal system.

Counting to 7 in the octal system uses all the allowed symbols, just as counting to 9 uses all the allowed symbols in the decimal system. The number "7 plus one additional unit" is represented by 10 in the octal system, just as the number "9 plus one additional unit" is represented by 10 in the decimal system. To clarify which system is being used, 10 is called *octal* 10, or *octal one zero*, and *decimal* 10, or *decimal one zero*.

Thus, the octal system is built up using the base 8 in the same way as the decimal system using base 10. After octal 10 are octal 11, 12, 13, and so on. After octal 17 is octal 20, and after octal 177 is octal 200.

Numbers in the octal system do not, of course, have the same value as similar numbers in the decimal system. Octal 10 is equivalent to decimal 8, not decimal 10. In the decimal system, two more numbers beyond 7 are counted before 10 is reached, while in the octal system the very next number after 7 is 10. (Table 2-2 shows the construction of the first 16 numbers of the octal system along with their decimal equivalents.)

All terms applied to decimal numbers are also applicable to octal numbers. The octal number 3642 also has four digits. The zeroth-order digit is a 2, the first-order digit is a 4, the second-order digit is a 6, and

the third-order digit is a 3.   However, in the octal system, the digits
represent powers of 8 rather than powers of 10.   Actually, if the octal
system were in common use, the people who used it would say that the
digits in the octal system represented powers of 10, i.e., powers of octal 10.

TABLE 2-2   *Octal and*
Decimal Numbers

Octal	Decimal equivalent
0	0
1	1
2	2
3	3
4	4
5	5
6	6
7	7
10	8
11	9
12	10
13	11
14	12
15	13
16	14
17	15
20	16

They would also say that the decimal system was not in powers of 10 but
rather in powers of 12.   They would mean octal 12, of course, since octal
12 is equivalent to decimal 10.   Either system, decimal or octal, can be
built up completely independent of the other.   Furthermore, any number
can be readily translated from one system to the other.   Table 2-3
illustrates the conversion of octal 3642 to the decimal system.

TABLE 2-3   *Octal-to-decimal Conversion*

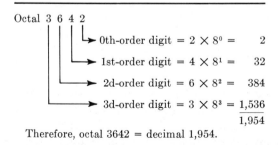

Octal 3 6 4 2

0th-order digit $= 2 \times 8^0 =$ 2

1st-order digit $= 4 \times 8^1 =$ 32

2d-order digit $= 6 \times 8^2 =$ 384

3d-order digit $= 3 \times 8^3 =$ 1,536

1,954

Therefore, octal 3642 = decimal 1,954.

2-6   *The Binary Number System*

Another number system, the one of greatest importance in the study of computers, is the binary number system.   The rules for the construction of the binary number system are identical to those for the decimal and octal systems.   The only difference is that the base for the binary system is 2 instead of 10 or 8.

In the binary system, since the base is 2, only two symbols are necessary.   The symbols used are the numerals 0 and 1.   All the available symbols are used just in counting to 1; the number "1 plus one additional unit" is represented in the binary system by the binary number 10.   This number is called *binary* 10, or *binary one zero*, and is equivalent to decimal 2.   The next number in the binary system is binary 11, which is "binary 10 plus one additional unit."   Another additional unit then results in the binary number 100.   The binary system is built up just as the decimal and octal systems are built.   Table 2-4 shows the first 16 binary numbers along with their decimal equivalents.

TABLE 2-4 *Binary and Decimal Equivalents*

Binary	Decimal equivalent
0	0
1	1
10	2
11	3
100	4
101	5
110	6
111	7
1000	8
1001	9
1010	10
1011	11
1100	12
1101	13
1110	14
1111	15
10000	16

The terms "digit," "number," and "order" are applicable to binary numbers as well as to decimal and octal numbers.   In the six-digit binary number 110101, the zeroth-, second-, fourth-, and fifth-order digits are 1s and the first- and third-order digits are 0s.   The binary digits stand for powers of decimal 2, just as the octal digits stand for powers of decimal 8 and the decimal digits stand for powers of decimal 10.

2-7 *Binary-to-decimal Conversion*

If the construction of the binary system is understood, conversion of binary numbers into equivalent decimal numbers is easily learned.   For example, take the binary number 110101 again.   The 1 in the zeroth-order digit is equivalent to 1×2^0, or 1.   The 0 in the first-order digit means that the first power of 2 is not present; that is, $0 \times 2^1 = 0$.   The 1 in the second-order digit is equivalent to 1×2^2, or 4.   The 0 in the third-order digit is evidence that the 2^3 term is also missing, or equal to 0.   The fourth and fifth orders both contain 1s, indicating that the 2^4 and 2^5 terms, or 16 and 32, respectively, are present.   The decimal equivalent of binary 110101 must then be the sum of all nonzero terms, or $32 + 16 + 4 + 1 = 53$.   The entire conversion process for the binary number 110101 is shown in Table 2-5.

T A B L E 2 - 5   *Conversion of Binary 110101*

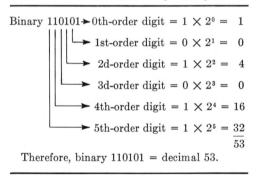

Binary 110101➤0th-order digit $= 1 \times 2^0 =$ 1

1st-order digit $= 0 \times 2^1 =$ 0

2d-order digit $= 1 \times 2^2 =$ 4

3d-order digit $= 0 \times 2^3 =$ 0

4th-order digit $= 1 \times 2^4 =$ 16

5th-order digit $= 1 \times 2^5 =$ 32

$$\overline{53}$$

Therefore, binary 110101 $=$ decimal 53.

A second method of binary-to-decimal conversion is called *doubling and dabbling*.   To illustrate this process, take the binary number 110101 again.   The highest-order digit is the starting point for the process.   The 1, which is always present in the highest-order digit, provides a base for the doubling operation.   Proceeding to the second-highest-order digit, the original 1 is doubled if that digit is a 0.   If the next-lower-order digit is a 1, the original 1 is doubled and another 1 is added to it.   This addition of 1 is called *dabbling*—thus the name "doubling and dabbling." The process then continues until there are no more digits, doubling if a 0 appears and doubling and dabbling if a 1 appears.   Table 2-6 illustrates the process.

TABLE 2-6 *Doubling and Dabbling*

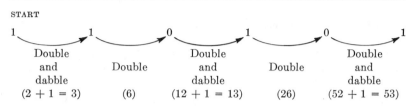

Therefore, binary 110101 is equivalent to decimal 53.   Another example:

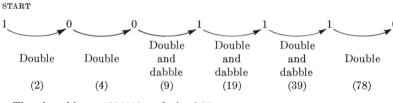

Therefore, binary 1001110 = decimal 78.

2-8 *Decimal-to-binary Conversion*

Decimal-to-binary conversion is handled by reversing the binary-to-decimal conversion process.   The decimal number is first inspected to determine the highest power of decimal 2 that it contains.   For example, in the case of decimal 177, 2^7 (decimal 128) is the highest power of 2 which is smaller than 177.   The next power of 2, 2^8, equals decimal 256 and therefore is too large.   Subtracting 2^7 (128) from 177 leaves 49. The highest power of 2 in 49 is then 2^5, or 32, 2^6 (64) being too large. Subtracting 32 from 49 leaves 17, which in turn contains the fourth power of 2, or 16.   Further subtraction leaves only 1, which contains only the zeroth power of 2, or 1.   Since 2^7, 2^5, 2^4, and 2^0 are exactly contained in decimal 177, the binary representation of 177 is as shown in Table 2-7.

This process can be cumbersome for large numbers, and a simpler scheme consisting of division by 2 is often handy.   Here the decimal number is repeatedly divided by 2 to determine which powers of 2 are present.   If division by 2 produces a remainder, then the number must be odd or, what amounts to the same thing, must contain 2^0.   A 1 must therefore appear in the zeroth-order digit.   If division by 2 does not produce a remainder, then the number must be even; that is, it does not contain 2^0.   In this case, a 0 appears in the zeroth-order digit.   The process is then repeated until no further division is possible.

For example,

Remainder

$$
\begin{aligned}
177 \div 2 &= 88 + 1 && 2^0 \text{ is present} \\
88 \div 2 &= 44 + 0 && 2^1 \\
44 \div 2 &= 22 + 0 && 2^2 \\
22 \div 2 &= 11 + 0 && 2^3 \\
11 \div 2 &= 5 + 1 && 2^4 \text{ is present} \\
5 \div 2 &= 2 + 1 && 2^5 \text{ is present} \\
2 \div 2 &= 1 + 0 && 2^6 \\
1 \div 2 &= 0 + 1 && 2^7 \text{ is present}
\end{aligned}
$$

TABLE 2-7 *Binary Representation of Decimal 177*

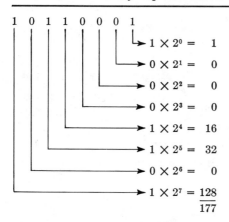

Here is the entire conversion process in review:

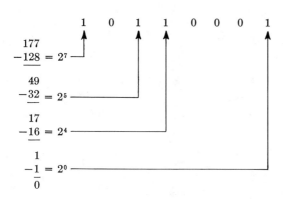

The binary representation of decimal 177 is then 10110001. Note that the highest-order digit is the last to be derived. This process is the exact opposite of doubling and dabbling.

2-9   *Binary Addition*

Binary addition is done in the same way as ordinary decimal addition except that the rules are much simpler. Binary addition follows these four rules:

$$
\begin{array}{cccc}
0 & 0 & 1 & 1 \\
+0 & +1 & +0 & +\,1 \\
\hline
0 & 1 & 1 & 10 \ (\text{or } 0 \text{ and carry } 1)
\end{array}
$$

For example,

$$
\begin{array}{ll}
1101 & (\text{decimal } 13) \\
+\ 100 & (\text{decimal }\ \ 4)
\end{array}
$$

The zeroth-order digits are combined to form a sum of 1; the first-order digits are combined to form a sum of 0; and the second-order digits are combined to form a sum of 10, or "0 and carry the 1." The third-order digits are then combined, with the carry from the second order, to form the sum 10. Note that in the lower number there is no third-order digit. In this case, the missing digit is simply taken as 0.

The result is

$$
\begin{array}{lllll}
\text{Carry:} & 1\!\!\leftarrow \\
 & 1 & 1 & 0 & 1 \\
+ & & 1 & 0 & 0 \\
\hline
10 & \!\!\leftarrow\!\!0 & 0 & 1
\end{array}
$$

The decimal equivalent of 10001 is

$$
\begin{array}{lcl}
1 \times 2^4 = 1 \times 16 = 16 \\
0 \times 2^3 = 0 \times\ \ 8 =\ \ 0 \\
0 \times 2^2 = 0 \times\ \ 4 =\ \ 0 \\
0 \times 2^1 = 0 \times\ \ 2 =\ \ 0 \\
1 \times 2^0 = 1 \times\ \ 1 =\ \ \underline{1} \\
17
\end{array}
$$

This is the same as the decimal sum

$$
\begin{array}{r}
13 \\
+\ 4 \\
\hline
17
\end{array}
$$

Another example:

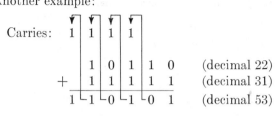

	1	0	1	1	0	(decimal 22)
+	1	1	1	1	1	(decimal 31)
1	1	0	1	0	1	(decimal 53)

In this example, the second-order digits are both 1s. When these are combined with the carry from the previous order, the sum is 11, or "1 and carry the 1."

Practice problems to illustrate further the mechanics of binary addition are given at the end of this chapter. The reader should be able to perform these additions and convert the binary result to decimal numbers before continuing.

2-10 *Binary Subtraction*

In binary subtraction, borrows are used instead of carries. The rules for subtraction are

$$(1) \quad \text{borrow}$$

1	1	0	0
-1	-0	-0	-1
0	1	0	1

To illustrate the borrow, consider the following example:

Borrow:	0	10	0	0

	1	0	1	1	(decimal 11)
$-$		1	0	1	(decimal 5)
		1	1	0	(decimal 6)

In the second order, 10 must be borrowed from the third order before subtraction can be accomplished. After borrowing, the problem may be assumed to look like this:

0	(10)	1	1
$-$		1	0	1
		1	1	0

Compare this with the procedure in decimal subtraction:

Borrow:	0 10 0 0	0 10

$$
\begin{array}{r}
8 \\
9 \quad 0\ 9\ 9 \\
-\quad \ 9\ 0\ 9 \\
\hline
8\quad 1\ 9\ 0
\end{array}
\text{ or } -
\begin{array}{r}
\not{9}\quad 0\ 9\ 9 \\
\ 9\ 0\ 9 \\
\hline
8\quad 1\ 9\ 0
\end{array}
$$

Sometimes it is necessary to transmit the borrow through more than one digit:

	1
Borrows:	0 0 ~~10~~ 10 0

$$
\begin{array}{rl}
1\ 1\ \ 0\ \ 0\ 1 & \text{(decimal 25)} \\
-1\ 0\ \ 1\ \ 1\ 0 & \text{(decimal 22)} \\
\hline
1\ 1 & \text{(decimal \ 3)}
\end{array}
$$

The borrow in the second order must be transmitted to the third order before complete subtraction is possible.   In effect, the fourth-order digit supplies borrows to both the third- and second-order digits.   The same process is used in the following decimal subtraction:

	9
Borrows:	~~10~~ 10

$$
\begin{array}{r}
8 \\
9\ \not{9}\ 0\ \ 0\ 9 \\
-9\ 0\ 9\ \ 9\ 0 \\
\hline
8\ 0\ \ 1\ 9
\end{array}
$$

Practice problems are given at the end of this chapter.

2-11   *Binary Multiplication*

Multiplication in the binary system is extremely simple.   Here are the multiplication rules:

$$0 \times 0 = 0$$
$$0 \times 1 = 0$$
$$1 \times 0 = 0$$
$$1 \times 1 = 1$$

In binary multiplication, multiplier and multiplicand are arranged just as in decimal multiplication.   For example,

Multiplicand	10110	(decimal 22)
Multiplier	$\times$ 101	(decimal 5)

However, since all multiplication is by either 1 or 0, the formation of partial products amounts to nothing more than either recopying or not copying the multiplicand.

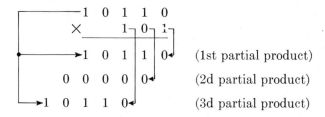

	(1st partial product)
	(2d partial product)
	(3d partial product)

As in normal multiplication, the lowest order of each partial product is placed beneath the appropriate order of the multiplier.   In other words, each partial product is shifted one place to the left of the previous partial product.   Summing the partial products is then straightforward addition.

```
   10110     (decimal 22)
×    101     (decimal  5)
   10110
   00000
   10110
 1101110     (decimal 110)
```

Another example of binary multiplication is

Binary	*Decimal*
110011	51
$\times$ 1011	$\times 11$
110011	
110011	
000000	
110011	
1000110001	561

2-12 *Binary Division*

Binary division, like binary multiplication, is also much simpler than the decimal process.   The numbers are arranged as in decimal division:

Divisor →   101 |‾1101110‾   ← Dividend
                   (decimal 5) (decimal 110)

Inspection reveals that the three-digit divisor is less than the three highest orders of the dividend; that is, 101 "goes into" 110 one time. This determines the highest-order digit of the quotient.   Division then proceeds in the same manner as decimal division:

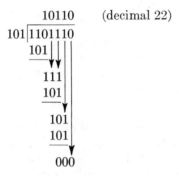
                  10110   (decimal 22)

Two other examples of binary division are

Binary	*Decimal*	*Binary*	*Decimal*
111	7	110	6
1101|1011011	13|91	10101|1111110	21|126
1101		10101	
10011		10101	
1101		10101	
1101		000	
1101			

Further exercises are provided at the end of this chapter.   With a little practice, the reader should quickly master binary arithmetic.

2-13 *Application of the Binary and Binary-coded Systems*

The binary number system is of great importance in the study of computers because, of all number systems, the binary is translated most readily into electronic language.   The decimal system, while quite appropriate for human calculation, has drawbacks in a machine system.

For one thing, the 10 symbols of the decimal system, although easily recognized, present certain problems when represented by electronic signals. Each symbol must be clearly differentiated from every other symbol, so that 9, for instance, will look nothing at all like 7. One way to do this is to represent each symbol by a distinct voltage level. This, however, requires 10 separate voltage levels, plus amplification and wave-shaping equipment to ensure that 9s are not distorted or attenuated into 7s. The binary system, on the other hand, has only two symbols, 1 and 0. These are easily represented by relays being either *open* or *closed* and by transistors being either *conducting* or *not conducting*. There are many electrical and mechanical devices that are suitable to implement binary notations.

A second advantage of the binary system is that the rules of arithmetic are much simpler. For example, the rules for binary addition are simply

$$
\begin{array}{cccc}
0 & 0 & 1 & 1 \\
+0 & +1 & +0 & +\,1 \\
\hline
0 & 1 & 1 & 10
\end{array}
$$

This is a considerable improvement over the 100 possible combinations of symbols used as rules in decimal addition. In the same manner, the rules for binary subtraction, multiplication, and division are substantially simplified over the same operations using decimal arithmetic.

In addition to the straight binary system, there are a number of coding schemes which represent decimal numbers by means of binary codes. In this way, decimal arithmetic can be done directly, although at the expense of equipment complexity. These codes, which are described in Chap. 5, are also widely used in other electronic equipment.

Because of their ease of representation and simplicity of design, the binary system and related octal system are generally used in computer design. The next chapter describes logic implemented with binary notations.

EXERCISES

2-1. Write the Roman numbers for 19, 26, 4, and 8. Attempt to add these numbers.

2-2. Define symbol, numeral, order, number, and digit.

2-3. How many digits are in the number 572,937? Which numeral is the third-order digit?

2-4. Determine the octal equivalents of the decimal numbers 21, 35, 43, 59, 80, and 105.

2-5. Determine the decimal equivalents of the octal numbers 15, 47, 53, 111, and 173.

2-6. Determine the decimal equivalents of the binary numbers 1011, 11010, 1011101, and 110101101.

2-7. Determine the binary equivalents of the decimal numbers 18, 43, 77, and 111.

2-8. How many symbols are required for a number system using a radix, or base, of 5?

2-9. Construct the first 20 numbers of the radix-5 system (quinary system).

2-10. Determine the decimal equivalents of the following numbers of the radix-5 system: 432, 2341, 4423, and 3114.

2-11. Add the following numbers and check your answers:

Binary	*Decimal*	*Binary*	*Decimal*	*Binary*	*Decimal*
10110	22	111101	61	101101	45
+ 1110	+14	+ 11101	+29	+100111	+39

2-12. Add the following binary numbers:

(*a*) 1101	(*b*) 110111	(*c*) 1011101
+ 101	+101101	+1101010

2-13. Perform the following subtractions:

Binary	*Decimal*	*Binary*	*Decimal*	*Binary*	*Decimal*
1011	11	110111	55	101101	45
− 111	− 7	− 11010	−26	− 10111	−23

2-14. Perform these problems in binary subtraction:

(*a*) 1011	(*b*) · 11101	(*c*) 1011101
− 101	− 1110	− 101110

2-15. Multiply. Check your answers by converting to the decimal system.

(*a*) 1010	(*b*) 10110	(*c*) 11011
× 101	× 110	× 1101

2-16. Divide. Check your answers.

(*a*) 11110 by 101   (*b*) 111000 by 1000   (*c*) 10010110 by 1111

THREE

Computer Logic

3-1 *Introduction to Logic*

Chapters 1 and 2 have introduced the history and concepts of digital computers, the relative constructions of number systems, and the influence of the binary number system on digital-computer operations. This chapter on computer logic presents the relationships of logic techniques to the "reasoning" operations of the computer, that is, to the performance of calculations and the manipulation of logic statements.

A brief description of logic reasoning will be presented and related to the symbols for expressing logic statements and to diagrammatic methods of expression: truth tables and Venn diagrams. Truth tables and Venn diagrams are pictorial presentations of the relationships (or conditions) of a logic statement. This chapter also presents the concepts of the basic computer operators—AND, OR, and NOT—and relates these to truth-table and Venn-diagram presentation. The final section of the chapter presents a study of Boolean algebra that is based on previous discussions.

The material in the rest of this book is designed to be studied as clearly defined units. Therefore, from this point on, a most important function while using this text will be faithful study and performance of demonstrations and the associated exercises. These demonstrations have been carefully selected to instruct the reader graphically in the computer operations that are the subject of this text. An understanding of these demonstrations is an important background for advanced computer study.

3-2 *Logic Reasoning*

The strength of the digital computer is its ability to perform logic operations. The computer can follow varying instructions that are signified by binary 1 and 0 notations, as described earlier. Addition and subtraction are simple counting functions that can be performed by desk calculators and adding machines. However, with the desk calculators and adding machines, the operator must supply the associative control function to satisfy the requirements of logical reasoning, such as "Subtract this number from the sum." In a computer, the associative

control functions are built in.   The relationship of the numbers is prescribed by the *program* for the computer, or by the fixed arrangement of
the computer operations.   Also, the computer can make decisions that
are governed by the conditions or states of various logic statements.   In
other words, the computer can automatically make correct responses to
variable conditions.   All this is accomplished through the use of logic.

Logic is often defined as the science of reasoning.   More properly, it is
the science of necessary inference, because it describes when a statement
follows from other statements.

The fundamental rules of logic list those situations in which correct
inference or reasoning is possible.   By listing all the circumstances where
correct inference is possible and by being careful to rely on inference only
in those situations where correct inference is possible, the pitfalls of
faulty reasoning are avoided.

For example, if it is true that "All boys like baseball" and if it is also
true that "Harry is a boy," then logic says that Harry must like baseball.
In other words, the statement "Harry likes baseball" can be inferred
from the statements "All boys like baseball" and "Harry is a boy."
Harry has to like baseball if, in fact, the other two statements are true.

Logic, however, makes no guarantees about the statement "All boys
like baseball."   Such a statement is assumed to be true.   Statements like
"The sky is blue" and "The grass is green" are also assumed to be true.
These statements do not stem from logic but from experience.   Statements like these, which are based on experience and cannot logically be
shown to be true, are called *observably true* statements.

Logic does, however, make guarantees about correctly drawn inferences.
If it is true that "All grass is green" and if it also is true that "Harry's
lawn is grass," then logic guarantees that Harry's lawn is green.   However, this guarantee is still based on the grass being green and Harry's
lawn being grass in the first place.   Statements drawn from correct
inference are called *demonstrably true* if (1) a correct inference has been
drawn, and (2) the inference has been drawn from true statements.

There is a third kind of truth, which is *obviously true* just by its nature.
A statement such as "Either John has a bicycle or he does not" is obviously true.   John must either have a bike or not have a bike; there is no
other alternative.   Essentially, an obviously true statement divides the
universe into two segments.   In John's case, the universe is divided into
a segment of bike owners and another segment of those who do not own
bikes.

3-3   *Logic Symbols and Truth Value*

For a computing machine to use logic, the logic statements must be
broken down into symbols and equations.   Some means must be pro-

vided whereby everyday verbal statements can be translated into symbolic statements. The most elementary of these symbols are the symbols for true and false.

In logic, all statements are either true or false. There is no place for "maybe" or "perhaps." Therefore, to express completely the conditions of true and false, only the binary symbols 1 and 0 are needed. If a statement is true, it equals 1. If a statement is false, it equals 0. Moreover, any statement used in logic must be one or the other. A statement can equal 1, or it can equal 0, but it must equal one or the other, i.e., be true or false.

Statements themselves can be represented by symbols. For example, "The sun is shining" might be represented by the letter S. Wherever the letter S appears, it is understood that S stands for "The sun is shining." If it is true that the sun is shining, then this is expressed by the logic equation $S = 1$. If the sun is not shining, then $S = 0$. The logic equation $S = 0$ means it is false that the sun is shining, or in other words, the sun is not shining.

The numerical values 1 and 0 are associated with the truth and falsity of logic statements. If a statement is true, it has a truth value of 1. If a statement is false, it has a truth value of 0.

The two truth values 1 and 0 are readily translated into electronic language as either of two voltage levels. One voltage level represents the truth value 1, or the *assertion* of a statement. The other voltage level represents the truth value of 0, or the *negation* of a statement. The terms "assertion" and "negation" are translations of the truth values 1 and 0 into electronic language.

During the remainder of the book, illustrated demonstrations are used to implement logic functions discussed in the text. The illustrations are made up of functional block diagrams. Each of the functional block types, hereafter referred to as *modules*, performs a specific operation. A summary of the various module types, with their symbols and functional operation, is given in the Appendix.

The demonstrations are presented such that they can be readily implemented in a laboratory using the equivalent logic modules and auxiliary equipment, including power supplies and interconnection wires.

Demonstration 3-1 *True-False Implementation*

Purpose

To introduce the electronic implementation of assertion-negation, true-false, 1-0 by use of a level switch.

Equipment

1—Level switch

LOGIC ONE SOURCE

LOGIC ZERO SOURCE

OUTPUT

Fig. 3-1   Manual two-position switch.

Discussion and Implementation

In logic, statements are either true or false; that is, a statement is either asserted or negated.   Throughout the remainder of this text, statements or conditions are symbolically represented by alphabetic notations and the assertion and negation of the statements are represented by the binary symbols 1 and 0, respectively.

Implementation of these binary symbols in electronic terms is accomplished by using different voltage levels to stand for logic 1 and 0.   The assignment of the particular voltage levels that define the logic states is somewhat arbitrary and is usually a circuit-design consideration.

In most of the demonstrations shown in this text, level-switch modules are used to provide a source for binary 1s and 0s.   Each level-switch module has four independent outputs which can be switched manually to a logic 1 or a logic 0.

The output of the manual switch represented in Fig. 3-1 can be set to a logic 0 or a logic 1 by selection of the proper manual position.   This operation is very similar to that of a light switch which turns a light bulb on and off.   In the illustration, a symbol may be assigned to the output. The assigned symbol may represent a logic statement or a logic condition. By manually operating the switch, the operator can then select a truth value for the logic condition represented by this output.

The level-switch module in Fig. 3-2 has four of the switches represented in Fig. 3-1.   Each of the outputs of the two-position switches can be set to a logic 1 or a logic 0.   The letters A, B, C, and D are used to represent the four discrete switches and have no logic significance.   When this module is used in the demonstrations, the symbolic assignments to each output will be made external to the rectangle.

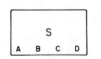

Fig.   3-2   The   level-switch module.

Although most computers use a few manual switches to enter a set of preconditions into the machine prior to solving a problem, these switches are not normally used within a computational cycle since the gating elements in the computer may operate at speeds in excess of a million times per second. However, with the exception of the increased speed, the operations are identical to those described in this chapter.

Exercises 3-1 and 3-2 at the end of this chapter demonstrate the use of the level-switch module.

3-4 *The Logic Operators:* AND, OR, NOT

The truth or falsity of an individual statement standing alone is of little logical interest. It is only when two or more statements are joined together that logical inferences can be drawn.

AND *Operator.* For example, a friend may tell you that if and only if the weather is good AND he has the day off, he will play golf Saturday. This means that if you know the weather is good AND he is not scheduled to work, you may infer that he is playing golf. Let S stand for "The weather is good," and let C stand for "He has the day off." If S is true (S = 1) AND if C is true (C = 1), you will find your friend playing golf Saturday. However, if either S or C or both are false (S = 0 or C = 0 or both), you may be assured that your friend will not be playing golf. He will only play if both "The weather is good" and "He has the day off" are true.

Whether or not your friend plays golf is determined by the truth of both S and C. The truth of S or C standing alone will not determine whether he is playing. You are only interested in *both* S and C being true. A symbolic representation is therefore needed to show that both S and C are true. The logic equation $S \cdot C = 1$ means both S and C are true. To put it another way, $S \cdot C = 1$ means that S and C are both true at the same time. The dot ($\cdot$) defines the logic *conjunction*, i.e., the logic AND operation.

Note that there are only four possible combinations of S and C. If S = 1, C must be either 1 or 0; and if S = 0, C must again be either 1 or 0. These four combinations are listed in Table 3-1.

TABLE 3-1

S	C
1	1
1	0
0	1
0	0

A third column can be added to the table showing the value of the expression S · C for each pair of values for S and C. This has been done in Table 3-2.

TABLE 3-2

S	C	S · C
1	1	1
1	0	0
0	1	0
0	0	0

This *truth table* lists every possible combination of the two variables S and C along with the resultant output S · C. From this simple truth table, one can observe that S · C is true only when S is a 1 and C is a 1.

OR *Operator*. Assume now that your friend is a carefree sort and that he will play golf Saturday if EITHER "The weather is good" OR "He has the day off" OR both. Now the truth of S OR C determines your friend's whereabouts. This is not to say that S or C standing alone will necessarily tell you whether or not your friend is playing golf. If S = 0 ("The weather is not good"), you still have no information about his work schedule. Your friend may have gone to play golf anyway. A symbolic representation is needed to show that EITHER S OR C OR both are true. The logic equation S + C = 1 means that EITHER S OR C OR both are true, that is, at least S = 1 OR C = 1. The plus sign (+) defines the logic *disjunction*, i.e., the logic OR operation. This logic symbol (+) is entirely different from the arithmetic plus sign, and the two should not be confused. The logic disjunction is not equivalent to arithmetic addition but merely implies the logic operation OR. Table 3-3 is a truth table that expresses this relationship.

TABLE 3-3

S	C	S + C
1	1	1
1	0	1
0	1	1
0	0	0

The truth table shows that S + C = 1 if at least one term, either S or C, equals 1. S + C only equals 0 when both S and C equal 0.

NOT *Operator*. The third basic logic operator is the NOT operator, or the logic *inversion*. To illustrate this operator, reexamine the conditions concerning your friend. If you used C to represent symbolically the fact that "He has the day off" and if, within the same reasoning process, you desired to represent symbolically the fact that "He is scheduled to work," would a new symbol be required? The answer is "No." A new symbol is unnecessary and can lead to confusion. A better technique is to modify the original symbol to show that it is an opposite, or inverse, of the new statement.

Since C = 1 already means that it is true that "He has the day off," a modification of the original symbol is needed to show that "He does not have the day off." The logic equation $\overline{C} = 1$ fulfills this need. Note that $\overline{C}$ is the opposite, or inverse, of C. If C is true, then $\overline{C}$ must be false. If C = 1, then $\overline{C} = 0$. This basic logic relationship is shown in Table 3-4. $\overline{C}$ is always the inverse of C and may be read as NOT C.

TABLE 3-4

C	$\overline{C}$
1	0
0	1

3-5 *Venn Diagrams*

Another way to represent the meanings of the logic operators is by the use of geometric diagrams. Such diagrams are called *Venn diagrams* after John Venn, a mathematician and logician who began using them in the middle of the nineteenth century. To illustrate the use of Venn diagrams, assume that every person in the world is contained in a rectangle (Fig. 3-3).

All Americans, as distinct from other persons, can then be grouped together in a circle, such as the one in Fig. 3-4. For everyone inside the circle, the statement "That person is American" is true. Outside the circle, the statement "That person is American" is false. The circle defines for whom the statement "That person is American" is true. If

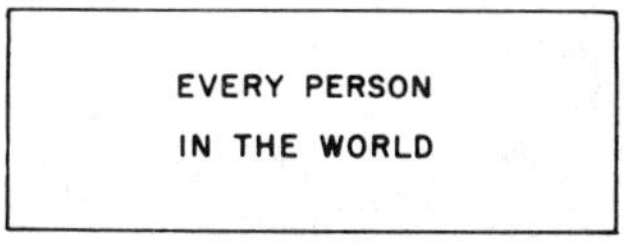

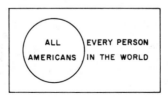

EVERY PERSON
IN THE WORLD

ALL AMERICANS   EVERY PERSON IN THE WORLD

Fig. 3-3   Venn diagram, one variable.

Fig. 3-4   Venn diagram, two variables.

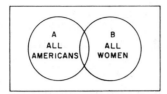

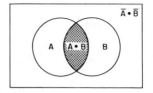

Fig. 3-5   Venn diagram,   *Fig. 3-6   Venn diagram,*
three variables.   A · B.

such a statement is represented by the letter A, then within the circle
A = 1 and outside the circle A = 0, or $\overline{A}$ = 1.

In Fig. 3-5, a second circle, representing all women, has been added.
For everyone inside circle B, the statement "That person is a woman"
is true.   At every point inside circle B, B = 1; and at every point outside
B, B = 0, or $\overline{B}$ = 1.

Now consider the area which is common to both circles.   This is the
shaded area in Fig. 3-6.   In this area, A = 1 AND B = 1; that is,
A · B = 1.   In this area, it is true that "That person is an American
woman"; she is American AND she is a woman.   Outside the shaded
area, $\overline{A \cdot B}$ = 1, or A · B = 0.   Outside the shaded area, it is never true
that "That person is an American woman."   A person outside the shaded
area in the circles may be a woman or may be an American but cannot be
both.   The shaded area, then, represents the logic AND function.

This corresponds, in a truth table, to both A AND B being 1.   The
shaded row of the truth table in Fig. 3-7 corresponds to the shaded area
in Fig. 3-6.   In this row, A = 1 and B = 1.

The logic OR function is represented by the area contained in either or
both circles.   This area has been shaded in Fig. 3-8.   In this area, A = 1
OR B = 1; that is, A + B = 1.   In this area, it is true that "That
person is American or is a woman"; that person does not have to be both
but must be one or the other.   Outside the shaded area, A + B = 0, or
$\overline{A + B}$ = 1; it is never true that "That person is American or is a woman."
That person may be a Chinese man or African man but cannot be American and cannot be a woman.

The Venn diagram for the OR operation corresponds in a truth table

A	B	A · B
I	O	O
I	I	I
O	O	O
O	I	O

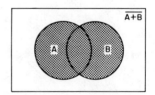

Fig. 3-7   Truth table,   *Fig. 3-8   Venn diagram,*
A · B.   A + B.

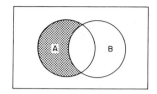

A	B	A+B
1	1	1
1	0	1
0	1	1
0	0	0

Fig. 3-9 Truth table,
A + B.

Fig. 3-10 Venn diagram
A · B̄.

to A OR B being 1.   The shaded rows in the truth table in Fig. 3-9 correspond to the shaded area in Fig. 3-8.   In these rows, A = 1 or B = 1.
More complicated representations can also be drawn.   In Fig. 3-10, the shaded portion represents A · B̄, which means "All Americans that are not women."   Notice that this is true only for that area of A which is not included in the overlap.

3-6 *Implementation:* AND, OR, NOT

A physical system can be designed to implement the logic AND, OR, and NOT operations previously discussed.   Take, for example, the faucets on a sink, as shown in Fig. 3-11.   This system can implement the logic OR operation.   If either the hot faucet or the cold faucet is on or if both are on, that is, are in the 1 state, then water flows from the tap and the tap is in the 1 state.   If, however, both faucets are off, or in the 0 state, then no water can flow from the tap and it is in the 0 state.

To construct a system for the AND operation, the faucets must be placed in series, one after the other, as shown in Fig. 3-12.   When in series, both faucets must be on (in the 1 state) if water is to flow from the tap.   If either is off (in the 0 state), then no water can come out of the tap and it is in the 0 state.

Electrical switches can also be arranged to represent logic operations.   Figure 3-13 shows two switches in parallel.   If either switch is closed or if

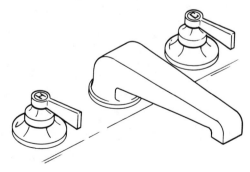

Fig. 3-11 Physical OR gate.

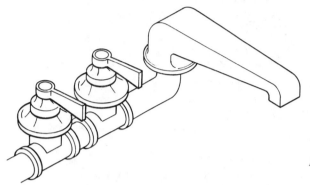

Fig. 3-12   Physical AND gate.

both are closed, then current flows through the system.   However, if both switches are open, then no current can flow.   The two parallel switches represent the logic OR function just as the two parallel water faucets do.   By placing the switches in series, as shown in Fig. 3-14, the system represents the logic AND function.   In this case, both switches must be closed to have current flow through the system.   If either switch is open or if both switches are open, then no current can flow.

The logic NOT function is implemented merely by an open switch rather than a closed switch.   The switch in Fig. 3-15A represents $X = 1$, and the switch in Fig. 3-15B represents $\overline{X} = 1$, or $X = 0$.

These examples show how mechanical switches, such as those used in light switches, can be used to implement logic functions.   In computing machinery, such switches are never used.   Mechanical switches are far too slow and difficult to operate to be useful in a computer.

Early computers used relays instead of mechanical switches.   In relays, springs and magnets operate the switch rather than the human hand.   Vacuum-tube switches are even faster than relays and are operated using electricity.   No slow-acting springs are required.   Beginning with the Eniac, most wartime and postwar digital computers used vacuum tubes to perform the logic operations.   In the mid-1950s, the vacuum tubes were in turn replaced by transistors, which are faster, smaller, and

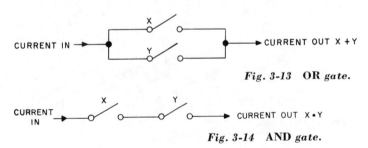

Fig. 3-13   OR gate.

Fig. 3-14   AND gate.

more reliable and offer many advantages over vacuum tubes. The newest generation of computers has replaced discrete transistors with microelectronics. The use of semi-

(A)   (B)

Fig. 3-15   Logic NOT.

conductor and film integrated circuitry allows highly reliable switching to be performed in extremely small packages. As a result of improvements in the switching properties of gating elements, faster, more reliable, more complex, and lower-cost computers have been made available.

The AND Gate.   The logic AND gate implements the function A · B. If the two inputs to an AND gate are A and B, then the output is A · B. The inputs can be thought of as closing two switches arranged in series. The output of the gate can be a 1 (assertion) only if both inputs (A and B) are 1s.   Therefore, A · B = 1 only if A = 1 and B = 1.   If either input to an AND gate is 0, then the AND-gate output also must be 0 (negation). Hence A · B = 0 if A = 0 or B = 0.

If the inputs A and B are represented as circles on a Venn diagram, then the AND gate reflects that area where A and B overlap. The shaded portion of Fig. 3-16 shows the overlap of A and B.   It is in this area that both A and B exist together, or symbolically, A · B exists (equals 1).   To represent the AND function with a truth table, the output is a 1 only if both inputs are 1.   (See Table 3-5.)   In all other cases, the output is 0.   Note that this truth table is identical to Table 3-2.

TABLE 3-5

A	B	Output
1	1	1
1	0	0
0	1	0
0	0	0

AND gates may, of course, have more than two inputs.   AND gates with 10 inputs are not uncommon.   The AND-gate modules used in the demonstrations have as many as four inputs and can implement four-variable functions, such as A · B · C · D.   The rules for three- or four-input gates are identical to the rules for the two-input AND gate, except that all four inputs must be 1 to provide a 1 output.   Any unused input or inputs will not affect the gate; any 0 input causes the gate's output to be 0.

The symbol for the AND-gate module is

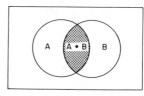

Fig. 3-16   Venn diagram of AND function.

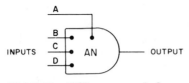

Fig. 3-17 AND gate symbol.

shown in Fig. 3-17. The output provides the AND function for inputs A, B, C, and D. This gate can be implemented by various electrical or mechanical devices, the only restriction being that the device has two discrete states to represent binary 1 and 0. For demonstration purposes, assume that the gates illustrated are electronic in nature and that an electronic switch inside the gate switches the output to the 1 state only when all the inputs are logic 1s; otherwise, the output is a logic 0.

Demonstration 3-2 The AND *Operation*

Purpose

To illustrate the implementation of the logic AND operation with the AND-gate module (AN).

Equipment

   1—Level switch (S)
   3—AND gates (AN)

Discussion and Implementation

The AND-gate modules provide electronic implementation of the AND operation. Each module can accept up to four inputs (A, B, C, and D), allowing up to four signals or propositions to be ANDed together. The gate's output appears at the far right of the AND-gate symbol.

The level switch in Fig. 3-18 provides a source of 1s and 0s for the four variables A, B, C, and D. A is gated into AND gate AN1 along with the signal B. Thus the resultant output of AN1 is the logic conjunction of A and B, or symbolically, A · B. AND gate AN2 and its output are symbolically represented as C · D. Module AN3 gates the outputs of the other

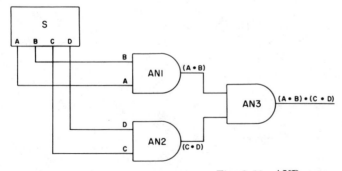

Fig. 3-18 AND gates.

TABLE 3-6

A	B	C	D	A · B	C · D	(A · B) · (C · D)
0	0	0	0	0	0	0
0	0	0	1	0	0	0
0	0	1	0	0	0	0
0	0	1	1	0	1	0
0	1	0	0	0	0	0
0	1	0	1	0	0	0
0	1	1	0	0	0	0
0	1	1	1	0	1	0
1	0	0	0	0	0	0
1	0	0	1	0	0	0
1	0	1	0	0	0	0
1	0	1	1	0	1	0
1	1	0	0	1	0	0
1	1	0	1	1	0	0
1	1	1	0	1	0	0
1	1	1	1	1	1	1

two AND gates and provides as an output the conjunction of the four variables. Since each of the variables can assume two states (binary 1 or 0), there can be 16 different possible combinations of the four inputs.

Table 3-6 shows every possible combination of the four variables along with the logic states of the outputs of each gate. From the table, one can observe that the output of AN1 is a 1 only when A is 1 and B is 1. The same logic holds true for the other two gates in that their outputs are in the 1 state only when both inputs are 1s.

Verify the truth table for all input conditions.

The OR Gate. The logic OR gate implements the function A + B. If the two inputs to an OR gate are A and B, then the output is A + B. In this case, the two inputs can be thought of as closing two switches arranged in parallel. The output of the gate is 1 if at least one of the inputs (A or B) is a 1; that is, A + B = 1 if A = 1 or B = 1. If all inputs to an OR gate are 0, then the OR-gate output must be a 0; that is, A + B = 0 if A = 0 and B = 0.

If the inputs A and B are represented as circles on a Venn diagram, then the OR gate reflects that area which includes both circles. This area is shown by shading in Fig. 3-19. At every point in this area, either A or B exists (equals 1).

To represent the OR function with a truth table, the output is a 1 if at least one input is 1. (See Table 3-7.) The only time the output is 0 is when both inputs are 0. Here again, the

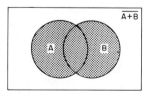

Fig. 3-19   Venn diagram of **OR** *function.*

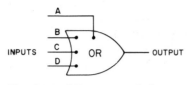

Fig. 3-20   OR-gate symbol.

truth table is identical to that describing the OR operation (Table 3-3).

The OR gate may have more than two inputs. The OR-gate modules used in the demonstrations, like the AND gates, accept up to four inputs. These OR gates can implement four variable functions, such as $A + B + C + D$. The rules for three- or four-input gates are identical to the rules for two-input gates. At least one input must be 1 to "open the gate." If all inputs are 0, the gate output is 0. Unused inputs have no effect on gate operation.

TABLE 3-7

A	B	Output
1	1	1
1	0	1
0	1	1
0	0	0

The symbol for the OR-gate module is shown in Fig. 3-20.

Demonstration 3-3   **The OR *Operation***

Purpose

To illustrate the implementation of the logic OR operation using the OR-gate module (OR).

Equipment

   1—Level switch (S)
   3—OR gates (OR)

Discussion and Implementation

An OR gate accepts inputs and provides an output which is the disjunctive representation of the inputs. If any input (one or more) is a 1, it will cause the output to be in the 1 state. The operation of an electronic OR gate is analogous to that of the OR gate shown in Fig. 3-11, where the inputs are hot and cold faucets and the output is a water tap. The inputs and output of an electronic gate are voltage levels, one level representing a logic 1 and another representing a logic 0. Thus, if any input to an OR gate is a 1 level, the output will be a 1 level.

The inputs to gates OR1 and OR2 are generated on the level switch S. Each of the inputs from the level switch can be set to the 1 or 0 level. Assume that inputs A, B, and C are at the 0 state and that D is a logic 1. What will the state of the OR-gate outputs be in Fig. 3-21 with these input

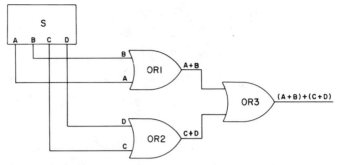

Fig. 3-21 OR gates.

conditions? The output of OR1, which represents the logic disjunction (A + B), will be a 0 since both inputs are 0s. The output of OR2 will be a 1 since D is a 1, and the output of OR3 will be a 1 since the input received from OR2 is a 1. A truth table can be constructed for the 16 possible combinations of inputs using the above reasoning process, and this can be verified by implementing the demonstration with actual modules.

3-7 *Implementation:* **NAND, NOR**

The NOT (negation) operation is performed by the use of logic inversion in a gate with one input and one output. If the input is a 1, the output is a 0, and vice versa, as listed in Table 3-4. Logic inversion is usually performed in connection with another gate.

The combination of an AND gate followed by an inverter is called an *inverted*-AND, or NAND, gate. The combination of an OR gate followed by an inverter is called an *inverted*-OR, or NOR, gate. Although a computer could be designed using only AND gates, OR gates, and inverters, both the NAND and NOR gates are used extensively.

The NAND Gate. The NAND gate is an inverted-AND gate, or NOT AND. The NAND gate performs the logic operation $\overline{A \cdot B}$ (the bar extends across both terms). This operation is exactly opposite to that performed by the AND gate. If the two inputs to a NAND gate are A and B, then the output is $\overline{A \cdot B}$. With an AND gate, the output is 1 if both inputs are 1s. With a NAND gate, if both inputs are 1s, the output is 0. Conversely, if either input to an AND gate is 0, the output is 0; but if either input to a NAND gate is 0, the output is 1. If the inputs A and B are represented as circles on a Venn diagram, then the NAND gate represents that area outside the area of overlap. The shaded portion of Fig. 3-22 shows this area. At every point in the shaded area, A and B never exist (equal 1) at the same time. Therefore, sym-

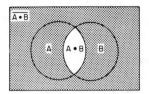

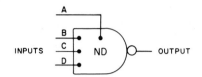

*Fig. 3-22 Venn dia-
gram of NAND function.*

Fig. 3-23   NAND gate symbol.

bolically, $\overline{A \cdot B} = 1$.   The Venn diagram shows that $\overline{A \cdot B}$ is the inverse of $A \cdot B$.

Table 3-8 shows that the output of a NAND gate is 0 only when both inputs are 1.   In all other cases, the output is 1.

TABLE 3-8

A	B	Output
1	1	0
1	0	1
0	1	1
0	0	1

Note that the output column in this truth table is exactly opposite to that for an AND gate (Table 3-5).

The NAND gate may have more than two inputs.   The NAND-gate module shown in Fig. 3-23 has four inputs; the function $\overline{A \cdot B \cdot C \cdot D}$ can be represented.   In this case, if any input to the gate is 0, the output is 1, and all inputs must be 1s for the output to be 0.

The symbol for a NAND-gate module is shown in Fig. 3-23.   The small circle to the right of the AND symbol identifies the gate as an inverted-AND, or NAND, gate.

When a NAND gate is used with a single input, it does not perform the gating function but it does perform logic inversion.   In other words, the NAND gate can be used to implement the logic NOT operation.   If X were the symbolic input to a NAND gate, the output would be $\overline{X}$.

Demonstration 3-4   *The* NAND *Operation*

Purpose

To implement the logic NAND operation using the NAND-gate module (ND).

Equipment

1—Level switch (S)
3—NAND gates (ND)

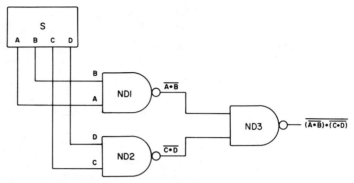

Fig. 3-24 **NAND gates.**

Discussion and Implementation

The NAND-gate modules provide implementation of the inverted-AND, or NAND, operation. Furthermore, like the NOR gate to be described next, the NAND gate can be used as an inverter. The output of a NAND gate is a 0 only if all its inputs are 1. Any 0 input to a NAND gate sends its output to a 1. Therefore, as with a NOR gate, if a single input is presented, the gate output will be the inverse of the input.

The output of a NAND gate will be a 0 only when all its inputs are 1s; thus any 0 input will make the corresponding output a 1. The truth table (Table 3-9) can be constructed to illustrate the output conditions of each of the NAND gates in Fig. 3-24 for all the possible combinations of the four variables and can be verified in the demonstration.

TABLE 3-9

A	B	C	D	ND1	ND2	ND3
0	0	0	0	1	1	0
0	0	0	1	1	1	0
0	0	1	0	1	1	0
0	0	1	1	1	0	1
0	1	0	0	1	1	0
0	1	0	1	1	1	0
0	1	1	0	1	1	0
0	1	1	1	1	0	1
1	0	0	0	1	1	0
1	0	0	1	1	1	0
1	0	1	0	1	1	0
1	0	1	1	1	0	1
1	1	0	0	0	1	1
1	1	0	1	0	1	1
1	1	1	0	0	1	1
1	1	1	1	0	0	1

The **NOR** *Gate.*   The final logic gate to be discussed is the inverted-OR, or NOR, gate (NOT OR), which is similar to the NAND gate.

The NOR gate performs the logic operation $\overline{A + B}$.   As with the NAND gate, the bar extends across both terms.   If the two inputs to a NOR gate are A and B, then the output is $\overline{A + B}$.   This operation is exactly opposite to the operation performed by the OR gate.   With an OR gate, any input at logic 1 results in a 1 output; with a NOR gate, any input at logic 1 results in a 0 output.   Conversely, with an OR gate, all inputs must be 0s to have a 0 output; with a NOR gate, all inputs must be 0s to have a 1 output.

If the inputs A and B are represented as circles on a Venn diagram, then the NOR gate reflects that area lying outside of both circles.   This area is shown by the shaded portion of Fig. 3-25.   At every point in this area, NEITHER A NOR B exists (equals 1).   Symbolically, $\overline{A + B}$ exists (equals 1).   The Venn diagram helps to point out that $\overline{A + B}$ is the inverse of A + B.

In the truth table (Table 3-10), the output is a 1 only if neither input is 1.   If at least one input is 1, the output is 0.   The output column in Table 3-10 is the exact opposite, or inverse, of that in Table 3-3.

TABLE 3-10

A	B	Output
1	1	0
1	0	0
0	1	0
0	0	1

Like AND, OR, and NAND gates, the NOR gate may have more than two inputs.   The NOR-gate module illustrated in Fig. 3-26 can accept four inputs and can represent the function $\overline{A + B + C + D}$.   Like a two-input NOR gate, if any input is 1 the gate output will be 0.   Only if all inputs are 0s will the gate output be 1.

With only one input connected, the NOR gate serves the function of an inverter.   Symbolically, if the input is X, the output is $\overline{X}$.   The symbol

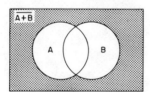

Fig. 3-25 Venn diagram of **NOR** *function.*

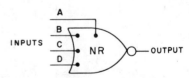

Fig. 3-26 **NOR** *gate symbol.*

for NOR-gate modules is shown in Fig. 3-26.   The small circle at the point of the OR symbol identifies the gate as an inverted-OR, or NOR, gate.

The NOR, AND, OR, and NAND gates are the four basic gating elements that can be used in a computer.   There are no others.   Furthermore, some computers are designed using only one type of gate, e.g., NAND, to perform all the logic required.   A medium-size machine requires on the order of four to five thousand gating elements, while a larger computer can require between one and two orders of magnitude more gating.

Demonstration 3-5   **The NOR** *Operation*

Purpose

To implement the logic NOR operation using the NOR-gate   module (NR).

Equipment

   1—Level switch (S)
   3—NOR gates (NR)

Discussion and Implementation

The NOR-gate modules provide implementation of the inverted-OR, or NOR, operation.   Furthermore, with a single input, the NOR gate can be used as an inverter.

As described in the text, the output of a NOR gate is 1 only if all its inputs are 0.   Any 1 input to a NOR gate makes its output 0.   Thus, if there is only one input to a NOR gate, the output of the gate is 1 if the input is 0 and 0 if the input is 1; that is, the output is always the inverse of the input.   Used in this way, the NOR gate performs the NOT operation and functions as an inverter in the same manner as a NAND gate.

In Fig. 3-27, assume that A and D are 1s and that B and C are 0s.

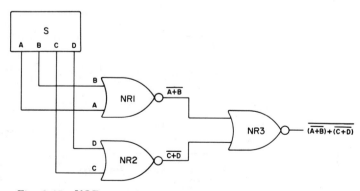

Fig. 3-27   **NOR** *gates.*

What will be the logic state of each of the three NOR-gate outputs? The outputs of NR1 and NR2 will both be logic 0 since each of these gates has a 1 input. The output of NR3 will obviously be a 1 since both its inputs are 0s. Note that the symbolic representation of each of the outputs has a single bar extending over the input terms connected by the disjunctive symbol (+). The proper symbolic representations must be recorded clearly and exactly; otherwise, they can easily be misinterpreted.

3-8 *Boolean Algebra*

The AND, OR, and NOT operators make up all the basic symbols of digital logic. However, in solving logic problems, the operators do not appear individually, but as parts of an equation. Since by their very nature these problems are too complicated to reason out verbally, it is necessary to derive an abstract system of rules whereby the operators can be manipulated to form different equations or solutions to equations. Boolean algebra, named for its inventor, George Boole, provides just such a system.

The basic rules, or postulates, of Boolean algebra are similar to the rules of common numerical algebra and can be derived by induction, that is, by reasoning through every possible solution of each postulate. This is a rather simple task since each symbol can have only two logic states. The use of Venn diagrams aids in this task.

The Postulates of Boolean Algebra. Figure 3-28 is a Venn diagram. By definition, the rectangle is the entire universe and contains all logic conditions. Everything within the circle represents $A = 1$, and everything outside the circle represents $A = 0$, or $\overline{A} = 1$.

The expression $A \cdot 1$ is represented by the area where A overlaps the rectangle. But exactly 100 percent of A overlaps the rectangle, no more and no less. Therefore,

$$A \cdot 1 = A \tag{3-1}$$

Similarly, the expression $A \cdot 0$ must equal 0. Since 0 represents no area at all within the rectangle, $A \cdot 0$ also represents no area at all. Therefore,

$$A \cdot 0 = 0 \tag{3-2}$$

The expression $A \cdot A$ is just a repetition of the occurrence of A. It is merely a second area A, identical to the first, which exactly overlaps the

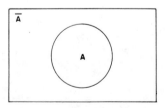

Fig. 3-28   Venn diagram for postulates.

original A.   Therefore,

$$A \cdot A = A \tag{3-3}$$

The expression $A \cdot \overline{A}$ represents that portion of the Venn diagram where A overlaps $\overline{A}$.   Since there is no such portion, $A \cdot \overline{A} = 0$.   Nothing can be A and NOT A at the same time.   Thus,

$$A \cdot \overline{A} = 0 \tag{3-4}$$

The expression $\overline{\overline{A}}$ stands for NOT NOT A.   Since what is not NOT A must in fact be A,

$$\overline{\overline{A}} = A \tag{3-5}$$

Equations (3-6) to (3-9) for $A + 1$, $A + 0$, $A + A$, and $A + \overline{A}$ can also be reasoned inductively from the Venn diagram in Fig. 3-28.   All nine postulates of Boolean algebra are listed below in tabular form.

	Equation No.			Equation No.
$A \cdot 1 = A$	(3-1)		$A + 1 = 1$	(3-6)
$A \cdot 0 = 0$	(3-2)		$A + 0 = A$	(3-7)
$A \cdot A = A$	(3-3)		$A + A = A$	(3-8)
$A \cdot \overline{A} = 0$	(3-4)		$A + \overline{A} = 1$	(3-9)
$\overline{\overline{A}} = A$	(3-5)			

Demonstration 3-6   The Postulates of Boolean Algebra

Purpose

To demonstrate the proofs of the postulates of Boolean algebra using logic modules.

Equipment

1—Level switch (S)
1—AND gate (AN)
2—OR gates (OR)
1—NAND gate (ND)

Discussion and Implementation

Just as the postulates of Boolean algebra can be inductively reasoned to be true with the aid of Venn diagrams, they can also be proved with logic modules.   For example, if a constant 1 source is gated into an AND gate along with the variable A, the output of the AND gate will always assume the state of the input A.   If A is a 1, then the output will be a 1; and if A is a 0, the output will be 0.   A few of the postulates are implemented in Fig. 3-29.

One of the two Inputs to OR1, a constant 1, is gated with A.   If any input to an OR gate is a 1, the output will be a 1.   Thus the output of OR1 will be a 1 regardless of the state of A.   The two inputs to AN1 are the

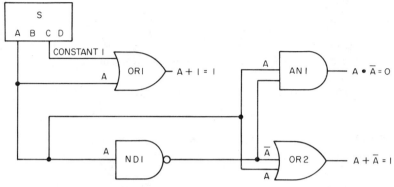

Fig. 3-29   Postulates.

complement of one another; thus if one of them is a logic 0, the other is a logic 1.   With this situation, one of the inputs to AN1 will always be 0, which guarantees that the output will be 0 and proves that $A \cdot \overline{A} = 0$. A similar situation occurs at the input of OR2, where A and its complement $\overline{A}$ are ORed together.   This guarantees that one of the two inputs will be a logic 1; consequently, the output of OR2 will always be a 1.

Note that the output of gate ND1 fans out to two different inputs. Logically, there is no limit to the number of different gates an output may drive, i.e., be connected to.   However, there are circuit limitations, and the logic designer must be aware of the particular rules associated with the hardware (modules) at his disposal.   Typically, a gate would be allowed to drive a maximum of 5 to 10 other gates, although some specifically designed for high fan-out can drive 25 or more gates.

Laws of Boolean Algebra.   In Fig. 3-30, a circle labeled B has been added to the Venn diagram of Fig. 3-28.   The area A + B is exactly equal to the area B + A.   The order of the terms is of no significance. Note also that $A \cdot B = B \cdot A$.   Again, the order is insignificant.   These are the commutative laws of Boolean algebra.

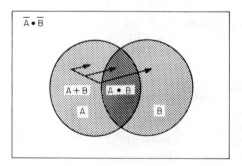

Fig. 3-30   Venn diagram for commutative laws.

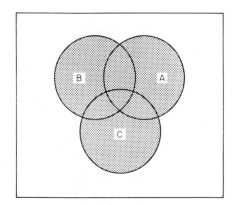

Fig. 3-31   Venn diagram for associative laws.

Commutative laws

$$A + B = B + A \tag{3-10}$$
$$A \cdot B = B \cdot A \tag{3-11}$$

In Fig. 3-31, a third circle has been added to the Venn diagram, representing C. Note that the area $A + (B + C)$ is exactly the same area as $(A + B) + C$. Furthermore, the area $A \cdot (B \cdot C)$ is exactly the same area as $(A \cdot B) \cdot C$. Therefore, $A + (B + C) = (A + B) + C$ and $A \cdot (B \cdot C) = (A \cdot B) \cdot C$. These are the associative laws of Boolean algebra.

Associative laws

$$(A + B) + C = A + (B + C) \tag{3-12}$$
$$(A \cdot B) \cdot C = A \cdot (B \cdot C) \tag{3-13}$$

The associative and commutative laws are used in Boolean algebra. In Eqs. (3-12) and (3-13), the parentheses could be omitted without causing error. These simple examples are used merely to illustrate the laws governing the use of parentheses.

The three-circle Venn diagram (Fig. 3-31) can also be used to show the distributive laws of Boolean algebra. Thus $A \cdot (B + C)$ is identical to the area $A \cdot B + A \cdot C$. By shading the appropriate areas, area $A + B \cdot C$ can be proved to be identical to $(A + B) \cdot (A + C)$.

Distributive laws

$$A \cdot (B + C) = A \cdot B + A \cdot C \tag{3-14}$$
$$A + B \cdot C = (A + B) \cdot (A + C) \tag{3-15}$$

Demonstration 3-7   The Laws of Boolean Algebra

Purpose

To demonstate proofs for the associative laws of Boolean algebra using logic modules.

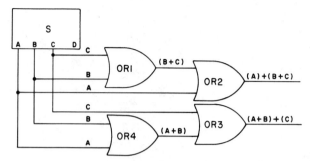

Fig. 3-32   *Logic for associative law 1.*

Equipment

 1—Level switch (S)
 4—AND gates (AN)
 4—OR gates (OR)

Discussion and Implementation

 Proofs for the laws of Boolean algebra are as straightforward as the proofs for the postulates of Boolean algebra. Although they require more modules, the laws are conceptually simpler.

 The associative law, in terms of electronic modules, merely says that it does not matter how groups of AND gates are ANDed together. Where the commutative law points out that the order in which similar operations are performed is immaterial, the associative law points out that the way in which similar operations are grouped is also immaterial.

 Figure 3-32 illustrates that the grouping of the three variables by use of parentheses is immaterial since the outputs of OR2 and OR3 are identical for all combinations of states of input variables. The outputs of AN2 and AN3 in Fig. 3-33 will also be equivalent for all possible input conditions. This should be verified in the demonstration.

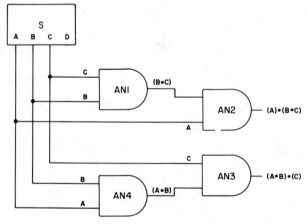

Fig. 3-33   *Logic for associative law 2.*

Simplifying Theorems of Boolean Algebra.   The laws of Boolean algebra can now be used to derive additional useful expressions:

$$
\begin{aligned}
A + A \cdot B &= A \cdot 1 + A \cdot B && \text{by (3-1)} \\
&= A \cdot (1 + B) && \text{by (3-14)} \\
&= A \cdot 1 && \text{by (3-6)} \\
A + A \cdot B &= A && \text{by (3-1)} && \text{(3-16)}
\end{aligned}
$$

$$
\begin{aligned}
A \cdot (A + B) &= A \cdot A + A \cdot B && \text{by (3-14)} \\
&= A + A \cdot B && \text{by (3-3)} \\
A \cdot (A + B) &= A && \text{by (3-16)} && \text{(3-17)}
\end{aligned}
$$

$$
\begin{aligned}
A + \overline{A} \cdot B &= (A + \overline{A}) \cdot (A + B) && \text{by (3-15)} \\
&= 1 \cdot (A + B) && \text{by (3-9)} \\
A + \overline{A} \cdot B &= A + B && \text{by (3-1)} && \text{(3-18)}
\end{aligned}
$$

These expressions can also be inferred from Venn diagrams, and the reader may wish to do so.

3-9   *De Morgan's Theorems*

Two other powerful expressions can be inferred from Venn diagrams. These are called *De Morgan's theorems.*   In the three-circle Venn diagram in Fig. 3-34, the shaded portion represents the area $\overline{A + B + C}$, that is, the area where neither A nor B nor C exists, or $\overline{A + B + C} = 1$.   But this is also the area where $\overline{A}$ and $\overline{B}$ and $\overline{C}$ all exist together, or symbolically, $\overline{A} \cdot \overline{B} \cdot \overline{C} = 1$.   Therefore,

$$\overline{A + B + C} = \overline{A} \cdot \overline{B} \cdot \overline{C} \tag{3-19}$$

The converse is also true.   The shaded portion of Fig. 3-35 represents the area $\overline{A \cdot B \cdot C} = 1$, but this is exactly the area in which

$$\overline{A} + \overline{B} + \overline{C} = 1$$

Therefore,

$$\overline{A \cdot B \cdot C} = \overline{A} + \overline{B} + \overline{C} \tag{3-20}$$

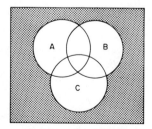

Fig. 3-34   Venn diagram 1, De Morgan's theorem.

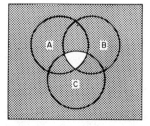

Fig. 3-35   Venn diagram 2, De Morgan's theorem.

Both of De Morgan's theorems are completely general. The theorems simply state that the inverse of any series of OR operations is exactly equivalent to the same series of inverted-AND operations and, similarly, that the inverse of any series of AND operations is exactly equivalent to the same series of inverted-OR operations. For the two-variable case, consider Table 3-11.

TABLE 3-11

1	2	3	4	5	6	7
A	B	$\overline{A}$	$\overline{B}$	$A \cdot B$	$\overline{A \cdot B}$	$\overline{A} + \overline{B}$
1	1	0	0	1	0	0
1	0	0	1	0	1	1
0	1	1	0	0	1	1
0	0	1	1	0	1	1

Columns 1 and 2 list all possible combinations of the inputs A and B. In columns 3 and 4 are the inverses of these inputs. When $A = 1$, then $\overline{A} = 0$; when $B = 1$, then $\overline{B} = 0$; and so on. Column 5 represents $A \cdot B$. In this column, a 1 appears when A and B are both equal to 1. Column 6 is the inverse of column 5, representing the inverse of $A \cdot B$, or $\overline{A \cdot B}$. Column 7 then represents $\overline{A} + \overline{B}$. A 1 appears in this column whenever a 1 appears in either the $\overline{A}$ or the $\overline{B}$ column. Verification of De Morgan's theorems is reflected by the fact that the column for $\overline{A \cdot B}$ is identical to the column for $\overline{A} + \overline{B}$; that is, $\overline{A \cdot B} = \overline{A} + \overline{B}$. A similar truth table can be constructed to show that $\overline{A + B} = \overline{A} \cdot \overline{B}$. Four examples are

$$\overline{A \cdot B \cdot C} = \overline{A} + \overline{B} + \overline{C}$$
$$A \cdot B \cdot C = \overline{\overline{A} + \overline{B} + \overline{C}}$$
$$\overline{A + B + C} = \overline{A} \cdot \overline{B} \cdot \overline{C}$$
$$A + B + C = \overline{\overline{A} \cdot \overline{B} \cdot \overline{C}}$$

Demonstration 3-8   The Theorems of Boolean Algebra

Purpose

To demonstrate the proofs for De Morgan's theorem and two simplifying theorems [Eqs. (3-20), (3-16), and (3-17), respectively] by use of logic modules.

Equipment

1—Level switch (S)
1—AND gate (AN)
1—OR gate (OR)
4—NAND gates (ND)

Discussion and Implementation

De Morgan's theorem states that the negation of a series of conjunctions (AND) is equivalent to the disjunctive (ORing) of a series of negations. In terms of logic modules, this says that one multi-input NAND gate (the negation of a series of conjunctions) is equivalent to many single-input NAND gates ORed together (the disjunction of a series of negations). The NAND gates in the latter case perform logic inversions rather than gating functions. Electronically, this implementation is limited by the number of inputs a NAND gate will accept. Obviously, a series of seven conjunctions would require a seven-input NAND gate. Figure 3-36 and Table 3-12 illustrate the equivalence of De Morgan's theorem $\overline{A \cdot B \cdot C} = \overline{A} + \overline{B} + \overline{C}$.

NAND gate ND1, in Fig. 3-36, is the output which provides the equivalent to the output of the OR gate. The equivalence is readily apparent upon examining the truth table for all possible combinations of the three inputs. The simple rules to remember when relating the diagram to Table 3-12 are (1) any 0 input to a NAND gate will display a 1 at its output, (2) any 1 input to the OR gate will display a 1 at its output.

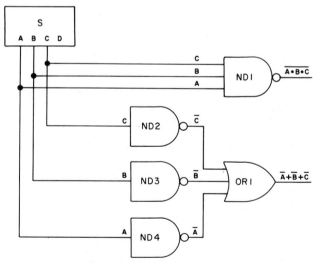

Fig. 3-36   Logic for De Morgan's theorem.

TABLE 3-12

A	B	C	$\overline{A \cdot B \cdot C}$	$\overline{A} + \overline{B} + \overline{C}$
0	0	0	1	1
0	0	1	1	1
0	1	0	1	1
0	1	1	1	1
1	0	0	1	1
1	0	1	1	1
1	1	0	1	1
1	1	1	0	0

The condition where all inputs are logic 1s presents all 0 inputs to the OR gate and causes its output to go to 0.   This situation is shown on the diagram when all the switches are positioned to the logic-1 source; thus the logic inverters ND2, ND3, and ND4 present all 0s to the OR gate.

The simplifying theorems state that if any input to an AND gate is ORed together with the output of the AND gate, the output of the OR gate will be equivalent to the input that is common to both gates.   Conversely, if any input to an OR gate is ANDed together with the output of the OR gate, the resultant output of the AND gate will be equivalent to the input

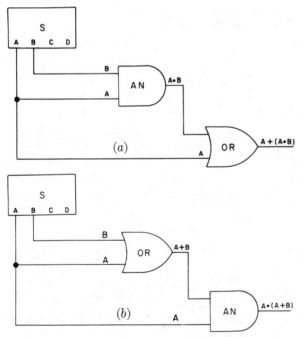

Fig. 3-37   *Logic for simplifying the-orems.*

that is common to both gates.   Here again, the validity of the statements is evident by inspection of the block-diagram implementation.

In Fig. 3-37a, the simplifying theorem $A + A \cdot B = A$ can be inferred logically by switching B from 1 to 0 for both conditions of A. By doing this, it can be seen that the output of the OR gate reflects the logic state of A regardless of what B does.   Thus, it can be stated that the two gates are not performing logic and are redundant, or logically useless.   The same criterion applies to Fig. 3-37b, which shows a proof of the simplifying theorem $A \cdot (A + B) = A$.

3-10   *Simplification and Conversion*

Simplification.   Quite often an apparently complex logic equation can be reduced to a much simpler one by the application of the rules of Boolean algebra.   Consider the expression

$$A \cdot B + A \cdot B \cdot C + A \cdot B \cdot \overline{C} + \overline{A} \cdot B \cdot C$$

From Eq. (3-14), the term $A \cdot B$ can be factored out of the first and third terms and the term $B \cdot C$ can be factored from the second and fourth terms.   The result is

$$A \cdot B \cdot (1 + \overline{C}) + B \cdot C \cdot (A + \overline{A})$$

Now, from Eqs. (3-6) and (3-9), $(1 + \overline{C})$ and $(A + \overline{A})$ are both equal to 1, reducing the expression to

$$A \cdot B \cdot 1 + B \cdot C \cdot 1$$

From Eq. (3-1), this simplifies further to

$$A \cdot B + B \cdot C$$

which, from Eq. (3-14), simplifies again to

$$B \cdot (A + C)$$

This is a considerable improvement over the original expression.

If desired, the same terms could have been used many times in factoring. As an example, $A \cdot B$ could have been factored from the first three terms and $B \cdot C$ could have been factored from the second and fourth terms. This is equivalent to adding $A \cdot B \cdot C$ to the expression.   From Eq. (3-8), any term can be ORed with itself without changing the value of the expression.

Sometimes, in the process of simplification, it is useful to expand by multiplying one or more terms of an expression by the form $A + \overline{A}$. Any expression can be multiplied by 1 without changing its value; from

Eq. (3-9), $A + \overline{A} = 1$. Consider the expression

$$A \cdot B + \overline{A} \cdot \overline{C} + B \cdot \overline{C}$$

If the last term is multiplied by $A + \overline{A}$, the result is

$$A \cdot B + \overline{A} \cdot \overline{C} + A \cdot B \cdot \overline{C} + \overline{A} \cdot B \cdot \overline{C}$$

Factoring $A \cdot B$ from the first and third terms then gives

$$A \cdot B \cdot (1 + \overline{C}) + \overline{A} \cdot \overline{C} + \overline{A} \cdot B \cdot \overline{C}$$

which, from Eq. (3-6), simplifies to

$$A \cdot B + \overline{A} \cdot \overline{C} + \overline{A} \cdot B \cdot \overline{C}$$

Factoring $\overline{A} \cdot \overline{C}$ from the last two terms gives

$$A \cdot B + \overline{A} \cdot \overline{C} \cdot (1 + B)$$

or, from Eq. (3-6),

$$A \cdot B + \overline{A} \cdot \overline{C}$$

Note that the third term of the original expression has been eliminated. The third term was not necessary to specify the expression completely.

Rearrangement of an expression may also be desirable. Consider the expression

$$A \cdot \overline{B} + \overline{A} \cdot B$$

Adding $A \cdot \overline{A} = 0$ and $B \cdot \overline{B} = 0$ does not change the value of the expression:

$$A \cdot \overline{A} + A \cdot \overline{B} + \overline{A} \cdot B + B \cdot \overline{B}$$

Factoring,

$$A \cdot (\overline{A} + \overline{B}) + B \cdot (\overline{A} + \overline{B})$$

Factoring once more,

$$(A + B) \cdot (\overline{A} + \overline{B})$$

Although this expression is no simpler than the original one, it may be easier to implement in a particular design where one of the terms may be available from a previous implementation.

A general theorem of Boolean algebra is that any logic expression can be stated as either a conjunction of disjunctive terms or a disjunction of conjunctive terms. In other words, any expression can be stated either as OR operations connected by AND operations or as AND operations connected by OR operations. For example, the expression

$$(A + B) \cdot (C + D)$$

is said to be in the OR-to-AND form.   By multiplying the terms out to form

$$A \cdot C + A \cdot D + B \cdot C + B \cdot D$$

the expression is converted to AND-to-OR form.

Conversion.   Frequently, the logic designer desires to convert a logic expression to a form which is readily implemented by the type of logic circuits he has at his disposal.   Economic reasons frequently limit the type or types of gates the logic designer may use to implement his logic. Designing a system exclusively of NAND gates or NOR gates may simplify the manufacturing process since there are fewer types of modules in the system.   Cost reductions are realized in the design and fabrication process.   The three widely used approaches to logic implementation are NAND gates exclusively, NOR gates exclusively, or AND-OR gating elements with logic inverters.   Inverters are necessary with AND-OR logic since the negation signals are often required in a logic expression.

A logic designer may be restricted, as is often the case, to the use of NAND gates exclusively.   Thus, he must transform the AND-OR expressions to the NAND form which is readily implemented with NAND gates.   As mentioned previously the basic logic circuits are the AND, OR, NOR, and NAND circuits.   Any Boolean expression can be written in any one of the following forms:

$$
\begin{aligned}
\text{AND-OR:} \quad & A \cdot B + \overline{C} \cdot D \\
\text{OR-AND:} \quad & (A + \overline{C}) \cdot (A + D) \cdot (B + \overline{C}) \cdot (B + D) \\
\text{NAND:} \quad & \overline{\overline{A \cdot B} \cdot \overline{\overline{C} \cdot D}} \\
\text{NOR:} \quad & \overline{\overline{A + \overline{B}} + \overline{C + \overline{D}}}
\end{aligned}
$$

All these expressions are equivalent, although this is not readily apparent by inspection.   The conversion from AND-OR to NAND is accomplished easily by using De Morgan's theorem.   Consider the conversion of $A \cdot B + \overline{C} \cdot D$ in Fig. 3-38 to the NAND form.

The two variable terms can be substituted using single variables.   Let

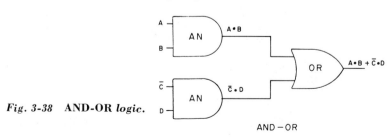

Fig. 3-38   **AND-OR logic.**

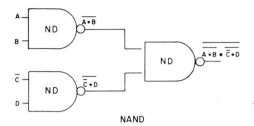

NAND

Fig. 3-39   **NAND** *logic.*

$A \cdot B = X$ and $\overline{C} \cdot D = Y$.   From De Morgan's theorem [Eq. (3-19)],

$$X + Y = \overline{\overline{X} \cdot \overline{Y}}$$

By resubstituting the original terms,

$$A \cdot B + \overline{C} \cdot D = \overline{\overline{A \cdot B} \cdot \overline{\overline{C} \cdot D}}$$

This expression can now be implemented entirely by NAND gates, as shown in Fig. 3-39.

Conversion from AND-OR expressions to the NOR form requires the repetitive use of De Morgan's theorem, which changes all conjunctives to disjunctives.   Consider the conversion of $A \cdot B + \overline{C} \cdot D$ to the NOR form.   By use of Eq. (3-20),

$$A \cdot B = \overline{\overline{A} + \overline{B}}$$

and

$$\overline{C} \cdot D = \overline{\overline{\overline{C}} + \overline{D}} = \overline{C + \overline{D}}$$

Thus

$$A \cdot B + \overline{C} \cdot D = \overline{\overline{\overline{A} + \overline{B}} + \overline{C + \overline{D}}}$$

Figure 3-40 demonstrates how the function $A \cdot B + \overline{C} \cdot D$ is implemented strictly with the use of NOR gates.   Although the NOR and NAND configurations are equivalent, it can be seen that the NAND configuration is more economical in implementing this particular expression because it takes one less gate.   The final expression in Fig. 3-40 is

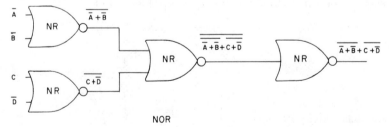

NOR

Fig. 3-40   **NOR** *logic.*

entirely in terms of NOR operations. By alternate use of Eq. (3-5) and De Morgan's theorems [Eqs. (3-19) and (3-20)], all the ANDs or all the ORs can be eliminated from any logic equation by converting it to either the NOR or the NAND form.

This is useful because it means that any logic expression can be implemented using different gating types. Any equation can be reduced to the NAND or NOR form and implemented using only NAND or NOR gates.

The conversion from AND-OR to OR-AND requires the repeated use of the distributive law [Eq. (3-15)]. Consider transferring the expression $A \cdot B + \overline{C} \cdot D$ to the OR-AND form:

$$
\begin{aligned}
A \cdot B + \overline{C} \cdot D & \\
&= (A \cdot B + \overline{C}) \cdot (A \cdot B + D) && \text{by (3-15)} \\
&= (\overline{C} + A \cdot B) \cdot (D + A \cdot B) && \text{by (3-10)} \\
&= [(\overline{C} + A) \cdot (\overline{C} + B)] \cdot [(D + A) \cdot (D + B)] && \text{by (3-15)}
\end{aligned}
$$
(AND-OR)

(OR-AND)
$$
\begin{aligned}
A \cdot B + \overline{C} \cdot D & \\
&= (\overline{C} + A) \cdot (\overline{C} + B) \cdot (D + A) \cdot (D + B) && \text{by removal} \\
& && \text{of primary} \\
& && \text{parentheses}
\end{aligned}
$$

The conversion from OR-AND to AND-OR is performed easily by multiplying the terms out as is normally done in conventional algebra. This type of conversion usually involves a simplification process to obtain the minimized expression:

$$
\begin{aligned}
& [(\overline{C} + A) \cdot (\overline{C} + B)] \cdot [(D + A) \cdot (D + B)] \\
&= (\overline{C} \cdot \overline{C} + \overline{C} \cdot B + A \cdot \overline{C} + A \cdot B) \\
& \qquad\qquad\qquad \cdot (D \cdot D + D \cdot B + A \cdot D + A \cdot B) && \text{by (3-14)} \\
&= [\overline{C} \cdot (1 + B + A) + A \cdot B] \cdot [D \cdot (1 + B + A) + A \cdot B] \\
& && \text{factor} \\
&= (\overline{C} \cdot 1 + A \cdot B) \cdot (D \cdot 1 + A \cdot B) && \text{reduce by (3-6)} \\
&= (\overline{C} + A \cdot B) \cdot (D + A \cdot B) && \text{by (3-1)} \\
&= \overline{C} \cdot D + \overline{C} \cdot A \cdot B + A \cdot B \cdot D + A \cdot B \cdot A \cdot B && \text{expand} \\
&= \overline{C} \cdot D + A \cdot B \cdot (\overline{C} + D + 1) && \text{factor} \\
&= \overline{C} \cdot D + A \cdot B \cdot 1 && \text{reduce by (3-6)} \\
&= \overline{C} \cdot D + A \cdot B && \text{by (3-1)} \\
&= A \cdot B + \overline{C} \cdot D && \text{by (3-10)}
\end{aligned}
$$

In summary, Table 3-13 illustrates each particular conversion process (two arrows indicate conversion in either direction) and the associated equation to be used.

TABLE 3-13

1. AND-OR → OR-AND	Repeated use of Eq. (3-15)
2. AND-OR ⇆ NAND	De Morgan's theorem, Eq. (3-19)
3. AND-OR ⇌ NOR	De Morgan's theorem, Eq. (3-20)
4. OR-AND → AND-OR	Repeated expansion by distributive law, Eq. (3-14)
5. OR-AND ⇆ NAND	De Morgan's theorem, Eq. (3-19)
6. OR-AND ⇆ NOR	De Morgan's theorem, Eq. (3-20)
7. NAND ⇆ NOR	De Morgan's theorems, Eqs. (3-19), (3-20)

To convert from NAND to NOR or from NOR to NAND, a double conversion process can also be used. The paths shown on Table 3-13 provide the directions. For example, to convert from NAND to NOR, first perform conversion 2 in the direction of NAND to AND-OR. Second, perform conversion 3 in the direction of AND-OR to NOR. To convert from NOR to NAND, first perform conversion 6 in the direction of NOR to OR-AND; then perform conversion 5 in the direction of OR-AND to NAND.

As a final aide to an understanding of simplification and conversion as used in solving Boolean algebra problems, Table 3-14 presents all simplifying expressions. At this time, the most comprehensive check for the individual is self-assurance that the implications of all expressions are

TABLE 3-14

Equation No.

(3-1)	$A \cdot 1 = A$	
(3-2)	$A \cdot 0 = 0$	
(3-3)	$A \cdot A = A$	
(3-4)	$A \cdot \overline{A} = 0$	
(3-5)	$\overline{\overline{A}} = A$	Postulates
(3-6)	$A + 1 = 1$	
(3-7)	$A + 0 = A$	
(3-8)	$A + A = A$	
(3-9)	$A + \overline{A} = 1$	
(3-10)	$A + B = B + A$	Commutative laws
(3-11)	$A \cdot B = B \cdot A$	
(3-12)	$(A + B) + C = A + (B + C)$	Associative laws
(3-13)	$(A \cdot B) \cdot C = A \cdot (B \cdot C)$	
(3-14)	$A \cdot (B + C) = A \cdot B + A \cdot C$	Distributive laws
(3-15)	$A + B \cdot C = (A + B) \cdot (A + C)$	
(3-16)	$A + A \cdot B = A$	Simplifying theorems
(3-17)	$A \cdot (A + B) = A$	
(3-18)	$A + \overline{A} \cdot B = A + B$	
(3-19)	$\overline{A + B + C} = \overline{A} \cdot \overline{B} \cdot \overline{C}$	De Morgan's theorems
(3-20)	$\overline{A \cdot B \cdot C} = \overline{A} + \overline{B} + \overline{C}$	

thoroughly understood. A number of exercises are given at the end of this chapter for practice.

Demonstration 3-9 AND-*to*-OR, OR-*to*-AND, *and* NAND *Conversion*

Purpose

To demonstrate the conversion of an OR-to-AND expression to AND-to-OR format, to NAND, and back to OR-to-AND, and to demonstrate their implementation with various gating configurations.

Equipment

   3—OR gates (OR)
   3—AND gates (AN)
   5—NAND gates (ND)
   3—NOR gates (NR)
   1—Level switch (S)

Discussion and Implementation

Conversion to the AND-to-OR form is normally accomplished by multiplying out the terms of the OR-to-AND expression and removing the unnecessary terms. For example, the OR-to-AND expression $(A + B) \cdot (B + \overline{C}) \cdot (A + D)$ can be multiplied out to

$$(A \cdot B + A \cdot \overline{C} + B \cdot B + B \cdot \overline{C}) \cdot (A + D)$$

or

$$A \cdot A \cdot B + A \cdot A \cdot \overline{C} + A \cdot B \cdot B + A \cdot B \cdot \overline{C} + A \cdot B \cdot D \\ + A \cdot \overline{C} \cdot D + B \cdot B \cdot D + B \cdot \overline{C} \cdot D$$

Simplifying by $A \cdot A = A$, we get

$$A \cdot B + A \cdot \overline{C} + A \cdot B + A \cdot B \cdot \overline{C} + A \cdot B \cdot D \\ + A \cdot \overline{C} \cdot D + B \cdot D + B \cdot \overline{C} \cdot D$$

Factoring, we obtain

$$A \cdot B(1 + 1 + \overline{C} + D) + A \cdot \overline{C}(1 + D) + B \cdot D(1 + \overline{C})$$

But since $(1 + A) = 1$, the expression can be reduced to

$$A \cdot B + A \cdot \overline{C} + B \cdot D$$

This is the AND-to-OR form which is implemented in Fig. 3-41.

The NAND gate ND1 in Fig. 3-41 is used as an inverter and does not perform a logic operation.

Conversion to the NAND form is performed easily by the use of De Morgan's theorem. For example, convert $(A \cdot B) + (A \cdot \overline{C}) + (B \cdot D)$ to the NAND form. By Eq. (3-19),

$$A \cdot B + A \cdot \overline{C} + B \cdot D = \overline{\overline{A \cdot B} \cdot \overline{A \cdot \overline{C}} \cdot \overline{B \cdot D}}$$

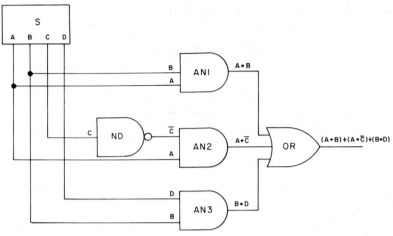

Fig. 3-41 **AND-OR** *equivalent.*

Each of the two variable terms in the original expression is treated as a single variable in this particular conversion. If desired, each variable in the original expression could be acted upon independently. But this would only lead to a more complicated expression which could not be implemented by the use of NAND gates exclusively since it would contain disjunctives. Figure 3-42 illustrates the NAND implementation. Note that the same number of gates is required

Conversion to the OR-to-AND form is accomplished by repeated use of the theorem

$$A + B \cdot C = (A + B) \cdot (A + C)$$

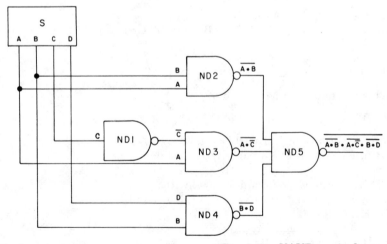

Fig. 3-42 **NAND** *equivalent.*

For example, convert to the OR-to-AND form

$$A \cdot B + A \cdot \overline{C} + B \cdot D$$

Factoring,

$$A \cdot (B + \overline{C}) + B \cdot D$$

From the theorem $X + Y \cdot Z = (X + Y) \cdot (X + Z)$ [Eq. (3-15)],

$$A \cdot (B + \overline{C}) + B \cdot D = [A \cdot (B + \overline{C}) + B] \cdot [A \cdot (B + \overline{C}) + D]$$

After rearrangement,

$$[A \cdot (B + \overline{C}) + B] \cdot [A \cdot (B + \overline{C}) + D]$$
$$= [B + A \cdot (B + \overline{C})] \cdot [D + A \cdot (B + \overline{C})]$$

Using $X + Y \cdot Z = (X + Y) \cdot (X + Z)$ again,

$$[B + A \cdot (B + \overline{C})] \cdot [D + A \cdot (B + \overline{C})]$$
$$= \{(B + A) \cdot [B + (B + \overline{C})]\} \cdot \{(D + A) \cdot [D + (B + \overline{C})]\}$$

Simplifying by Eqs. (3-12) and (3-8),

$$(B + A) \cdot (B + \overline{C}) \cdot (D + A) \cdot (D + B + \overline{C})$$

Now let $B + A = X$, $B + \overline{C} = Y$, and $D + A = Z$.   By substitution,

$$
\begin{aligned}
X \cdot Y \cdot Z \cdot (D + Y) &= (X \cdot Y \cdot Z \cdot D) + (X \cdot Y \cdot Z \cdot Y) &\text{by (3-14)} \\
&= (X \cdot Y \cdot Z \cdot D) + (X \cdot Y \cdot Z) &\text{by (3-3)} \\
&= X \cdot Y \cdot Z \cdot (D + 1) &\text{by (3-14)} \\
&= X \cdot Y \cdot Z &\text{by (3-6)}
\end{aligned}
$$

Now resubstitute:

$$
\begin{aligned}
&= (B + A) \cdot (B + \overline{C}) \cdot (D + A) \\
&= (A + B) \cdot (B + \overline{C}) \cdot (A + D) &\text{by (3-10)}
\end{aligned}
$$

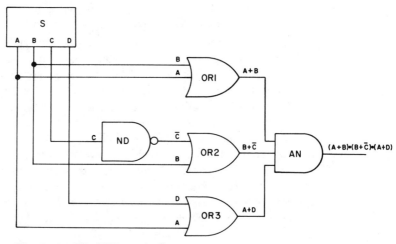

Fig. 3-43   OR-AND *equivalent.*

This leads to the original expression, the one that we started with at the beginning of this discussion. Figure 3-43 illustrates the implementation of this expression.

To verify each of the three demonstrations, prepare truth tables for all values of A, B, C, and D and compare all three truth tables:

3-11 *Minimization by Truth Tables*

The designer of digital equipment is inevitably concerned with the need to obtain the simplest, most direct implementation of logic functions. This minimizes the amount of equipment needed to implement the functions and maximizes the economy and reliability of the overall system. Previous sections in this chapter have shown how minimization can be achieved using Boolean algebra. A second method of minimization, which has achieved widespread acceptance because it is relatively easy to use, is the truth table. Minimization truth tables differ from those previously introduced in this chapter because their method of construction requires a special configuration. The use of truth tables for minimization is based on a simple rule: *If two logic expressions result in the same truth table, the two expressions must be equivalent.*

The two-variable chart is the most elementary version of a truth table. It is of minimum complexity, and it points out some of the principles behind the use of truth tables.

Figure 3-44 is a truth table which implements the expression $A \cdot \overline{B} +$ $A \cdot B$. Note that each shaded block represents one term of the expression, which is in the AND-OR form. Thus, in each shaded block, the expression is a 1; and in every unshaded block, the expression is a 0. If another expression results in the same two and only two blocks being shaded, it must be an equivalent expression.

The *first rule* for using truth tables is to convert the expression to be reduced to the AND-OR form. This results in a series of AND terms ORed together. Each of the AND terms is represented by one of the blocks on the table. Consider the example shown in Fig. 3-44. There are four possible combinations (2^n, where n equals the number of variables) of the variables A and B. These terms are $A \cdot B$, $\overline{A} \cdot B$, $A \cdot \overline{B}$, and $\overline{A} \cdot \overline{B}$. Each of the four terms is represented by an equivalent area on the table. The example shown has two terms ORed together, $A \cdot \overline{B}$ and $A \cdot B$. The area $A \cdot \overline{B}$ may be read as the square where A is 1 and B is 0. By following the coordinates, one can easily identify and shade the square where A is 1 and B is 0. When all the terms are implemented by shading the appropriate squares, we can then proceed to reduce the expression to the simplest form.

The *second rule* for using truth tables is that all terms of the AND-OR

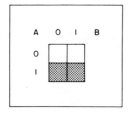

A	B	0	I	C
0	0	0	I	
0	I	2	3	
I	I	4	5	
I	0	6	7	

Fig. 3-44 Two-varia-
ble truth table.

Fig. 3-45 Three-vari-
able truth table.

expression should be represented by an equivalent shaded area on the chart.

The *third general rule* is to read all the shaded areas on the chart using the minimum number of terms and the minimum number of variables in the terms. By using the chart in Fig. 3-44, the term $A \cdot \overline{B} + A \cdot B$ can be reduced to A. This means that the logic expression A would result in the same truth table and implies that it does not matter whether B is a 1 or a 0 as long as A is a 1.

A truth table must be constructed so that squares which are adjacent either horizontally or vertically have only one of the variables change between their respective statements. This is clearly shown in a three-variable truth table, where a special reflected code is used to construct the chart. This code is called the *Gray code* and is described in Chap. 5.

A three-variable truth table (Fig. 3-45) has eight (2^3) squares. These eight squares can be arbitrarily numbered 0 to 7 for the purpose of this explanation. Although A, B, and C could have been set down in any order (for example, B = 0 for squares 4 and 5 and a 1 for squares 6 and 7), the use of the reflected Gray code presents certain advantages. By "reflected," we mean that the code can be generated by using a mirrored image. If a mirror were placed on the line between squares 2 and 3 and 4 and 5, we would see a reflected code about this center point of B and C and A would be changed from a 0 to a 1. The chart can be considered continuous, so that square 0 is also below 6 and square 1 is below 7.

It can be seen that only one variable changes state in any two adjacent squares. Thus squares 2 and 3 differ only in the value of C, 6 and 4 only in the value of B, and 1 and 7 only in the value of A. Use of a reflected code provides for easy identification of squares with common terms. Any two adjacent squares can be expressed by a term which has only two variables; the third variable is not necessary.

Figure 3-46 is shaded to implement the AND-OR expression

$$\overline{A} \cdot \overline{B} \cdot \overline{C} + \overline{A} \cdot B \cdot \overline{C} + \overline{A} \cdot B \cdot C + A \cdot B \cdot C + A \cdot \overline{B} \cdot \overline{C}$$

$$\quad 0 \qquad\qquad 2 \qquad\qquad 3 \qquad\qquad 5 \qquad\qquad 6 \quad \text{square number}$$

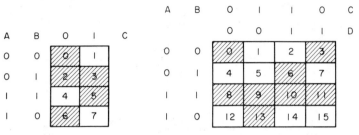

Fig. 3-46 Three-variable chart.   **Fig. 3-47 Four-variable chart.**

Any logic expression which results in these and only these squares being shaded is an equivalent expression. With truth tables having more than three variables, there are often many equivalent expressions which describe the function. The following not only describes the function but is a minimum expression (a minimum expression is one having a minimum number of terms and a minimum number of variables in each term):

Squares 2 and 3 are equivalent to $\overline{A} \cdot B$
Squares 0 and 6 are equivalent to $\overline{B} \cdot \overline{C}$
Squares 3 and 5 are equivalent to $B \cdot C$

Note that square 3 was used twice in the reduced term and that squares 0 and 1 are adjacent to one another in terms of reflection properties.

Thus, since each expression produces the same truth table,

$$\overline{A} \cdot B + \overline{B} \cdot \overline{C} + B \cdot C$$
$$= \overline{A} \cdot \overline{B} \cdot \overline{C} + \overline{A} \cdot B \cdot \overline{C} + \overline{A} \cdot B \cdot C + A \cdot B \cdot C + A \cdot \overline{B} \cdot \overline{C}$$

In similar fashion, charts for four, five, six, or more variables can be created. While the three-variable chart had eight squares, a four-variable chart would have 16, or 2^4, squares. The additional eight squares are generated by constructing the mirrored image at the right-hand margin of Fig. 3-46 and adding values for the variable D. Figure 3-47 shows the result. The squares are numbered arbitrarily and do not reflect the value of the squares in the Gray code. The chart is continuous, so that square 12 is adjacent to squares 0 and 15 in addition to being adjacent to squares 8 and 13.

Consider the simplification of

$$\overline{A} \cdot \overline{B} \cdot \overline{C} \cdot \overline{D} + A \cdot B \cdot \overline{D} + A \cdot C \cdot \overline{D} + A \cdot B \cdot C \cdot D$$
$$\quad\;\; 0 \qquad\qquad 8, 9 \qquad\;\; 9, 13 \qquad\qquad 10$$
$$+ A \cdot B \cdot \overline{C} + B \cdot C \cdot D + \overline{A} \cdot \overline{B} \cdot \overline{C} \cdot D$$
$$\quad\; 8, 11 \qquad\; 10, 6 \qquad\quad 3 \qquad\qquad \text{square number}$$

Any expressions which produce the same truth table are identical. Thus,

Squares 8, 9, 10, 11 are equivalent to A · B
Squares 0 and 3 are equivalent to $\overline{A} \cdot \overline{B} \cdot \overline{C}$
Squares 9 and 13 are equivalent to A · C · $\overline{D}$
Squares 6 and 10 are equivalent to B · C · D

and the original expression can be reduced to

$$A \cdot B + \overline{A} \cdot \overline{B} \cdot \overline{C} + A \cdot C \cdot \overline{D} + B \cdot C \cdot D$$

Note that squares 0 and 3 were combined to eliminate the D variable. This was brought about by the continuous feature of the chart in the horizontal direction. This chart is also continuous in the vertical direction. The final expression in its simplified form is easily checked now by shading in the squares on a clean chart. Then the two charts can be compared to make sure they are identical.

EXERCISES

3-1. Represent the following logic statements on the level switches:

A is true; B is false; C and D are true.
A is false; B, C, and D are true.
A and B are true; C and D are false.

3-2. Show the counts of 0000 through binary 1111 (decimal 15) using level switches.

3-3. Prepare truth tables similar to Tables 3-2 and 3-3 for the following expressions:

(a) $A + \overline{B}$ (b) $\overline{A} \cdot B$
(c) $\overline{A} \cdot \overline{B}$ (d) $\overline{A} + \overline{B}$

3-4. Construct Venn diagrams for each of the following expressions and shade the representative area where the expression is true. Also construct truth tables for them.

(a) $A \cdot \overline{B}$ (b) $\overline{A} + B$
(c) $A \cdot B \cdot C$ (d) $A \cdot B \cdot \overline{C}$
(e) $A \cdot \overline{B} \cdot \overline{C}$ (f) $A + B + C$

3-5. Using Demonstration 3-2, prove that $(A \cdot B) \cdot (C \cdot D)$ is equivalent to $(A \cdot C) \cdot (B \cdot D)$.

3-6. Prepare a truth table and Venn diagram for Demonstration 3-3.

3-7. Compare the truth table and Venn diagram for the NAND gate, Demonstration 3-4, with those for the AND Gate, Demonstration 3-2. What is the relationship between them?

3-8. Show that the NAND gate and the NOR gate can both perform the NOT function. Prove that they are identical when only one input is used.

3-9. Construct a truth table showing the output state of each NOR gate in Fig. 3-27 for the 16 possible combinations of the four variables. Check your answer.

3-10. If each of the signals A, B, and C are connected in common to an AND gate, an OR gate, a NAND gate, and a NOR gate, prepare a common truth table showing the outputs of each of the gates for all combinations of input signals.

3-11. Implement De Morgan's theorem [Eq. (3-19)] using logic modules. Construct a truth table for all combinations of the three variables showing all output gates.

3-12. Show that $A + \overline{A} \cdot B = A + B$. Construct a wiring diagram showing all gates and all inputs and outputs. Check your answer using a Venn diagram.

3-13. Convert $A \cdot B + A \cdot C + B \cdot D$ to NOR form. Implement and check the truth table against Demonstration 3-9.

3-14. Convert to AND-to-OR form:

$$(A + D) \cdot (B + C)$$
$$(A + C) \cdot (B + C) \cdot (A + B + D)$$

3-15. Convert to OR-to-AND form:

$$A \cdot B + B \cdot C + A \cdot \overline{C}$$

3-16. Convert to NAND form:

$$A \cdot C + B \cdot \overline{D} + A \cdot D$$
$$(A + C) \cdot (\overline{B} + C) \cdot (\overline{B} + \overline{D})$$

3-17. Convert to NOR form:

$$A \cdot B + A \cdot C + \overline{B} \cdot \overline{C}$$
$$(A + \overline{B}) \cdot (B + C) \cdot (\overline{A} + \overline{D})$$

3-18. Using the laws of Boolean algebra, simplify the following algebraic expressions:

(a) $A \cdot B + B \cdot C + A \cdot B \cdot C$ (b) $(A + \overline{C}) \cdot (A + B) \cdot (\overline{A} + C)$
(c) $A \cdot (\overline{B} + C) + A + \overline{B} \cdot C$
(d) $(\overline{A} \cdot \overline{B} \cdot \overline{C} + A \cdot B \cdot C) \cdot (A + \overline{B}) \cdot (B + \overline{C}) \cdot (C + \overline{A})$

3-19. Simplify the expressions in Exercise 3-18 using truth tables. Conversion to the AND-OR form is necessary for (b), (c), and (d).

3-20. Simplify the following expressions using the four-variable truth tables:

(a) $A \cdot B \cdot \overline{C} + \overline{A} \cdot \overline{B} \cdot (C \cdot D + \overline{C} \cdot \overline{D}) + A \cdot \overline{B} \cdot C \cdot D$
(b) $B \cdot C \cdot D + A \cdot B \cdot C \cdot \overline{D} + A \cdot B \cdot \overline{C} \cdot D + \overline{A} \cdot B \cdot C$
$\qquad\qquad\qquad\qquad + \overline{A} \cdot \overline{B} \cdot \overline{C} \cdot \overline{D} + A \cdot \overline{B} \cdot \overline{C} \cdot D$

FOUR

Flip-flops and Storage Registers

4-1 *Storage*

Performing arithmetic requires more than just knowing the rules. Large additions and subtractions would be extremely difficult, if not impossible, without the aid of storage. When a person does arithmetic, pencil and paper perform the storage function. By using these he keeps track of what he is doing. He records those operations that have been performed and what the results were. In this way, he can concentrate on one thing at a time and store information until he is ready for it.

A computer also must store information. For example, in a multiplication problem, as each partial product is generated, it is stored until the other partial products are produced.

Furthermore, different portions of a computer operate at different speeds. If one part of a problem is finished before another, the part that is ready first must be stored until the second part can be completed. Otherwise, the first part may appear as the answer to one problem and the second part, arriving later, as the answer to another. Numbers would then run back and forth through the computer, arriving in various places at random times and triggering subsequent operations either too early or too late. In this case, the internal operation of the computer would be out of control. To keep everything on schedule and to allow the computer to keep track of what it is doing, storage devices are necessary.

What are the necessary attributes of a storage device? First, it must accept inputs. Just as paper accepts inputs from a pencil, so an electronic storage device must accept inputs from other electronic devices. Second, a storage device must be able to hold or store data until needed. Pencil and paper would not be much good if the pencil marks faded as soon as they were put down. Third, a storage device must be able to return stored information to the system when required.

Other important attributes of storage devices are the length of time over which they retain information and the amount of information they can retain. A slide rule, for example, stores information only so long as the cursor is not moved, and it stores only one number at a time. Pencil and paper, on the other hand, will store more information and store it long after the problem is finished.

One type of computer storage device is the *delay circuit*. A delay circuit is capable of storing one digit of information for a period of time fixed by the design of the delay circuit. Delay devices provide a means for synchronizing a signal with other signals. Suppose the output of one OR gate must arrive at an AND-gate input after the output of some other OR gate has already arrived. In this case, the output of the first OR gate (the first signal to occur) must be temporarily slowed down. Slowing down such signals is accomplished by delay devices.

A *register* usually provides longer and higher-capacity storage. A register can store entire numbers, and its ability to store is not limited in time, as with the delay element. The familiar cash register, which holds entire numbers in temporary storage, is a good example of a mechanical register. In a register, a number remains in storage until a new number is entered, and then the old number disappears or is erased. In a computer, the register becomes an extremely useful device, as it is easily designed to perform a variety of functions. The flexibility of the register will become apparent in the later study of arithmetic functions.

A *buffer device* provides long storage and high storage capacity similar to a register. Buffer storage is primarily used to match the speeds of the various computer elements. For example, an input unit might accept a large number of signals from punched tape (an electromechanical device) at a comparatively low rate of speed and then, after a short storage interval, pass the signals on to the major computer memory element at a very high rate of speed. In this sense, the buffer is a function that can be accomplished by registers.

Large-capacity internal storage is accomplished by the computer's *memory*. Memory elements in a computer must be accessible in a very short amount of time since this memory is used in the computational cycle. Thus the memory element is usually an electrical device rather than a slower, electromechanical device. This memory can digest an entire program (data with instructions that control the sequence of computer operations) and retain it through a whole problem or series of problems. A program may contain data that are used over and over many times. The memory, therefore, must be able to store extensive quantities of information for comparatively long periods of time. Core memories are the most widely used type of memory element. A computer memory may contain over one million bits of storage capacity. Refer to Chap. 7 for more detailed information on memories.

Another form of storage is called *external storage*. Here the information is stored on paper or magnetic tapes, cards, magnetic disks, or other devices. Such storage provides great capacity and usually contains many millions of information bits.

When the computer requires information which is in external storage, the data are usually first transferred to the computer's internal memory and then used as needed by the computer.

4-2 The Flip-flop

An understanding of the basic storage element is fundamental to an understanding of the storage functions of a digital computer, just as mastery of basic rules is a prerequisite to an understanding of Boolean algebra.

The device most widely used as a storage element is the flip-flop circuit, or simply the *flip-flop*. A flip-flop is a network of electronic components which always exists in one of two stable states. For this reason, it is called a *bistable* device. As an example of a bistable device, consider the simple seesaw of Fig. 4-1.

If the left side of the seesaw is down, then the ball will be at the left end. The system is completely stable in this position. It will not change unless something comes along and changes it. When the right side of the seesaw is pushed down, the ball rolls to the right end. The new position, although opposite to the old, is also stable. The system has only these two stable states, which may be equated to the two binary symbols, 0 and 1, shown in the drawing. It is this equivalency that makes the flip-flop ideal for computer work.

There are several important points to be noted about this system. One side of the seesaw must be down, and the other up. There are no stable "in-between" states. Any other state is unstable. If an attempt is made to balance the system by putting the ball in the center, the slightest tilt causes the ball to move to one side, causing more tilt. This moves the ball even further, and the tilt increases until the system reaches a stable state. Such action, which forces the system to rapidly seek one of its stable states, is called *regenerative feedback*.

Since the system has only two stable states, one can be defined as the set state (S) and the other as the reset state (R). Pushing the left end down puts the seesaw in the set state; pushing the right end down puts it in the reset state. Once put into either state, the system will remain in that state and store the information regarding that state. By definition, when it is in the set state, it is storing

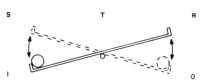

Fig. 4-1   Flip-flop physical analogy.

a binary 1; when it is in the reset state, it is storing a binary 0. Furthermore, it is easy to identify which state the system is in by looking at it. This physical system transmits a signal—in this case, a visual image— identifying its state.

The electronic flip-flop behaves in a manner similar to that of the physical example shown in Fig. 4-1. In the figure, the physical analogy is superimposed on the symbolic drawing of a flip-flop. For simplicity, the left side of the seesaw can be called the *set* or 1 side, and the right side can be called the *reset* or 0 side. To put the set side of the seesaw down, it is necessary to push down on that side.

In electronics, the physical up and down is correlated to the conditions of voltage levels. For example, when a light switch is turned off and a room is in darkness, the electric cord transmits no voltage, or 0 potential, to the light bulb. If the switch is turned on and the light comes on, the cord carries a discrete voltage of approximately 110 volts. No attempt is made here to define the voltage levels; we are merely illustrating that there are two discrete levels. The voltage levels used to define the 1 and 0 states of an output are identical to those used to define the output state of the gating elements, where the choice of voltage levels is primarily a circuit-design consideration.

Figure 4-2 illustrates both the two stable states which the flip-flop can assume and an additional concept in terms of logic. In stable state A, the flip-flop is said to be set. This means that the set output is in the binary-1, or logic-1, state, and from the seesaw analogy, this also means that the reset output is in the binary-0, or logic-0, state. In stable state B, the flip-flop is reset, with the set output in the logic-0 state and the reset output in the logic-1 state. In other words, either output of the flip-flop can provide a logic-1 signal level or a 0 signal level. In a flip-flop, only one side at a time can produce a 1; the other side must simultaneously be a logic 0.

There are many ways in which a flip-flop can be implemented electronically. For example, a flip-flop can be made by connecting the output of NAND gate ND1 (Fig. 4-3) to the input of NAND gate ND2

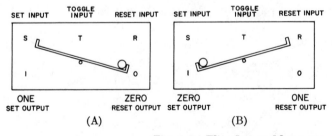

Fig. 4-2 Flip-flop stable states.

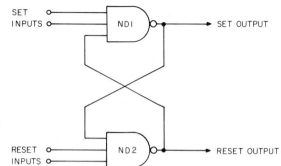

Fig. 4-3 Direct-coupled flip-flop.

and the output of NAND gate ND2 to the input of NAND gate ND1. Assume that all other inputs to the NAND gates are at the logic-1 condition. Thus, if ND1 has a 0 output, ND2 has a 1 output, which holds the output of ND1 to a 0. If one of the other inputs to ND1 is now made a 0, the output of ND1 becomes a 1 and ND2 becomes a 0. The input to ND1 can now be changed back to 1, and the output of ND1 remains in the 1 state. The flip-flop will change state by applying a 0 momentarily to the appropriate input. Thus, if the d-c (direct-coupled) flip-flop in Fig. 4-3 is in the set state (storing a binary 1), it could be reset (to store a binary 0) by momentarily making either of the reset inputs a logic 0. Once the flip-flop is put into the reset state, it will remain there until a momentary logic 0 is applied to a set input. This flip-flop is an acceptable storage device since it can accept inputs from other devices and store these data permanently and since its output can be detected. This particular flip-flop has a disadvantage in that applying 0s simultaneously to a set input and a reset input causes both outputs to become 1s and the flip-flop is then neither set nor reset. This is similar to both ends of the seesaw being up simultaneously. Although this type of configuration has extensive applications, a more versatile type of flip-flop will be described and then used throughout the remainder of this text.

A second type of flip-flop relies on transitions on its inputs rather than input levels to modify its outputs. When the flip-flop is in a stable state A (Fig. 4-2), a sharp transition from logic 1 to logic 0 at the reset input sends the flip-flop to stable state B. To get from stable state B to stable state A, a transition from 1 to 0 must be applied to the set input. It is important to remember that the flip-flop responds to a transition—in this case, a transition from 1 to 0. A transition from 0 to 1 does not change the state of the flip-flop. A flip-flop of this type is used in the demonstrations.

Any two voltage levels can be used to distinguish a logic 1 from a logic 0. The choice of the two levels is determined by the circuit designer. To illustrate the operations of a flip-flop better, two voltage levels will be assigned to represent the binary 1 and 0. Let +3 volts represent a logic 1 and 0 volts or ground represent a logic 0. The electronic flip-flop thus defined responds to a transition (+3 volts to ground) at its inputs. A transition from 1 to 0 (+3 volts to ground) on the set input will cause the set output to become a 1. A similar signal on the reset input will reset the flip-flop. Immediately following a 1-to-0 transition at the S terminal, the flip-flop is in the set state. It will remain in this state until a 1-to-0 transition is received at the R terminal; that is, it will store its signal until it is commanded to change.

When the flip-flop is used in the manner described, it is called a *set-reset* flip-flop. When sent into one of its states, the flip-flop then remains there until it receives a signal to go to its opposite state. The set-reset flip-flop responds only to set or reset inputs. Set inputs send it to the set state (1 output is logic 1); reset inputs send it to the reset state (0 output is logic 1). If a series of all set or all reset signals is received, only the first signal will have any effect. Once the flip-flop is either set or reset, it will remain in that state until a signal comes along on the opposite input terminal to send it to the opposite state. However, set-reset operation is only one way in which a flip-flop can be used.

Another way to use a flip-flop is as a toggle, or complementary, flip-flop. In this case, only one input terminal, the toggle or T terminal shown in Fig. 4-2, is used. Each new signal received at T sends the flip-flop into its opposite state. A series of signals, then, sends it back and forth between the set and reset, or 1 and 0, states. Operation in this manner is called *toggling* or *complementing*. This is analogous to a ball-point pen with a button which, when pushed, causes the pen point to extend or retract. Each time the button is pushed, the pen changes state.

In most cases, the designer must define exactly the time at which he wishes to trigger a particular flip-flop. Frequently, the signal used to control a flip-flop is also gated with the output of the flip-flop. For this reason, the flip-flop is designed to respond to only one part of a signal. The transition from 1 to 0 is usually chosen. When the input signal to the flip-flop is a logic 1, it can be ANDed with the output of the flip-flop. When the signal changes from 1 to 0, it changes the state of the flip-flop and, at the same time, inhibits any gating. After the flip-flop has changed to its new state, the input signal is changed to a logic 1 again and enables all gates. The flip-flop is then triggered on the next 1-to-0 transition. Figure 4-4 is a graphic representation of an electronic signal.

At time T_0, the signal is 0 volts, or ground potential. At time T_1, the signal goes to +3 volts, or logic 1.

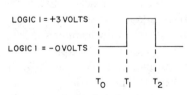

Fig. 4-4   Logic levels.

The signal stays here for a period of time and then, at time T_2, goes back to 0, or ground potential. It is this trailing edge, the edge of the signal which is going from logic 1 to logic 0, that is used to trigger a flip-flop.

It is important to comprehend this concept for an understanding of the operations utilizing flip-flops described later.

To summarize, the following may be said of a flip-flop:

1. It does not implement logic.

2. It is a storage device capable of storing one binary digit (bit) of information.

3. It can store either a 1 or a 0.

4. It has two outputs, referred to as the 1, set, or assertion output and the 0, reset, or negation output.

5. It has two possible stable states:

When FF stores	FF is in	1 output is	0 output is
1	Set state	1	0
0	Reset state	0	1

6. To change stable states, a transition from 1 to 0 must be sensed at the appropriate input.

7. It has two modes of operation:

Set-Reset Mode: Flip-flop is reset after a 1-to-0 transition is received at the reset input; it is set after a 1-to-0 transition is received at the set input.

Toggle Mode: Flip-flop changes state when a 1-to-0 transition is received at the toggle input.

8. A clear input may also be provided as a method of resetting the flip-flop prior to performing a sequence of operations. This operation is described in Demonstration 4-1.

Statements 1 to 5 hold true for any flip-flop, while statements 6 to 8 are peculiar to the type of flip-flop chosen for this text.

4-3 *Timing Diagrams*

Timing diagrams, such as that shown in Fig. 4-4, are used to show how the signal at a particular terminal varies over time. In Fig. 4-4, the voltage was 0 at time T_0, went up to $+3$ volts (logic 1) at time T_1, and came back to ground (logic 0) at time T_2. Such diagrams are useful in illustrating the operation of a flip-flop.

Figure 4-5 is a timing diagram showing the operation of a set-reset flip-flop. At time 0 (T_0), the flip-flop is in the reset state, with 0 volts at output terminal 1 and $+3$ volts at output terminal 0. When the trailing edge of a signal is received at the S terminal (set side), as at time (T_1), the 1-output terminal goes to logic 1, reflecting the set state.

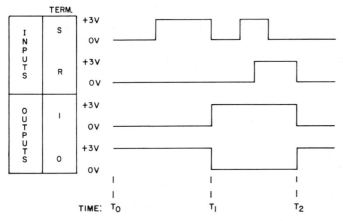

Fig. 4-5   *Flip-flop, set-reset timing.*

Naturally, the 0-output terminal goes to logic 0 at the same time.   The two must always be opposite.   The 1-output terminal then remains a logic 1 until a 1-to-0 signal is received at R.   The intervening set signal has no effect because the flip-flop is already set.   When, at time T_2, the flip-flop does receive a reset signal, the 1-output terminal becomes a 0 and the 0-output terminal becomes a 1, reflecting the reset state.

Operation of the flip-flop in the complementary mode is illustrated in Fig. 4-6.   Again, at time 0, the flip-flop is in the reset state.   At time 1, the trailing edge of a signal is received at T and the flip-flop complements to the set state.   The 1-output terminal goes to a logic 1 and the 0-output terminal goes to a logic 0.   At time 2, another signal is received at T and again the flip-flop complements, this time back to the reset state.   Finally, at time 3, a third signal is received and the flip-flop is complemented for the third time.

The time intervals on these diagrams are immaterial.   All triggering is done by the trailing edge of the input signal only.   The signals themselves could last for millionths of a second, seconds, or even hours.   The result would be the same.   In most computers, many such signals are of the

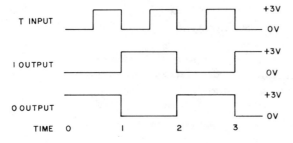

Fig. 4-6   *Flip-flop, toggle timing.*

order of one-millionth of a second in duration, but any length of time would produce satisfactory operation.

The electronic flip-flop fulfills all the requisites of a storage device. It accepts inputs, in the form of signals, which cause it to set or reset. It stores information by remaining in either the 1 or the 0 state until a new signal commands it to change state. It provides outputs by maintaining complementary logic levels at its two output terminals.

Demonstration 4-1   *The Flip-flop*

Purpose

To demonstrate the use and properties of the electronic flip-flop (FF) and to introduce the single-pulse generator (SPG).

Equipment

1—Flip-flop (FF)
1—Single-pulse generator (SPG)
1—Level switch (S)

Discussion and Implementation

The flip-flop in Fig. 4-7 responds only to the trailing edge of a pulse. This eliminates any ambiguity about when the flip-flop should be in the set or reset state. Only a sharp, definite transition (from +3 volts to ground) will trigger it.

The level switch, however, does not emit sharp, well-defined pulses. It puts out only steady up or down voltages. When changing between up and down, the level switch goes through relatively slow transitions, and the contacts of the switch are likely to bounce open and close many times before making final contact. For this reason, the level switch is not suitable for triggering flip-flops. To provide the sharp pulses required, the single-pulse generator (SPG) is used. When the push button on this module is depressed, the SPG emits a single, well-defined pulse, similar to the one illustrated in Fig. 4-4, with the necessary sharp transition for triggering a flip-flop.

The level switch is suitable, however, for clearing (that is, resetting) the flip-flop. Any signal momentarily at logic 0 will clear the flip-flop, whether it is from a logic-0 output (0 volts) or from a ground terminal. So long as the CL terminal is held to ground or to a logic-0 level, the flip-flop

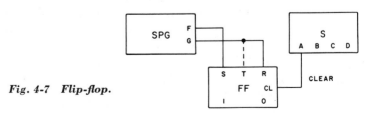

Fig. 4-7   Flip-flop.

will remain in the reset state.   On the other hand, a logic-1 input to the CL terminal allows the flip-flop to function normally.

The type of flip-flop illustrated in this and ensuing demonstrations operates exactly as the one described in Fig. 4-2.   After a pulse (similar to the one in Fig. 4-4) is applied to the S input terminal, the flip-flop will be in the set state.   Conversely, after a pulse is received at the reset input, the flip-flop will be in the reset state.   The SPG module is used as a source for single pulses.   It has two separate output channels, each having an associated push button.   Each time a button is depressed, the output channel associated with that push button emits a pulse.   Depressing each button alternately will alternately set and reset the flip-flop.

The clear input is connected to the A channel of the level switch.   When channel A of the level-switch module is momentarily put to a logic 0, the flip-flop will be reset.   This is an important operation in a computer. When power is initially applied to a computer, the flip-flops in the system may assume either of their bistable states and be set or reset.   This means that all information initially stored in the flip-flops is completely arbitrary. This is an undesirable situation prior to performing logic operations since the erroneous data stored in the flip-flops may trigger operations that are out of sequence, thus destroying the programmed instructions.   To get around this situation, all the flip-flops in the system are cleared simultaneously prior to the start of the first logic operation.

If the connections to the S and R inputs are removed and a connection is made to the T (toggle) input, illustrated by the dashed line in Fig. 4-7, the flip-flop can be used to demonstrate the toggle operation.   Each time the SPG is depressed, the flip-flop will change state.   The 1 and 0 outputs will respond in a fashion illustrated by the timing diagram in Fig. 4-5.

In the demonstration, pulses are supplied by a push button.   In a computer, pulses are supplied by a master clock and various counters.   A clock circuit puts out a steady, uninterrupted train of pulses at the rate of up to a few million per second.   This train of pulses is sent to a counter, which counts in the binary system.   Sequential operations are triggered in the computer as various counts are registered in this counter (usually referred to as the *program counter*).   The binary counter is discussed in the next paragraph.   The methods for decoding the counter and generating control signals for sequential operations will be covered in later chapters.

4-4   *The Binary Counter*

The four logic gates thus far described, AND, OR, NAND, and NOR, and the flip-flop storage devices provide the basic components needed to implement logic and arithmetic functions.   Circuits for performing complex operations are constructed simply by combining these basic components into larger networks.   In a large network, the principle of operation of any single gate remains unchanged.   All the techniques, such as truth tables, Venn diagrams, and timing diagrams, are just as applicable to the larger networks as they are to the individual gates.

One of the more elementary functions in digital logic is the counter circuit. Counting, in this case, amounts to nothing more than recording the number of signals passing through a circuit over a certain period of time. If a series of 12 signals is sent to a binary counter between time 0 and time X, then at time X, the counter must contain the number 12, or binary 1100. It must have counted to 12 and stored the result.

Counters are used in the control elements of computers. For example, a counter might count timing cycles, and based on the count, the computer would obtain data from the memory element and perform arithmetic operations on these data. Figure 4-8 shows a counter.

Each incoming pulse complements the first stage back and forth between 0 and 1, producing a 010101010101 . . . pattern at the first stage. The second stage, however, is only complemented when the first stage goes from 1 to 0. This means that the second stage must wait for the second incoming signal and every second signal thereafter before being complemented. This produces a 0011001100 . . . pattern at the second stage. The third stage, getting inputs only when the second stage goes from 1 to 0, complements only every fourth time. This produces a 000011110000111100 . . . pattern at the third stage. Later stages are complemented every eighth, sixteenth, thirty-second, etc., time. If the first stage represents the zeroth-order digit and the patterns from all subsequent stages are arranged as in Table 4-1, the development of the binary system can be readily seen. The states of the set outputs of the flip-flops are represented in the table.

This four-stage counter can continue to count up to 1111. When the

TABLE 4-1

Binary count (up)				Decimal count
Stage 4	Stage 3	Stage 2	Stage 1	
0	0	0	0	0
0	0	0	1	1
0	0	1	0	2
0	0	1	1	3
0	1	0	0	4
0	1	0	1	5
0	1	1	0	6
0	1	1	1	7
1	0	0	0	8

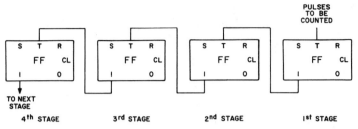

Fig. 4-8   Up counter.

counter reaches the next count after binary 1111, all stages revert to 0 and start over.   A four-stage counter, therefore, can count up to decimal 15 (binary 1111), or $16 - 1$.   In general, any binary counter can count up to $2^n - 1$, where n is the number of stages.   An eight-stage counter can count to $2^8 - 1$, or 255 (binary 11111111).

The binary counter just described counts only in one direction; that is, it counts up, or in the direction of higher numbers.   For some counter applications, it is desirable to count down, or in the direction of lower numbers.

Counting down is accomplished merely by using the 0 output of each flip-flop instead of the 1 output.   Figure 4-9 shows four flip-flops arranged for counting down.

This network is identical to the simple binary counter except that the 0 outputs now provide the connecting link and the 1 outputs are completely disconnected.   Assuming that, to start, all stages are set at 1, the incoming pulses complement the first stage back and forth between 0 and 1, producing the same 101010101 . . . pattern that was produced in the first stage of the binary counter.   However, the second stage is complemented when the first stage goes from logic 0 to 1, instead of from 1 to 0.   The 0-to-1 transition refers to the 1 output.   The actual triggering action is performed by the 0 output, which is making the 1-to-0 transition which is necessary for triggering operations.   This produces a pattern exactly opposite to that of the second stage of a simple binary counter.   Such a pattern would appear as 11001100110 . . . , where complementing only

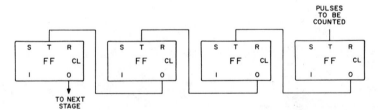

Fig. 4-9   Down counter.

TABLE 4-2

Binary count (down)				Decimal count
Stage 4	Stage 3	Stage 2	Stage 1	
1	1	1	1	15
1	1	1	0	14
1	1	0	1	13
1	1	0	0	12
1	0	1	1	11
1	0	1	0	10
1	0	0	1	9
1	0	0	0	8
0	1	1	1	7

occurs on 0-to-1 transitions from the first stage. The third and fourth stages are also the exact opposites of the third and fourth stages of the binary counter. These four patterns can then be combined, as in Table 4-2, to illustrate the down-counting process. Again, the set outputs are represented on this table.

In the down counter, the count starts at 1111. If all stages had been set at 0 to start, the first pulse would have sent all stages to the 1 state. This corresponds to the "starting-over" process in the simple binary counter; that is, in the down counter the count decreases to 0000, and at the next count all stages revert to 1111 and start over.

Demonstration 4-2   The Binary Counter

Purpose

To demonstrate the operation of the binary counter and to introduce the low-frequency-clock module (CK).

Equipment

    1—Level switch (S)
    1—Single-pulse generator (SPG)
    4—Flip-flops (FF)
    1—Low-frequency clock (CK)

Discussion and Implementation

To begin counting operations, all stages of the counter must first be cleared to all 0s. This is accomplished by putting channel D of the level switch momentarily to a logic 0. After clearing, the first pulse from the single-pulse generator (SPG) sends the first stage of the counter, FF1, to the 1 state. This, however, has no effect on the other three stages. The flip-flops change state only when their toggle inputs sense a transition from

1 to 0, marking the trailing edge of a pulse. The second pulse from the
SPG then sends the reset output of the first stage back to 1. Simultaneously, the 1-output terminal goes from 1 to 0. This transition at the
toggle input of the second stage causes the set output of that stage to go to
the 1 state. Each pulse from the SPG is then fed into the first stage of the
counter. After 15 pulses, all four stages of the counter will be in the 1 state,
and the next pulse will cause all stages to go back to the 0 state. The
sequence will then repeat itself as more count pulses are fed to the counter.
This four-stage counter can count up to 16 pulses before repeating the
sequence. Larger numbers can be counted in the same manner merely by
adding stages.

Figure 4-11 is a timing diagram showing how the four-stage counter
operates. The 1, or set, output of each stage is represented on the diagram.

Counter flip-flops change state only when the T input senses a transition
from logic 1 to 0. The amount of time between count pulses does not
alter the counting sequence. The counter stores the count until the next
count pulse is received. From the timing diagram, a table similar to Table
4-1 can be constructed to illustrate the counter operation.

In an actual system, pulses would rarely be received by a counter from a
push-button switching device such as an SPG module. To illustrate a more
realistic operation, a clock module is shown in Fig. 4-10. If the output of
the CK module is connected to the T input of the first stage (as shown by
the dashed line), the counter would operate continuously without requiring
manual operations. Assume for purposes of demonstration that the CK
module produces a pulse every 5 seconds. This is very low-frequency
operation compared with the millions of pulses per second produced by a
clock in a computer. The reason for this low frequency is to allow visual
indication of the states of the flip-flops. If indicators are used to show the
state of each flip-flop, the binary sequence in Fig. 4-11 is visually displayed
in 5-second increments. An indicator in the ON condition represents the
set state, and in the OFF condition, the reset state. One count cycle in
Fig. 4-11 would take 80 seconds to complete.

To count down, instead of up, it is only necessary to disconnect the 1
outputs and connect the inputs to the 0-output terminals. In this case,
signals from the SPG cause the counter to count down. Although the

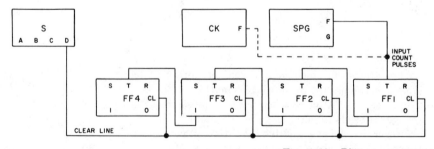

Fig. 4-10   Binary counter.

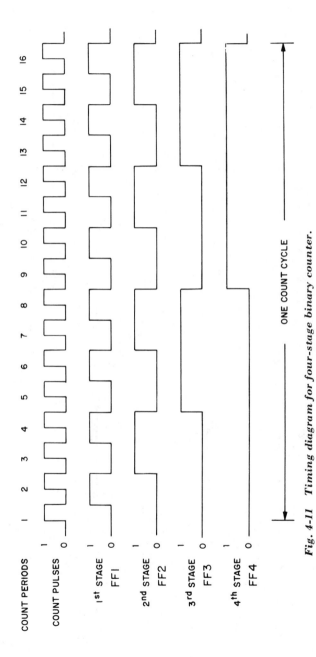

Fig. 4-11 Timing diagram for four-stage binary counter.

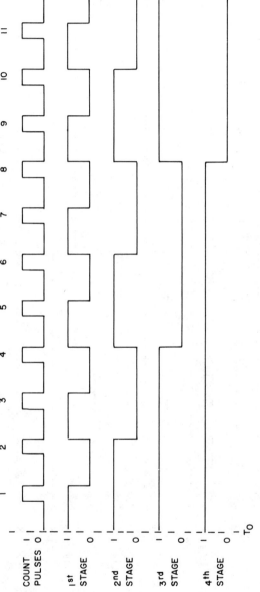

Fig. 4-12 Timing diagram for four-stage binary down counter.

first stage operates just as it did before, all subsequent stages now operate exactly opposite to the way they did in the up counter. Each stage is now complemented only on logic 0-to-1 transitions at the 1 terminal. The timing diagram for the down counter in Fig. 4-12 is exactly opposite to that for the up counter. Note that the 1 outputs are represented on the diagram.

In Fig. 4-12, be careful to distinguish between a flip-flop changing from state 0 to state 1 and one of its two outputs changing from 0 to 1. When the 1 terminal of a flip-flop changes from 0 to 1, the signal at its 0 terminal changes from 1 to 0. In other words, the diagram depicts the 1-output terminals of the four flip-flops; it does not depict the signals at the 0 terminals. A timing diagram showing the signals at the 0 terminals of a down counter would be identical to a timing diagram showing the signals at the 1 terminal of an up counter. This point is important to remember and should be thoroughly understood by the reader.

4-5   *The Up-Down Counter*

The binary counter can be used to perform either of two operations: It can count up (forward), or it can count down (backward). Although the binary counter can never do both at the same time, it can, by a slight alteration in the wiring, do either one.

A more powerful counter can count in either direction without any change in wiring. However, such a circuit must be provided with some means whereby an up command will cause the counter to count up and a down command will cause it to count down. The up command must automatically disable the down portion of the circuit, and the down command must similarly disable the up portion of the circuit. Logic gating fulfills this requirement.

To illustrate the principle of logic gating, consider Fig. 4-13, which shows a binary counter with counting-up connections in solid lines and counting-down connections in dotted lines. Such a configuration would be unsuitable if wired directly because the T terminals would be receiving signals from the 1 and 0 terminals at the same time. The flip-flops would not know which way to go. However, if the signals from one or the other

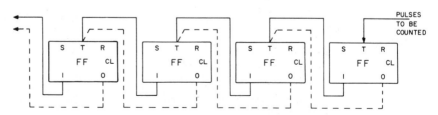

Fig. 4-13   Up-down counter, block diagram.

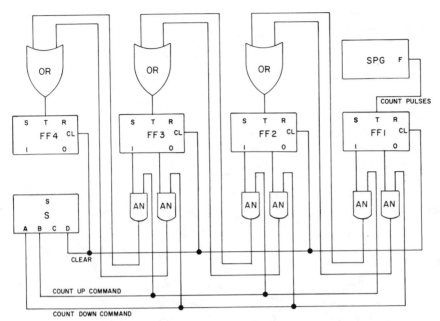

Fig. 4-14   Up-down counter.

set of terminals (but never both at the same time) can be presented at T, then the counter will operate either up or down, according to which signals are present.

In Fig. 4-14, the appropriate gating has been added to the circuit of Fig. 4-13, allowing only count-up signals to pass if an up command is present and only count-down signals to pass if a down command is present. The next demonstration describes the operation of an up-down counter.

Demonstration 4-3   *The Up-Down Counter*

Purpose

To demonstrate the operation of an up-down counter and to introduce the concept of gating.

Equipment

1—Level switch (S)
1—Single-pulse generator (SPG)
6—AND gates (AN)
3—OR gates (OR)
4—Flip-flops (FF)

Discussion and Implementation

The operation of the up-down counter is quite similar to that of the simple binary counter. The same transitions take place, and the same diagrams can be used. The only additional concept is that the up command allows signals from the 1 terminals to pass through one set of gates and the down command allows signals from the 0 terminals to pass through another. Both sets of signals are never allowed to pass at the same time.

Signals are passed to succeeding T terminals only if the previous stage is set and there is an up command (1 condition) present to gate the signal through or if the previous stage is reset and there is a down command to gate the signal through. The OR gates allow either set of signals to reach the T terminals, while the AND gates ensure that only one set of signals gets through at a time.

If it is desired to count up, the count-up command is activated by setting channel B of the level switch to a logic 1 and channel A to a logic 0. This enables the AND gates associated with the flip-flop 1 outputs. The counter is then cleared by momentarily putting channel D of the level switch to the 0 state. The counter counts input pulses as described previously and will produce a timing chart identical to Fig. 4-11 when pulses are received from the SPG.

In order to count down, a count-down command is activated by making channel A a logic 1 and channel B a logic 0. The register is then cleared by momentarily making channel D a 0. The counter will then produce a timing chart identical to that of Fig. 4-12 when count pulses are received.

If it is desired to switch the counter from up to down without clearing, a problem arises. When the up command is turned off (switched from 1 to 0), a 1-to-0 transition is sent to all AND gates in the count-up circuit. Gates receiving a logic-1 input from a set flip-flop will transmit the transition, causing some stages of the counter to be complemented. This means that after a period of counting up, the counter cannot be switched to counting down without changing the number in the counter. The same thing would happen when changing from counting down to counting up.

This difficulty can be eliminated by connecting the output of the SPG and all lower-order stages to the AND gates. In this case, transitions will only be transmitted if a command signal is present, all lower-order stages will be 1s, and a count pulse will be present. Switching the command from up to down or down to up will have no effect. Normally, the SPG has logic-0 output, and a transition can only get through the gates when a pulse is sent out from the SPG.

4-6　*The Ring Counter*

Another type of digital counter, called the *ring counter*, is analogous to the mechanical counting wheel. In a mechanical counting wheel, a

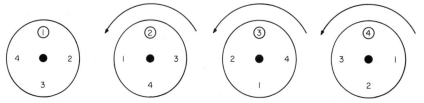

Fig. 4-15   Mechanical ratchet wheels.

count is registered when the wheel is rotated through a series of positions, as shown in Fig. 4-15.   In a ring counter, a count is registered when the 1 state is shifted around a ring of flip-flops, as shown in Fig. 4-16.   With this arrangement, a single count is registered each time the 1 state shifts to the next flip-flop.   Note that one flip-flop represents one position on the mechanical wheel.   A decimal ring counter would require 10 flip-flops, just as a decimal wheel would require 10 positions.   Furthermore, just as a mechanical counter can transmit its count to a second wheel after one full rotation, a ring counter can also shift its count to a second ring of flip-flops.

The operation of a ring counter is straightforward.   As shown in Fig. 4-17, only one flip-flop in the ring can be in the 1 state at a time.   All other flip-flops must be in the 0 state.   When a count signal is received, the 1 signal from the set flip-flop is gated into the next flip-flop, setting it into the 1 state.   The same signal is also used to reset the first flip-flop back to 0.   Each subsequent signal then gates the set signal around the ring.   The dotted line in Fig. 4-17 shows how the circuit can be connected back on itself to form a ring.   If desired, the last set signal can also be used to start a 1 moving in a second ring, thus implementing the carry mechanism, as in a two-wheeled counter.

This carry mechanism permits the connection of several ring counters in series.   If a 10-stage ring is connected to another 10-stage ring, 100 counts (10 × 10) can be registered.   After each full circuit of the first 10-stage ring, one count is registered on the second 10-stage ring.   Ninety-nine counts puts both rings to the ninth position, whereupon one additional count will return both counters to 0.   The highest count possible (in this case, 100) is called the *modulus* of the counter.

A ring counter requires more flip-flops for a given count, e.g., 16 flip-flops to count to 16, as opposed to 4 for a binary counter.   These flip-flops, however, provide automatic decoding since each flip-flop represents a weighted number.   Any one flip-flop in a ring counter is set only when the ring has counted to the weighted number assigned to that particular flip-flop.   The choice between a ring counter, which requires many

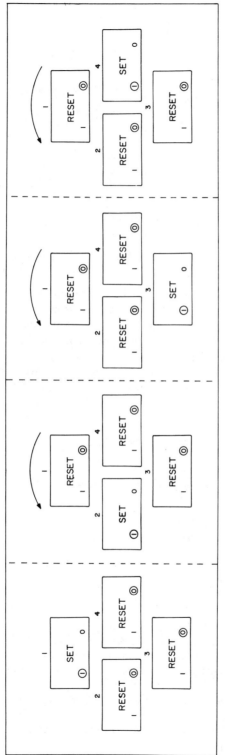

Fig. 4-16   Flip-flop ring-counter representation.

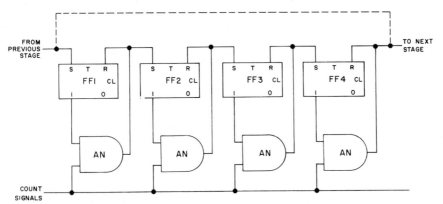

Fig. 4-17   Ring counter.

flip-flops, and a binary counter, which may require many decoding gates, is dependent on the particular system application.

One further attribute of the ring counter is that it can be used to count either up or down.   To count down, the gating is simply reversed.   A ring counter can therefore function as either an up or a down counter. Additional gating can be supplied to allow the counter to count in both directions.   Such a circuit could be used as a forward-backward ring counter.

Demonstration 4-4   The Ring Counter

Purpose

To demonstrate the operation of a ring counter.

Equipment

  1—Single-pulse generator (SPG)
  1—Low-frequency clock (CK)
  1—Level switch (S)
  4—Flip-flops (FF)
  5—AND gates (AN)

Discussion and Implementation

The ring counter can be thought of as a device for shifting one binary digit, in this case a 1, around a ring of flip-flops.   Since only one flip-flop at a time is set, the set flip-flop contains the binary digit 1.   A series of count signals then circulates this single binary digit, or bit, around the ring, passing it from stage to stage with each shift signal.   Figure 4-18 is a timing diagram for one cycle of operation of a four-stage ring counter.

The timing diagram shows how each succeeding stage in the ring counter is set as count pulses are received.   Note that the previous stage is also

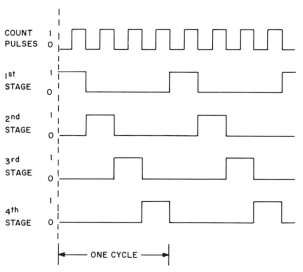

Fig. 4-18 Timing diagram for a four-stage ring counter.

reset at the same time. Here again, it is the trailing edge of the count pulse which causes both the set and the reset actions in adjacent stages.

Figure 4-19 illustrates a ring counter which is capable of providing four counts. A clear line is provided to clear all stages to the reset state prior to entering a 1 into the first stage. One of the properties of a ring counter is that one stage and only one stage should be in the set state at any time. Channel G of the single-pulse generator will put FF1 in the set state when the push button on that channel is depressed. Since FF1 was in the reset state, the pulse applied to the toggle input put it to the set state. Thus one stage of the ring is in the set state, and the ring is ready to accept count pulses. The first-stage FF1 represents a count of 0. When channel F of the SPG is activated, a pulse is applied to the count line. This pulse passes through AN1 since the other input to AN1 is a logic 1. It does not pass through AN2, AN3, or AN4 because an input to each of these gates is a logic 0. The pulse appearing at the output of AN1 is connected to the R input of FF1 and the S input of FF2, thereby resetting FF1 and setting FF2. This represents a count of 1 in the ring. Two subsequent pulses applied to the count line will cause FF4 to be in the set state. This is equivalent to a count of 3. When a fourth pulse is applied, FF1 returns to the set state and the cycle is complete. Refer to the timing diagram in Fig. 4-18 for the operation of a full timing cycle. The diagram presents the state of the 1 outputs of each stage relative to the count pulses. By connecting the output of FF4 as the count line to an identical four-stage ring count, two rings of four stages each would provide counts up to 16. The maximum count can also be increased by adding other stages to FF4 to change the size of the ring.

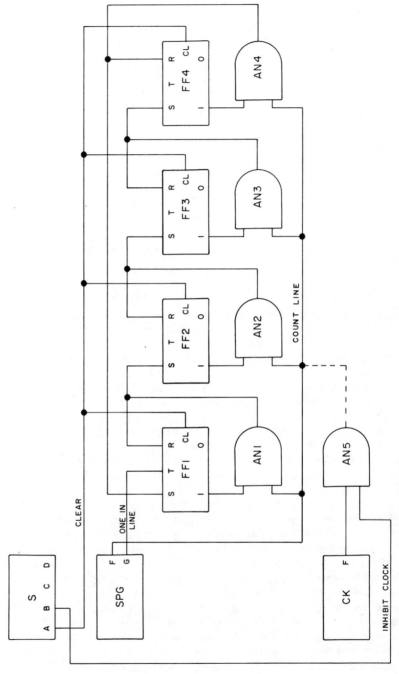

Fig. 4-19 Four-stage ring counter.

4-7 Registers

Another frequently encountered array of flip-flops is the register. A register is simply a set of flip-flops arranged side by side. As stated earlier, the register can store an entire binary number. The size of the number determines the number of flip-flops needed. Figure 4-20 shows a four-stage register storing the four-digit binary number 1011 (decimal 11).

The circled numbers in Fig. 4-20 identify the state of each flip-flop. Flip-flops 1, 3, and 4 are in the 1 state; flip-flop 2 is in the 0 state. Each flip-flop stores one binary digit, or 1 bit. Flip-flops 1, 3, and 4 are storing 1s, and flip-flop 2 is storing a 0.

Registers are frequently used in the arithmetic and control elements of computers, where they store commands, the results of arithmetic operations, and partial results while waiting for another phase of an operation to be concluded. Registers are extremely useful, not merely because of their storage capability, but because of the ease by which their contents can be transferred from one register to another at a specified point in time. In other words, information in a register is easily handled. The use of a gating signal permits the information to pass out of one register and into another on a definite command.

Many arithmetic operations require that the number stored in a register be shifted; that is, the number must occasionally be displaced bodily by one or more digits to either the right or the left. The register in Fig. 4-20 can be connected to perform this operation by the addition of the proper gating. The register shown in Fig. 4-21 is wired for shifting to the right and is called a *shift register*. By changing the interconnections, the register could be wired to shift left instead of right.

Each flip-flop presents signals representing the 1 or 0 state to the next flip-flop on the right. However, to reach the next flip-flop, the signal must pass through one of two AND gates. The AND gates block any signals from passing until a gating signal is received from the shift line. When the gating signal is received, all the proper AND gates (those with a 1 input from the previous stage) are opened and the number in the register is shifted one digit to the right. For example, if the register originally stores 0110, a shift pulse would shift the number one digit to the right

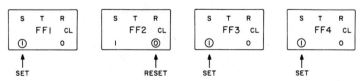

Fig. 4-20   Flip-flop register.

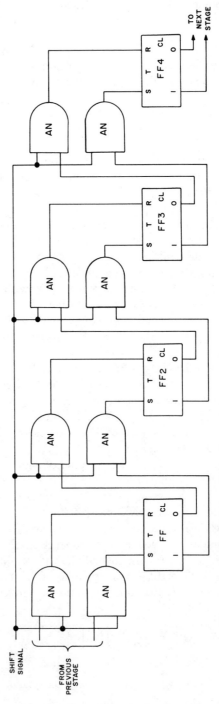

Fig. 4-21 Shift-register equivalent.

94

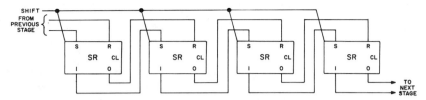

Fig. 4-22 Shift register.

to form 0011. A second shift right would then form 0001, with a 1 being shifted out of the register. This example assumes 0s are being shifted into the first stage.

Shift registers come into such frequent use that special modules have been developed which contain the necessary gating internally. If a shift signal is applied to the upper left-hand corner of a shift-register module (shown in Fig. 4-22), the module will behave like a flip-flop connected with the AND gates in Fig. 4-21. The circuit in Fig. 4-21 is reproduced in Fig. 4-22, using shift-register modules instead of flip-flops. Both circuits, however, perform the same function.

Demonstration 4-5 The Shift Register

Purpose

To demonstrate register storage and shifting operations.

Equipment

1—Level switch (S)
3—Flip-flops (FF)
3—Shift registers (SR)
6—AND gates (AN)
1—Single-pulse generator (SPG)
1—NAND gate (ND)

Discussion and Implementation

The shift-register circuit is similar to the up-down–counter circuit, except that the 1 and 0 outputs of one stage are taken to the S and R inputs of the next stage instead of to the T input. In this way, bits can be transferred unchanged from stage to stage. Where in the counter it is a carry which invariably complements the succeeding flip-flop, in the shift register the bit value itself is transferred. This means that the succeeding flip-flop may or may not be complemented, depending on the present state of the flip-flop and the data being transferred. Signals are gated into succeeding stages through AND gates. The common signal gated into each AND gate is called the *shift command.*

In Fig. 4-23, there are two independent 3-bit shift registers. One comprises three FF modules plus the six AND gates, and the other is illus-

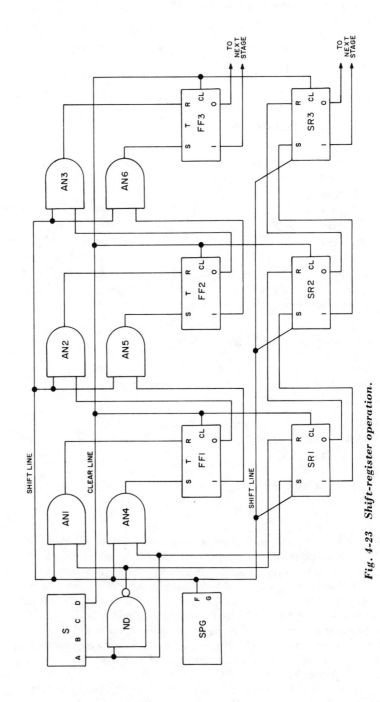

Fig. 4-23 Shift-register operation.

96

trated with three SR modules. One of the aims of this illustration is to
show the equivalency of these two registers. The SR module is actually a
flip-flop with two AND gates packaged into one module.

When the clear line is momentarily held to logic 0, all the stages of both
registers will be reset. Channel A of the level switch provides a source of
signals to be shifted serially into each register. The SR module requires
both the assertion and the negation of a signal to function properly. These
complementary input signals are presented to the inputs prior to activation
of the shift line with a pulse which enters the data into the register. The
first stage receives its complementary inputs from the A channel and the
inverted signal. Thus, if the input-data line is a logic 1, AN1 would have
a logic-0 input from the NAND gate while AN4 would have a logic-1 input.
Then, when channel F of the SPG is activated, the resulting pulse would
gate through AN4, but it would be inhibited in AN1. The pulse which
appears at the output of AN4 is connected to the set input of FF1 and sets
the flip-flop. Since FF1 was reset prior to the application of the initial
shift pulse, AN2 has a 1 on its input and AN5 has a 0. The initial shift
pulse is gated through AN2 and resets FF2. Since FF2 was already reset,
the reset signal has no effect. For similar reasons, a reset signal is also
applied to FF3.

If the input data on channel A are now changed to a 0, the next shift
pulse will pass through AN1 and will subsequently reset FF1. Since there
has been a 1 in FF1, this same shift pulse will pass through AN5, which is
enabled to set FF2. Since there has been a 0 in FF2, the same shift pulse
will pass through AN3 and reset FF3. Thus, it can be seen that the input
data shift into FF1; the data in FF1 shift into FF2; and the data in FF2
shift into FF3. The shift-register module is identical to a flip-flop with
the two AND gates; SR1 will have the same data as FF1, SR2 as FF2, and
SR3 as FF3. By setting the input-data line to a 1 or 0 and supplying a
shift pulse, any combination of 1s and 0s can be entered into the register.

4-8 *Serial and Parallel Modes*

Registers of the type described are used throughout a digital computer.
Constantly, they must accept new numbers, store them, and return them
on command to the other sections of the machine. There are two distinct methods of transmitting numbers to and from registers, and these
require detailed consideration.

The first technique for entering numbers into a register is called the
serial mode. When entering a register serially, the number comes in
1 bit at a time. For example, when the binary number 101 (decimal 5)
is entered serially into a register, the 1 in the zeroth-order digit (2^0)
is presented first and goes into the highest stage of the register. When
the first-order digit 0 is presented for entry, the 1 already in the highest
stage is shifted to the next-to-highest stage. A gating signal then allows

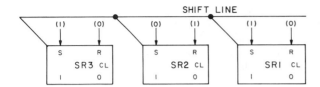

Fig. 4-24   Parallel transfer.

the first-order 0 to enter the register and the zeroth-order 1 to shift down to the next stage.   This process is repeated as each new digit comes into the register.   New digits keep entering the high-order stage, and those digits already in the register are continuously shifted down until the entire number has been entered, with the lowest-order bit in the zeroth stage.   Thus, in this operation, data arrive least significant digit first. The first bit in is shifted down through all orders to the lowest.   Succeeding entries are shifted down to their proper positions.

Serial operation normally requires a minimum amount of equipment and is often quite satisfactory.   However, numbers must be handled one digit at a time, and many shift operations are required.

A second method for entering numbers into a register is called the *parallel mode*.   Here the entire number is placed in the register in one shifting operation.

Consider binary 101 again.   Each digit of the number is presented at the input terminals of a separate stage of the register.   In this case, when the gating signal is received, the entire number enters the register all at once.   Figure 4-24 illustrates a register connected for parallel operation.

In Fig. 4-24, the number 101 is presented for parallel entry into a register.   The zeroth-order digit will go into the zeroth-order stage, the first-order digit into the first-order stage, and so on.   When a shift signal is received, the entire number will be sent into the register at one time. Note the logic states of the inputs prior to the shifting operation.   The input signals to the first order are opposite to those for the zeroth and second orders.

With a register, there are four possible modes of operation: (1) information can be entered serially and removed serially, i.e., serial in–serial out; (2) information can be entered into all stages simultaneously and removed from all stages simultaneously, i.e., parallel in–parallel out; (3) information can be entered serially and removed in parallel; and (4) information can be entered in parallel and removed serially.   All four modes are used in computers.

Demonstration 4-6 *Transfer of Information*

Purpose

To demonstrate how information is transferred from one register to another and to demonstrate serial and parallel modes of operation.

Equipment

1—Level switch (S)
1—NAND gate (ND)
1—Single-pulse generator (SPG)
6—Shift registers (SR)

Discussion and Implementation

In a computer, the output of one section must often become the input to another section. If, for example, a payroll is being computed, one step would be to multiply each man's rate of pay by the number of hours he worked. Each of these individual numbers is transferred from the computer memory element to the arithmetic section, where a total is accumulated. Furthermore, results must also be transferred from the arithmetic unit either to the output or back to the memory element.

These transfers can be accomplished in serial form, one bit at a time, or in parallel form, where all bits are transferred simultaneously. Furthermore, it is also possible to transfer a number into a register serially and then take it out in parallel form, or vice versa.

All transfers are accomplished by appropriate gating. When the transfer command is issued, the number under consideration is taken out of one register and placed in another. Serial transfer, of course, requires a transfer command for each bit, while parallel transfer can be accomplished on one command signal.

This demonstration illustrates how information can be transferred both in serial and in parallel within a computer. Refer to Fig. 4-25.

SR1 to SR3 are connected as a serial shift register. SR4 to SR6 are connected as a parallel register, which receives the output of the serial register.

Initially, the register is cleared by momentarily making channel B of the level switch a 0. Any three-digit number is entered into the serial register by using level-switch channel A and three shift pulses from channel F of the SPG. When it is desired to transfer the data in the upper register (SR1 to SR3) to the lower register (SR4 to SR6), channel G of the SPG is pressed. The upper and lower registers should then be identical. This operation illustrates the parallel transfer of information from one register to another. Note that only one pulse was required to shift the data in the upper register to the lower one, while it takes three pulses to enter the same data serially into the upper register.

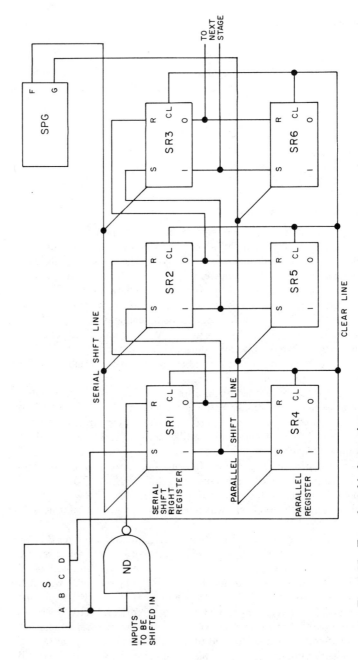

Fig. 4-25 Transfer of information.

EXERCISES

4-1. What three characteristics are required of a storage device?

4-2. Draw a d-c flip-flop made of two NOR gates. Write a truth table for all input conditions.

4-3. Describe the difference between a 1 level and the 1 output of a flip-flop. When a flip-flop is reset, what state is its 1 output?

4-4. Assume that a flip-flop is in the reset state. What state will the flip-flop be in after a 1-to-0 transition is applied to:

    (*a*) Reset input   (*b*) Set input
    (*c*) Toggle input   (*d*) Clear input

4-5. Draw a timing diagram showing the 1-output terminal with five sequential pulses applied to the toggle input. Assume that the flip-flop was reset at time T_0.

4-6. Assume that a flip-flop is in the reset state at time T_0. Complete the timing diagram (Fig. 4-26) by constructing the output pulse at the 1-output terminal. Note that the toggle input is not being used.

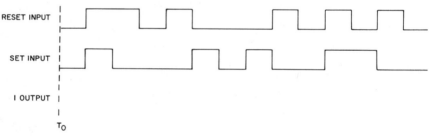

Fig. 4-26   Timing diagram.

4-7. Draw a timing diagram showing the set outputs of a three-stage up-down counter assuming the following sequence:

    (*a*) The register is cleared.
    (*b*) A count-up command is given, and 7 pulses are supplied to the count input.
    (*c*) A count-down command is given, and 4 pulses are supplied to the count input.

4-8. Construct a block diagram of an up-down counter similar to the one given in Demonstration 4-3, using an equivalent number of NAND gates in place of the AND and OR gates.

4-9. How many flip-flops would be needed to represent a decimal digit using a ring counter?

4-10. How many flip-flops would be needed to represent six decimal digits using ring counters?

4-11. Draw a timing chart for Demonstration 4-5 assuming 110011 is shifted into the register.

4-12. How many shift-register stages would be needed to store the binary equivalent of the decimal number 842?

4-13. Construct a block diagram similar to the one used in Demonstration 4-5 that will shift left rather than shift right.   Use shift-register modules.

4-14. Construct a timing diagram of a four-stage serial shift register which is initially cleared to 0000 and 4 shift pulses later registers 1011.

4-15. Construct a block diagram showing all interconnections of a 4-bit register which receives a parallel input and then shifts the data out serially.

FIVE

Codes and Decimal Arithmetic

5-1   *Coding in the Binary System*

Although the binary system is most widely used in computer design because of its ease of implementation and simplicity of design, other numbering systems are also used.   Of these, the most common are the octal system and a variety of coding systems which represent decimal numbers by means of binary codes.

The octal system has the advantage that numbers are more easily identified and yet can be converted directly into binary.   Thus octal 713 is more manageable than binary 111001011.   The octal number is converted directly into the binary number by converting each numeral to its binary equivalent; i.e., 7 is 111, 1 is 001, and 3 is 011.   Binary-to-octal and octal-to-binary conversion is always a direct operation requiring no arithmetic operations.   Binary 001011101 is octal 135; octal 627 is binary 110010111.

While there are advantages in designing the computer around the binary or octal number system, the computer inputs and outputs usually are decimal.   Scientists, engineers, and businessmen do their everyday thinking and calculating in the decimal system, and because of this, the methods used to process decimal numbers are important.

Any decimal number can be converted to binary either manually or inside the computer by following the conversion rules outlined in Chap. 2. Whether this conversion is to be performed within the computer or whether the entire problem is to be solved in the decimal numbering system, the decimal number must be represented in terms of 1s and 0s. Representation of decimal or octal symbols (or any other base number, for that matter) in the binary system is accomplished through the use of codes.   The word "code" is also used to describe a variety of programming languages as well as various methods for representing information in input-output equipment.   Programming and input-output codes are discussed in Chaps. 12 and 10.

Coding in the binary system is much like the familiar coding of the Morse system used in telegraphy.   Where Morse code uses dots and dashes to represent the letters of the alphabet, binary codes use 1s and 0s to represent the decimal numerals. Just as any telegraph operator learns to recognize · · · − as the letter V, a computer operator can learn to recognize 1001 as the decimal numeral 9. However, once numbers become large, it is difficult to translate a binary number into its decimal equivalent; therefore, binary-coded decimal (BCD) is used. The binary equivalent of 459 is 111001011. A binary-coded decimal equivalent can be formed which is much easier to convert. For example, 0100 0101 1001 equals 459.

Obviously, there is an important distinction between binary-coded decimals and binary numbers. Twelve binary digits, or bits, are required to represent 459 in binary-coded decimals, while only nine bits are necessary to represent 459 as a binary number. Each decimal numeral requires a minimum of 4 binary bits. Since only eight combinations of three binary digits are possible (i.e., 000, 001, 010, 011, 100, 101, 110, 111), it is impossible to represent all 10 decimal symbols with 3 bits. However, by using a 4-bit code, 16 possible combinations are available, and all the decimal symbols can be represented. In this case, though, 6 of the 16 combinations are never used and are, in fact, wasted. Coding of decimal numbers, therefore, involves a certain loss in economy. While 0100 0101 1001 is much easier to recognize as 459 than is 111001011, it requires 3 extra bits of information. This is the sacrifice required for ease of representation.

5-2 *Binary-coded Decimal*

The most obvious way to encode decimal numbers into binary symbols is to use the first 10 characters of the binary number system. In this way, the code shown in Table 5-1 can be prepared.

TABLE 5-1

Decimal	Binary-coded decimal			
	(8)	(4)	(2)	(1)
0	0	0	0	0
1	0	0	0	1
2	0	0	1	0
3	0	0	1	1
4	0	1	0	0
5	0	1	0	1
6	0	1	1	0
7	0	1	1	1
8	1	0	0	0
9	1	0	0	1

Using this code, the decimal number 382 appears as 0011 1000 0010. Each digit in the coded representation carries a characteristic weight. The lowest-order digit has a weight of 1; the first-order digit has a weight of 2; the second-order digit has a weight of 4; and the highest-order digit has a weight of 8. The numeral 7 (0111), then, is equivalent to $0 + 4 + 2 + 1$; the numeral 9 (1001) is equivalent to $8 + 0 + 0 + 1$. The natural binary code is therefore called a 4-*bit weighted code* and is often referred to as the 8-4-2-1 code.

The 8-4-2-1 code has the advantage of simplicity. Anyone who is at all familiar with the binary number system can quickly recognize binary-coded decimals in the 8-4-2-1 code. While counting in this code, 1001 is the largest number possible.

After reaching the count of 1001, the count returns to 0000 and a 1 is carried. The count cannot reach 1010 since this particular configuration is meaningless in the 8-4-2-1 code. The number 10 is represented as 0001 0000, not 1010. The following demonstration indicates how an 8-4-2-1 binary-coded decimal counter can be constructed.

Demonstration 5-1   The 8-4-2-1 BCD Counter

Purpose

To demonstrate the operation of a decimal counter which produces outputs in the 8-4-2-1 code.

Equipment

    1—Level switch (S)
    1—Single-pulse generator (SPG)
    1—Low-frequency clock (CK)
    4—Flip-flops (FF)
    2—AND gates (AN)
    1—OR gate (OR)

Discussion and Implementation

The 8-4-2-1 code is identical to the straight binary code from the count of 0 (0000) to 9 (1001). After 9, the next count must reset the counter to 0. There are many ways of accomplishing this. Figure 5-1 shows one method of building an 8-4-2-1 counter.

The four flip-flops are connected as in the normal binary counter, with the 1 output of each stage going to the toggle input of the next higher stage. The only exception is that 1-to-0 transitions from the first stage must pass through AND gate AN2 to reach the toggle input of stage 2. This AND gate is held open as long as the fourth stage is in the 0 state; therefore, as pulses are received at the first stage, the counter counts up to 1001 in the normal way. However, when the next pulse sends stage 1 back to the 0 state, this 1-to-0 transition is blocked from stage 2 by AN2. Since stage 4

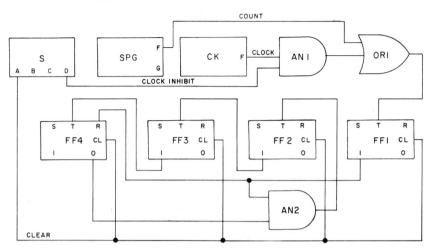

Fig. 5-1   8-4-2-1 BCD counter.

is now in the 1 state, AN2 is closed.   The 1-to-0 transition at stage 1 is
sent also to the reset input of stage 4, resetting it to the 0 state.   In this
way, all four flip-flops are 0 after the count of 9 is reached.   The circuit is
then ready to start over again and to count up to 1001.   On every tenth
count, a 1-to-0 transition is available at the 1 output of stage 4.   This signal
can then be used as the carry input to a second BCD counter.

A low-frequency clock has been included in this demonstration to provide
automatic operation.   If single-pulse operation is desired, the inhibit line is
held to a 0 level, making the output of AN1 a 0.   When channel D of the
level switch is set on 1, AND gate AN1 opens and admits count pulses
through OR1 into the first stage.   After each 10 pulses, the counter resets
to 0000 and begins counting again.   Channel A of the level switch provides
the CLEAR signal.

5-3   *Encoding and Decoding*

The BCD counter in Demonstration 5-1 not only performs a counting
operation but, in effect, also encodes decimal numbers.   If the decimal
number 326 is to be encoded, it is only necessary to send 326 pulses to a
12-stage counter.   After the last pulse is received, the counter is set at
0011 0010 0110 and the number 326 is encoded in the 8-4-2-1 code.
This, however, is a slow and involved approach.   What is really desired
is a system whereby when a key marked 9 is punched, the number 9 is
immediately converted to BCD form.   Such a system is actually quite
simple and is described below.

The BCD encoder in Fig. 5-2 accepts a decimal digit from keys 1 to 9
and converts it to BCD at the outputs of the OR gates.   Only one key at

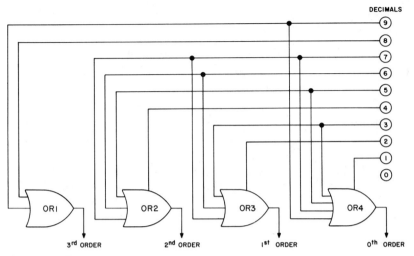

Fig. 5-2   Encoder.

a time can be activated.   Inactive keys have logic-0 outputs.   When a key is activated, it is defined as being a 1.   This signal is connected to OR gates and produces a 1 output on the appropriate gates.   The key marked 0 will give a 0000 output when it is depressed since it transmits no inputs to the gates.   If the key marked 9 is depressed, a signal will activate the zeroth order and the third order, giving a 1001 output.   It can be seen that the proper 8-4-2-1 representation of each key will occur at the output as each key is activated.

Decoding is almost the opposite of encoding.   To decode from the 8-4-2-1 BCD system to decimal, it is only necessary to recognize which decimal number is being represented and then to cause a signal to be emitted which identifies that decimal number.   For example, if a BCD register contains 1001, stage 1 is 1; stage 2 is 0; stage 3 is 0; stage 4 is 1. This is the only configuration that represents decimal 9, so the decoder should produce a signal on output 9.   If four signals, representing 1001, are connected to an AND gate, the gate will open and produce the required 9 signal.   For any other configuration, the AND gates will remain closed and no signal will be produced.   An example of this form of decoding is presented in Fig. 5-3.

The BCD counter in Fig. 5-3 is similar to that shown in Fig. 5-1.   As the counter goes through a count cycle, each of the gates is activated in succession.   When the counter is in the 1001 state, the output of the 9 gate is 1 and the outputs of gates 0 to 8 are 0.   The 9 output is a 1 since X_0 and X_3 are 1s and $\overline{X}_1$ and $\overline{X}_2$ are 1s, thus satisfying the condition of the AND that will produce a 1 output.

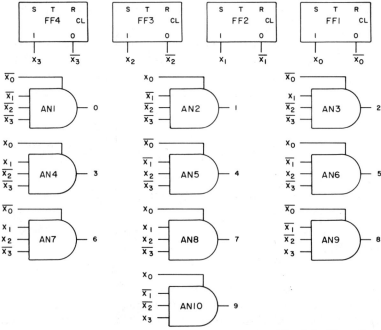

Fig. 5-3 Decoder.

5-4 *BCD-to-binary Conversion*

Once the BCD representation of a decimal number is formed, the conversion is only partially completed. The problem of converting this BCD number into a binary number still remains. This can be accomplished by a series of multiplications and additions. The following example illustrates the steps required in the process:

1. Select any decimal number, for example, 365.
2. Encode this number into the 8-4-2-1 BCD code as 0011 0110 0101.
3. Multiply the coded representation of the highest-order decimal digit by binary 1010 (decimal 10).

$$
\begin{array}{rr}
0011 & 3 \\
\times 1010 & \times 10 \\
\hline
0000 & \\
0011 & \\
0000 & \\
0011 & \\
\hline
0011110 & 30
\end{array}
$$

4. Add in the BCD representation of the second-highest-order decimal digit.

$$
\begin{array}{r} 11110 \\ +\ \underline{0110} \\ 100100 \end{array}
\qquad
\begin{array}{r} 30 \\ +\ \underline{6} \\ 36 \end{array}
$$

5. Multiply this result by binary 1010.

$$
\begin{array}{r}
100100 \\
\times\ \underline{1010} \\
000000 \\
100100 \\
000000 \\
\underline{100100} \\
101101000
\end{array}
\qquad
\begin{array}{r}
36 \\
\times 10 \\
\hline
\\
\\
\\
\\
\underline{} \\
360
\end{array}
$$

6. Add in the BCD representation of the lowest-order decimal digit.

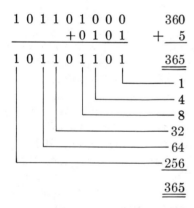

$$
\begin{array}{r}
1\ 0\ 1\ 1\ 0\ 1\ 0\ 0\ 0 \\
+0\ 1\ 0\ 1 \\
\hline
1\ 0\ 1\ 1\ 0\ 1\ 1\ 0\ 1
\end{array}
\qquad
\begin{array}{r}
360 \\
+\ 5 \\
\hline
365
\end{array}
$$

$$
\begin{array}{r}
1 \\
4 \\
8 \\
32 \\
64 \\
256 \\
\hline
365
\end{array}
$$

By successive multiplication by 1010 and then adding in the next lower-order BCD representation, any 8-4-2-1 binary-coded decimal number can be converted into the binary system. Methods used by the computer to add and multiply will be covered in Chap. 6.

5-5   *The Self-complementing 2-4-2-1 Code*

The 8-4-2-1 code is by no means the only BCD representation possible for decimal numbers; hundreds of different codes are possible, and many are in actual use. Some, however, have special properties and are illustrative of the more important things that can be done with different codes.

One such code is the 2-4-2-1 code.   This is also a weighted 4-bit code, but the weights are 2, 4, 2, and 1 instead of the natural binary weights of 8, 4, 2, and 1.   Table 5-2 illustrates the 2-4-2-1 code.

TABLE 5-2

Decimal	Binary-coded decimal			
	(2)	(4)	(2)	(1)
0	0	0	0	0
1	0	0	0	1
2	0	0	1	0
3	0	0	1	1
4	0	1	0	0
5	1	0	1	1
6	1	1	0	0
7	1	1	0	1
8	1	1	1	0
9	1	1	1	1

The major advantage of the 2-4-2-1 code is that it is self-complementing; that is, any two numbers which add up to 9 complement one another, or in other words, are opposite.   Thus 0 (0000) is the opposite of 9 (1111), and 1 (0001) is the opposite of 8 (1110).   This is true for all BCD numbers in the 2-4-2-1 code, and the code is therefore called *self-complementing*.   The self-complementing property can be advantageous in many subtraction applications, and several codes have been devised which have this property.   This feature will be discussed further in Chap. 6.

Decimal representations are not unique in this code.   The BCD representation for 6 can be either 1100 or 0110.   Both of these fit the weighting scheme to produce the numeral 6.   This, however, does not interfere with the self-complementing property of the code.   The 1s complements of 1100 and 0110 are 0011 and 1001, respectively, and either of these is an adequate representation for the numeral 3 using the 2-4-2-1 code.   Since 3 is the 9s complement of 6, the self-complementing property is preserved.

As with the 8-4-2-1 code, circuits can be constructed for the 2-4-2-1 code which encode, decode, and count in this particular BCD representation.   The 2-4-2-1 BCD counter is illustrated in Fig. 5-4.   Encoders and decoders for this system are quite similar to those for the 8-4-2-1 code.

Demonstration 5-2   **The 2-4-2-1 BCD Counter**

Purpose

To demonstrate the operation of a decimal counter which produces outputs in the 2-4-2-1 code.

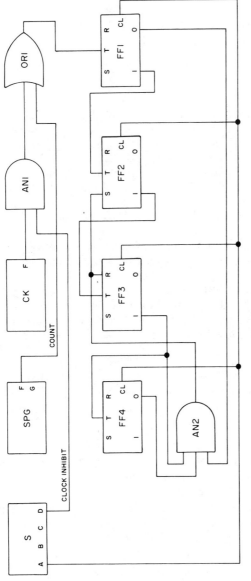

Fig. 5-4 2-4-2-1 BCD counter.

Equipment

    1—Level switch (S)
    1—Single-pulse generator (SPG)
    1—Low-frequency clock (CK)
    4—Flip-flops (FF)
    2—AND gates (AN)
    1—OR gate (OR)

Discussion and Implementation

The 2-4-2-1 code is identical to the straight binary code except in the transition from the count of 4 to 5, when it changes from 0100 to 1011. Figure 5-4 shows one method of implementing a 2-4-2-1 counter.

The four flip-flops are connected as in a binary counter, with the 1 outputs going to the toggle inputs of the next higher stage. Counting proceeds just as in the 8-4-2-1 counter until 0100 is reached. At this time, all three inputs to AND gate AN2 are 1 and the gate is open. However, no transitions are available until the next count. When the next count is received, stage 1 goes from 0 to 1 and the signal at the 0 output goes from 1 to 0. This transition is gated through AN2, setting stage 2 and resetting stage 3. When stage 3 is reset, a 1-to-0 transition is sent to stage 4, complementing it to the 1 state. Therefore, the next state after 0100 is 1011, which is correct for the 2-4-2-1 code. (Refer to Table 5-2.) Subsequent pulses up to the count of 1111 are counted in normal fashion, with AN2 remaining closed at all times. After the count of 1111 is reached, the counter reverts to 0000, just as a simple binary counter would, and the 2-4-2-1 sequence is maintained.

Automatic operation can be obtained by gating clock pulses through AN1, as was done in Demonstration 5-1. Channel A of the level switch provides the CLEAR signal.

5-6   *The Excess-3 Code*

Another important self-complementing code is the excess-3 code. This code is formed by adding 3 (binary 0011) to each coded decimal in the 8-4-2-1 code. The resulting BCD representation is given in Table 5-3. The excess-3 code is not a weighted code, and digit positions do not indicate the relative values of the representations in any way.

The excess-3 code is a self-complementing code; i.e., 0 (0011) is the opposite of 9 (1100), and 1 (0100) is the opposite of 8 (1011). This has advantages in subtraction, as will be discussed in Chap. 6. Beyond this, the excess-3 code also has properties that are quite useful for addition. To understand the importance of these properties, it is first necessary to understand how BCD arithmetic is performed.

TABLE 5-3 *Excess-3 Code*

8-4-2-1 code		Excess-3 code
0	0 0 0 0	↑
1	0 0 0 1	Unused
2	0 0 1 0	↓
3	0 0 1 1	0
4	0 1 0 0	1
5	0 1 0 1	2
6	0 1 1 0	3
7	0 1 1 1	4
8	1 0 0 0	5
9	1 0 0 1	6
↑	1 0 1 0	7
	1 0 1 1	8
Unused	1 1 0 0	9
	1 1 0 1	↑
	1 1 1 0	Unused
↓	1 1 1 1	↓

If two BCD numbers in the 8-4-2-1 code are to be added together, they are first arranged as in normal addition and combined to form a sum:

Decimal	BCD
683	0110 1000 0011
+ 542	+0101 0100 0010
1,225	1011 1100 0101

The least significant digit, 0101, is correct. The remainder of the sum, 1011 and 1100, are incorrect since they are forbidden codes in the 8-4-2-1 system. To correct the sum, a 6, which represents the six unused combinations of the 8-4-2-1 code, must be added to each order whose sum is greater than 9, or binary 1001.

```
Add 6:           1011            1100        0101
               +0110           +0110
             ⟋ 0001         ⟋ 0010          ____
  1 carry ⟋       1 carry ⟋
 ____            ____            ____        ____
0001            0010            0010        0101
 (1)             (2)             (2)         (5)
```

This produces a carry in each of the two highest orders and yields a correct result in the 8-4-2-1 code. Note, however, that the incorrect sums had to be recognized before the carries could be generated. Thus, the forbidden codes 1010 to 1111 must be recognized and a 6 (0110) added wherever they appear.

Now compare the above process to the addition of two BCD numbers in the excess-3 code. Again the numbers are arranged and summed in the normal manner:

Decimal		*Excess-3 Code*		
683		1001	1011	0110
+ 542		+1000	+0111	+0101
1,225		0001	0010	1011
	1 carry	1 carry		
	0001	0010	0010	1011

In this case, the correct decimal carries are generated immediately. However, the sums must still be corrected to achieve the proper result. In the lowest order, each original coded representation contained an excess 3, and the sum therefore contains an excess 6. To return it to excess 3, a 3 (0011) should be subtracted.

In the two higher orders, the excess 6 takes the sum right on through the six unused representations of the natural binary code. This causes the excess-6 sum to "catch up" with the 8-4-2-1 code, and the sum is, therefore, represented as an 8-4-2-1 number. However, it is also this catch-up process of going right through 1111 and back to 0000 that generates the carry. In other words, the sum is only in 8-4-2-1 form when a carry is generated. Therefore, if a carry is present, just adding 3 to the sum converts it back into the excess-3 code. To summarize the whole process: The coded representations are first added together. Then, if a carry is present, 3 is added to the sum; if no carry is present, 3 is subtracted from the sum. The result is the correct BCD sum in excess-3 form. The following example presents the entire process in detail:

Decimal		*Excess-3*		
683		1001	1011	0110
+542		+1000	+0111	+0101
		0001	0010	1011
	0001	1		
	0001	0010	0010	1011
	+0011	+0011	+0011	−0011
1,225	0100	0101	0101	1000
	(1)	(2)	(2)	(5)

Note that, instead of having to wait until after corrections are made, correct decimal carries are generated immediately and that these carries indicate which orders require correction.

5-7 *Reflected Codes: The Gray Code*

All the codes discussed in the previous sections must occasionally change the value of several digits at once to proceed from one representation to the next. For example, in the 8-4-2-1 code, both the zeroth- and first-order digits must be changed to get from 0101 to 0110. The zeroth order goes from 1 to 0, and the first order goes from 0 to 1. In going from 0111 to 1000, all four digits must be changed. For certain applications, this is undesirable, and a code that changes only one digit at a time is necessary. Reflected codes have just this property, and one such code, the Gray code, is the subject of this section. To form the reflected Gray code, first set down the two binary digits 0 and 1 in the following manner:

    0
    1

Then draw a reflection line under the 1 and form a mirror image of the 0 and 1 below the line.

    0
    1
    --------reflection line
    1
    0

Now add two 0s above the reflection line and two 1s below it.

    00
    01
    --------- reflection line
    11
    10

Next draw a new reflection line and reflect again.

    000
    001
    011
    010
    -----------reflection line 2
    110
    111
    101
    100

This is continued by adding four 0s above the line and four 1s below it and reflecting again, using a third reflection line.

After this is done, add eight 0s above reflection line 3 and eight 1s below it. The first 16 representations of the Gray code are then formed, as shown in Table 5-4.

TABLE 5-4

Decimal	Gray code
0	0 0 0 0
1	0 0 0 1
2	0 0 1 1
3	0 0 1 0
4	0 1 1 0
5	0 1 1 1
6	0 1 0 1
7	0 1 0 0
8	1 1 0 0
9	1 1 0 1
10	1 1 1 1
11	1 1 1 0
12	1 0 1 0
13	1 0 1 1
14	1 0 0 1
15	1 0 0 0

Actually, this process could be continued indefinitely, but the first 16 representations are sufficient to illustrate the code's important properties. In the Gray code, it is only necessary to change one digit to get to the next representation. This includes the transition from 15 back to 0.

Although the Gray code is not used in the computer, it is widely used in certain analog areas. One example is in the measurement of the angular rotation of a shaft. Angular rotation, being a continuous quantity, has an infinite number of possible positions. If a weighted code is used to measure shaft rotation, there is some position where all digits are changing. For example, in the 8-4-2-1 code, there is some position when the number is changing from 0111 to 1000. Erroneous codes will exist as some digits change before others. Use of the Gray code means that only 1 bit changes at any time and that there can be no more than 1 bit of uncertainty in the angular rotation.

5-8   *2-out-of-5 Code and Error Detection*

Each of the codes thus far described requires as many as three or four 1s in some representations. For example, the 8-4-2-1 representation for

7 is 0111, requiring three 1s; the 2-4-2-1 representation for 9 is 1111, requiring four 1s. For certain applications, design engineers sometimes prefer a code which uses only two 1s per character. This, however, requires that more digits be used to form the code. For example, if five digits are used, there are only 10 possible combinations which contain exactly two 1s. Table 5-5 illustrates just such a code.

TABLE 5-5

Decimal	2-out-of-5 code
0	1 1 0 0 0
1	0 0 0 1 1
2	0 0 1 0 1
3	0 0 1 1 0
4	0 1 0 0 1
5	0 1 0 1 0
6	0 1 1 0 0
7	1 0 0 0 1
8	1 0 0 1 0
9	1 0 1 0 0

The code is called the 2-out-of-5 code because it uses exactly two 1s out of five possible digits. This is also a weighted code, except for the numeral 0, and is often referred to as the 7-4-2-1-0 code.

The 7-4-2-1-0 code has the important property of being an error-detecting code. If an extra 1 appears or a 1 is dropped, there are no longer exactly two 1s in each character. This immediately identifies any erroneous presentations. For example, if the decimal numeral 5 is being transmitted properly as 01010 and then, because of some failure in the system, one digit is dropped, the representation might change to 01000. Since no such character appears in the 7-4-2-1-0 code, it is immediately identified as an error. In the 7-4-2-1-0 code, two digits must be changed to get from any one character to any other. A single change is therefore quickly detected as an error. Note, however, that if two errors are made simultaneously, they will go undetected. If 01010 is changed by two simultaneous errors to 00110, the error cannot be detected.

This error-detection property does not exist for any of the codes discussed previously. If the character 0110 in the 8-4-2-1 code erroneously changes to 0010, the 0010 is simply treated as decimal 2 and no error is detected.

5-9 *Summary of Codes*

There are many possible codes.   The preceding sections have illustrated a few of the more important ones used in the computer or in peripheral analog or digital equipment.   Individual codes have specific characteristics, e.g., being a weighted code and therefore easily derived, possessing particular arithmetic properties, allowing easy detection of most errors, or changing only one digit at a time.

All codes are similar in that they represent a decimal number or an analog quantity by a unique combination of 1s and 0s.   Binary representation is important since gates, flip-flops, and other logic building blocks possess only two states.   Thus any decimal number must be coded at the time of entry into the computer.

The conversion of coded representations into binary numbers follows the rules outlined in Chap. 2.   The amount of equipment required to convert from binary-coded decimal to binary is extensive.   In some cases, arithmetic operations are preferred in binary-coded decimal. Binary-coded decimal arithmetic whether in the 8-4-2-1 system, the 2-4-2-1 system, the excess-3 system, or another code requires more equipment and is less efficient than binary arithmetic.

In some cases, it is more economical to design the entire computer around binary-coded decimal arithmetic.   However, as the arithmetic section becomes larger, it is preferable to design the arithmetic section around binary arithmetic and to perform binary-coded-decimal-to-binary conversion on the input of the computer and binary-to-binary-coded-decimal conversion on the output of the computer.

The next chapter discusses basic arithmetic operations within the computer.

EXERCISES

5-1. Convert the following decimal numbers to the 8-4-2-1 BCD code and then to binary: 135, 273, 825, 107, 356.

5-2. Convert 135, 273, and 825 to the 2-4-2-1 BCD code.

5-3. Add 482 to 452 using the 8-4-2-1 code.   Check your answer.

5-4. Add the following decimal numbers using the excess-3 code:

673	521	279	724
+348	+373	+241	+ 27

5-5. Generate another weighted code and show the first 10 counts of the code.

SIX

Arithmetic Operations

6-1 *Introduction*

Computer operations can be generally classified into two categories: control and arithmetic. Although computers are certainly not limited to such operations, the major portion of the logic in a machine is designed to implement these two areas of operation. In this chapter, attention is focused on implementing some of the basic arithmetic functions.

The arithmetic section of a computer usually comprises a number of registers and some type of an adder configuration. The adder configuration can be utilized in performing other arithmetic operations, such as subtraction, multiplication, and division. Rules can be developed to enable these operations to be implemented in this way. These rules call for operations such as shifting, complementing, and comparing to be performed along with the addition process.

6-2 *Logical Addition; The Half Adder*

The basic addition operations performed in a computer follow the rules of binary arithmetic. Addition is the operation in which one number (an addend) is combined with a second number (an augend) to form a sum. Use of a binary counter is one technique of forming a sum. With this technique, a number of pulses equivalent to the augend are counted first, and then the counter continues by counting a series of pulses equivalent to the addend. Upon completion of both counts, the number in the counter is the total number of pulses that were sensed, or the sum of

TABLE 6-1

Y (augend)	0	1	0	1
Z (addend)	0	0	1	1
Sum digit	0	1	1	0
Carry digit	0	0	0	1

augend and addend.   This method is similar to tallying and is relatively slow; it also requires extensive equipment.   True arithmetic computation is much faster, uses less equipment, and simplifies data handling.

The rules for binary addition were given in Chap. 2 and are repeated, for convenience, in Table 6-1.

As an example of the addition of two binary numbers and their decimal equivalents, consider the following:

	Decimal		*Binary*	
Augend	93		1011101	
Addend	107		1101011	
Sum 1	190		0110110	Sum 1
Carry 1	01		1001001	Carry 1
Sum 2	100		10100100	Sum 2
Carry 2	1		001001	Carry 2
Sum 3	200		10000000	Sum 3
			01001	Carry 3
			11001000	Sum 4

When performing the pencil-and-paper addition of two decimal numbers, the sum and carry steps are mentally combined and the final sum is reached immediately.   However, when addition is broken down into fundamental steps, as shown in the previous example, augend and addend are first combined to produce an initial sum and carry, which are then combined to produce a second sum and carry.   Finally, these are added together to produce a third and final sum, which has no further carries.

In binary addition, similar steps are used.   First, a sum and carry are generated for each order of augend and addend.   Next, the sums and carries are combined to provide second sums and carries.   This process is continued until no more carries are present and a final sum is obtained.

To implement the sum-and-carry process electronically, it is necessary to transform the rules for addition into logic equations and then to construct a logic circuit which satisfies these equations.

Table 6-2 is a truth table which shows the logic operations required for addition.

TABLE 6-2

Y	Z	Carry	Sum
0	0	0	0
1	0	0	1
0	1	0	1
1	1	1	0

Inspection of this truth table reveals that the carry is 1 only if Y AND Z are 1 and the sum is 1 only if Y AND $\bar{Z}$ OR $\bar{Y}$ AND Z are 1; that is, the sum is 1 if Y or Z is a 1, but not simultaneously. Symbolically,

$$\text{Sum} \ \ = Y \cdot \bar{Z} + \bar{Y} \cdot Z \tag{6-1}$$
$$\text{Carry} = Y \cdot Z \tag{6-2}$$

A sum signal should exist only if $Y \cdot \bar{Z} = 1$ OR $Z \cdot \bar{Y} = 1$, and a carry signal should exist only if $Z \cdot Y = 1$.

It is sometimes advantageous, from a circuit point of view, to rearrange the symbolic expressions for sum and carry. By using De Morgan's theorems and the simplifying theorems, the expressions can be manipulated to arrive at the following equivalent representations:

$$\text{Sum} = Y \cdot \bar{Z} + \bar{Y} \cdot Z \tag{6-1}$$
$$= Y \cdot \bar{Y} + Y \cdot \bar{Z} + \bar{Y} \cdot Z + Z \cdot \bar{Z}$$
$$= (Y + Z) \cdot (\bar{Y} + \bar{Z}) \tag{6-3}$$
$$= (Y + Z) \cdot (\overline{Y \cdot Z}) \tag{6-4}$$
$$\text{Carry} = Y \cdot Z \tag{6-2}$$
$$= \overline{\bar{Y} + \bar{Z}} \tag{6-5}$$

Devices which perform these logic operations are called *half adders*. A half adder combines two binary digits and provides a resultant sum and carry. Any of the previous expressions can be used for the sum and carry terms of a half adder, and three are implemented in the demonstration that follows this section.

There are many possible implementations of the half adder. The particular one selected for use by a logic designer depends on a number of design considerations, including types of gates available, required speed, and available signals.

To make a complete addition, the carry digit from one order must be added in to the next higher order. This, however, requires another half adder. Therefore, in any one order, two half adders are needed to perform a complete addition; that is, to combine addend, augend, and input carry into a final sum and carry, two half adders or one full adder are required. The full adder is discussed in the next section.

In a computer, if more than two numbers are to be added, the usual procedure is to add two of them, take the partial sum and add to it a third number, and so on until all the numbers are combined into one sum.

Demonstration 6-1   *Half Adders*

Purpose

To show the properties of half adders by implementing various half-adder configurations. Three examples are given to indicate different design approaches.

Equipment

FIG. 6-1	FIG. 6-2	FIG. 6-3
1—Level switch (S)	1—Level switch (S)	1—Level switch (S)
3—AND gates (AN)	3—NAND gates (ND)	2—AND gates (AN)
2—NAND gates (ND)	2—OR gates (OR)	1—OR gate (OR)
1—OR gate (OR)	1—AND gate (AN)	1—NAND gate (ND)

Discussion and Implementation

There are many possible ways of implementing a half adder. Half adder 1 implements the expressions

$$\text{Sum} = Y \cdot \bar{Z} + \bar{Y} \cdot Z \tag{6-1}$$
$$\text{Carry} = Y \cdot Z \tag{6-2}$$

The logic expressions and the wiring for half adder 1 are shown in Fig. 6-1. The NAND gates ND1 and ND2 are used as inverters to produce the negation terms $\bar{Y}$ and $\bar{Z}$. $\bar{Y}$ is then gated together with Z in AND gate AN1, and $\bar{Z}$ is gated together with Y in AND gate AN2. Here the outputs of both AND gates are ORed together in OR1 to form the sum term. The sum digit is therefore a 1 if $Y = 1$ AND $Z = 0$ ($\bar{Z} = 1$) OR if $Y = 0$ ($\bar{Y} = 1$) AND $Z = 1$. To form the carry, Y and Z are gated together in AND gate AN3. The output of AN3 is $Y \cdot Z$ and is a 1 only if $Z = 1$ AND $Y = 1$.

Figure 6-2 presents a half adder that implements the expressions

$$\text{Sum} = (Y + Z) \cdot (\bar{Y} + \bar{Z}) \tag{6-3}$$
$$\text{Carry} = \overline{\bar{Y} + \bar{Z}} \tag{6-5}$$

The logic expressions and the wiring for half adder 2 are given in the diagram. NAND gates ND1 and ND2 are again used to produce the

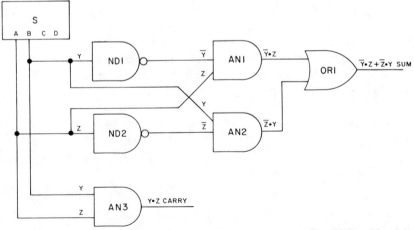

Fig. 6-1   Half adder 1.

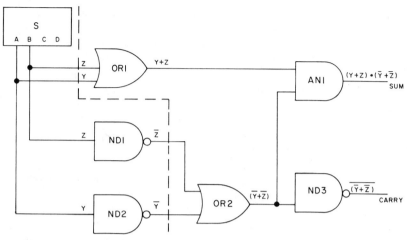

Fig. 6-2   Half adder 2.

negation terms $\overline{Y}$ and $\overline{Z}$.   These negation terms are ORed together in OR2 to produce the $(\overline{Y} + \overline{Z})$ term.   The assertion terms, Y and Z, are ORed together in OR1 to produce the $(Y + Z)$ term.   These two terms are then ANDed together in AN1 to produce the sum term $(\overline{Y} + \overline{Z}) \cdot (Y + Z)$. The NAND gate ND3 inverts the $(\overline{Y} + \overline{Z})$ term to produce the carry term $\overline{\overline{Y} + \overline{Z}}$.   By exercising all possible combinations of the two variables Y and Z, the sum and carry outputs will yield results similar to those in Table 6-2.

Figure 6-3 presents a half adder that implements the expressions

$$\text{Sum} = (\overline{Y \cdot Z}) \cdot (Y + Z) \tag{6-4}$$
$$\text{Carry} = Y \cdot Z \tag{6-2}$$

The logic expressions and the wiring for half adder 3 are given in the diagram.   The number of modules necessary to implement these expres-

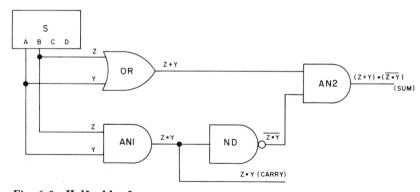

Fig. 6-3   Half adder 3.

sions is less than that required in the previous two demonstrations, although this is not easily determined from the logic expressions.

Y and Z are ORed together in OR to produce the term $(Y + Z)$, while the carry output is generated directly by ANDing Y and Z together in module AN1. Module ND inverts the carry function to produce $(\overline{Y \cdot Z})$. The outputs of OR and ND are then ANDed together in AN2 to produce the sum term $(\overline{Y \cdot Z}) \cdot (Y + Z)$. By using all possible combinations of Z and Y, the sum and output can be shown to be identical to Table 6-2. Thus, although the logic of the three figures is different, all three half adders produce the same result.

6-3   *The Full Adder*

Although a half adder performs the basic operation for addition, it does not consider the carry generated in the previous order. To perform a complete addition, a circuit must add three inputs: the augend, the addend, and the carry from the previous order. A half adder, however, accepts only two inputs. A device that accepts all three input variables and generates both sum and carry is called a *full adder*.

With three input variables, there are eight possible input combinations. These eight combinations are given in Table 6-3, along with the sum and carry outputs for each input condition.

TABLE 6-3

Y (addend input)	0 1 0 1 0 1 0 1
Z (augend input)	0 0 1 1 0 0 1 1
C (carry input from previous order)	0 0 0 0 1 1 1 1
Sum output	0 1 1 0 1 0 0 1
Carry output	0 0 0 1 0 1 1 1

Thus, if the two numbers

101000111	(decimal 327)
110011101	(decimal 413)

were to be added, the addition could be performed by following the rules given in Table 6-3. The result is given in Fig. 6-4.

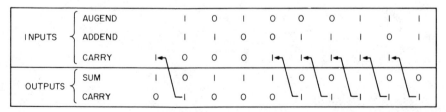

Fig. 6-4   Binary addition.

In Fig. 6-4, a final sum is reached in one step. If the carry in any order is 1, it is added into the next higher order, just as in pencil-and-paper addition. Note, however, that the correct final sum for any order can only be derived after the sums and carries for all previous orders have been computed. The carry must be passed on from order to order, one step at a time, until there are no more carries.

To derive the logic equations for full addition, Table 6-3 can be put in truth-table form (Table 6-4).

TABLE 6-4

Y	Z	C	Sum	Carry
0	0	0	0	0
1	0	0	1	0
0	1	0	1	0
1	1	0	0	1
0	0	1	1	0
1	0	1	0	1
0	1	1	0	1
1	1	1	1	1

Interpreting Table 6-4, the following expressions represent the input conditions that produce a 1 at the sum and carry outputs:

$$\text{Sum} = Y \cdot \bar{Z} \cdot \bar{C} + \bar{Y} \cdot Z \cdot \bar{C} + \bar{Y} \cdot \bar{Z} \cdot C + Y \cdot Z \cdot C \tag{6-6}$$
$$\text{Carry} = Y \cdot Z \cdot \bar{C} + Y \cdot \bar{Z} \cdot C + \bar{Y} \cdot Z \cdot C + Y \cdot Z \cdot C \tag{6-7}$$

The sum output is 1 whenever one, and only one, of the three input variables is 1 or when all three are 1s. The carry output is 1 whenever any two of the three inputs are 1s. Since it makes no difference what the third input is, the expression for the carry term reduces to

$$\text{Carry} = Y \cdot Z + Y \cdot C + Z \cdot C \tag{6-8}$$

These expressions can, of course, be manipulated to produce a wide variety of equations satisfying the conditions for full addition.

There are numerous possibilities for implementing a full adder. The particular configuration used by a logic designer is determined by many factors. The components available to him, the economics involved in minimizing these components, and the speed with which a particular configuration operates must all be given consideration. In design, these factors may be in conflict. Speed of operation frequently is obtained at the cost of additional equipment.

Speed of operation is largely determined by the number of gates through which signals must pass to perform one complete operation. Each time a signal passes through a gate, there is a small delay. The total delay through a network of gates is called *circuit delay* and is measured by the time it takes for the output of a circuit to respond to its inputs. Obviously, a circuit in which the signals must find their way through a large number of gates is slower than one in which additional gating provides parallel, "shortcut" paths.

The following demonstration presents three full-adder configurations with different circuit delays and numbers of gates.

Demonstration 6-2   *Full Adders*

Purpose

To show the properties of full adders by implementing several full-adder configurations. Three examples are given to indicate different design approaches.

Equipment

FIG. 6-5	FIG. 6-6	FIG. 6-7
1—Level switch (S)	1—Level switch (S)	1—Level switch (S)
7—AND gates (AN)	4—AND gates (AN)	5—AND gates (AN)
3—NAND gates (ND)	2—NAND gates (ND)	3—OR gates (OR)
2—OR gates (OR)	3—OR gates (OR)	1—NAND gate (ND)

Discussion and Implementation

In the first implementation, inverters are used to generate the negations of the three input variables. In a computer, however, assertion and negation signals are often already available and the need for inverters can be

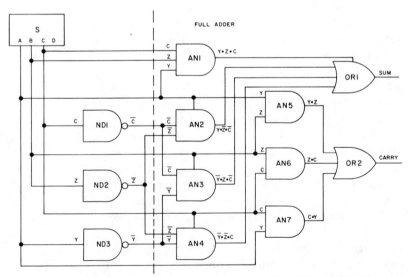

Fig. 6-5   Full adder 1.

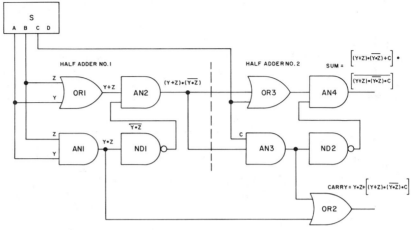

Fig. 6-6   Full adder 2.

eliminated. This is the case if inputs are from the outputs of flip-flops, which present both the assertion and the negation outputs (1 and 0 outputs).

The configuration in Fig. 6-5 directly implements the expressions

$$\text{Sum} = Y \cdot Z \cdot C + Y \cdot \bar{Z} \cdot \bar{C} + \bar{Y} \cdot Z \cdot \bar{C} + \bar{Y} \cdot \bar{Z} \cdot C$$
$$\text{Carry} = Y \cdot Z + Z \cdot C + C \cdot Y$$

Modules ND1 to ND3 are used as inverters to give the negation of the three inputs Y, Z, and C. The C input, although coming from the level switch, represents a carry input from the previous lower-order digit. The Y and Z inputs, on the other hand, represent signals coming from the addend and augend registers.

The outputs of AND gates AN1 to AN4 are ORed together in OR1. The output of OR1 therefore represents the sum term for the full adder. AND gates AN5 to AN7 are then ORed together in OR2 to generate the carry term. Note that only two levels of gating plus the inverters are required in this circuit to generate both sum and carry.

Frequently, full adders are implemented by combining the outputs of two half adders. In Fig. 6-6, one half adder adds the augend and addend digits while the second half adder adds the sum from the first half adder to the previous lower order.

The carry outputs from both half adders are then ORed together to produce the final carry. The expressions for this configuration are

$$\text{Sum} = [(Y + Z) \cdot (\overline{Y \cdot Z}) + C] \cdot [\overline{(Y + Z) \cdot (\overline{Y \cdot Z}) \cdot C}]$$
$$\text{Carry} = Y \cdot Z + [(Y + Z) \cdot (\overline{Y \cdot Z}) \cdot C]$$

By algebraic manipulation, these expressions can be shown to be equivalent to the expressions for full adder 1. This is given as an exercise at the

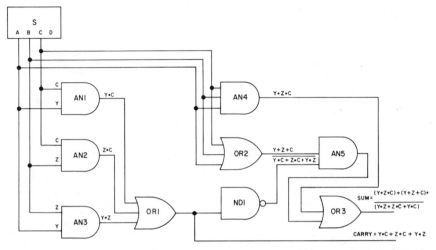

Fig. 6-7   Full adder 3.

end of this chapter.   Half adder 1 combines augend and addend digits
(Y and Z) to produce the carry term $Y \cdot Z$ and the sum term $(\overline{Y \cdot Z}) \cdot (Y + Z)$.
Half adder 2 then combines this sum term with the carry from the previous
order and produces the final sum term.   The carry terms generated by each
half adder are then ORed together in OR2 to give the final carry term.   By
varying Y, Z, and C through all possible values, this adder can be shown to
produce the results given in Table 6-4.

Figure 6-7 illustrates another approach to the full adder.   This configuration, like that of full adder 2, uses only assertion input signals, and it,
too, can be implemented with only nine modules.   However, in full adder 3,
the maximum number of gates through which a signal must pass is five
instead of the six of full adder 2.   On the other hand, full adder 3 requires
four more gate inputs and, therefore, more interconnection and wiring.
While full adders 2 and 3 are both slower than full adder 1 (which has only
two gate delays), they also require fewer gates and interconnections.

Full adder 3 implements the expressions

$$\text{Sum} = (Y \cdot Z \cdot C) + (Y + Z + C) \cdot (\overline{Y \cdot Z + Z \cdot C + Y \cdot C})$$
$$\text{Carry} = Z \cdot Y + Z \cdot C + Y \cdot C$$

Verification of the accuracy of these expressions is again left as an exercise
at the end of this chapter.   AN1 to AN3 gate together the three input
variables, Z, Y, and C, producing the terms $Z \cdot C$, $Y \cdot C$, and $Z \cdot Y$.   These
are then gated together in OR1 to produce the carry expression $Z \cdot Y +$
$Z \cdot C + Y \cdot C$.   The three variables are also gated together in AN4 and
OR2 to produce the $(Y \cdot Z \cdot C)$ and $(Y + Z + C)$ terms.   The $(Y + Z + C)$
term is then gated in AN5 along with the inverted carry expression.   The
$(Y \cdot Z \cdot C)$ term is then ORed together with the output of AN5 to produce
the final sum expression.   The full-adder truth table should be verified
using this demonstration.

6-4 *Serial Addition*

Without the aid of storage devices, one full adder could not form sums from binary numbers larger than a single binary digit. Although the full adder performs all the required logic operations, it has no means of retaining the results of its operations since it has no storage capability. Old results disappear as quickly as new results are formed. By connecting the output of the full adder to a shift register, these results are retained, and the addition of large binary numbers is possible.

One method of adding large binary numbers is by processing the augend and the addend into the full adder serially, starting with the lowest-order digits first and collecting the output of the full adder in a shift register. This is known as *serial addition*.

To perform serial addition, the lowest-order bits of both augend and addend are paired and presented at the input terminals of a full adder, as shown in Fig. 6-8. A_1, B_1, S_1 correspond to the lowest-order digits, while A_4, B_4, and S_5 are the highest-order digits. The S_5 stage of the shift register is necessary to store the carry bit generated in the addition of A_4 and B_4.

In the full adder, the augend and addend bits are combined to form a sum and carry, which appear at the output terminals of the adder. When a shift signal is applied, the sum bit is gated into the shift register and the carry bit is gated into a temporary carry-storage register. As soon as this occurs, the next higher-order bits of augend and addend are pre-

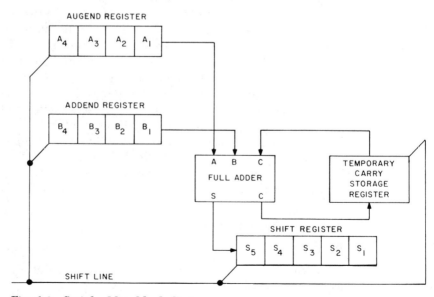

Fig. 6-8 Serial adder, block diagram.

sented to the input terminals of the full adder by shifting the augend and addend registers. Again, these two bits are combined, this time with the carry bit from the previous order, and a new sum and carry appear at the output terminals. Another shift signal then gates this sum into the shift register and the carry into the temporary storage register. In addition to admitting the new sum bit to the shift register, this shift signal also commands the right-shift operation. This is done as in a normal shift register by gating the first sum into the second stage of the shift register. As bits from subsequent orders are sent to the adder, new sum bits are sent to the highest-order stage of the register and previous sum bits are shifted to lower-order stages.

Thus, at the beginning of the addition, A_1 and B_1 are added. The sum digit is placed in S_5, and the carry digit in temporary storage. Upon application of the first shift pulse, the number in S_5 is shifted to S_4. The same pulse causes A_2 and B_2 to be shifted and become the new inputs to the full adder, along with the carry digit of the previous addition. The next sum digit placed in S_5 is the sum of A_2, B_2, and the carry digit from the addition of A_1 and B_1. The carry digit from the new addition is stored in the temporary carry-storage register. This procedure is continued until sufficient shift pulses have been presented so that the digit in S_1 is the sum of A_1 and B_1 and the digit in S_4 is the sum of A_4, B_4, and the carry of the preceding sum. Five shift pulses are required to add the four-digit numbers. The fifth shift pulse will shift the final carry bit into S_5 if one is generated.

Upon completion of the addition, all bits in both augend and addend registers have been shifted out, and the sum of the two binary numbers appears in the shift register. The shift register then contains all the information generated by the addition operation.

Two important things to be noted about serial addition are (1) only one full adder is required to add completely any two binary numbers, no matter how large; and (2) the time required for the complete addition is equal to the time required to process any single sum multiplied by the number of sums to be formed. With serial addition, it takes twice as long to add eight-digit numbers as it does to add four-digit numbers. If greater speed is desired, as is usually the case, and if additional equipment is permissible, parallel addition would be used. Parallel addition is the subject of the next section.

Demonstration 6-3   *Serial Addition*

Purpose

To demonstrate the construction and operation of a logic circuit which performs serial addition.

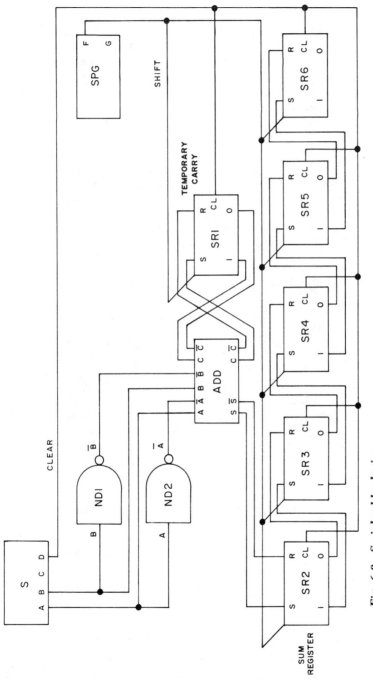

Fig. 6-9 Serial-adder logic.

Equipment

    1—Full adder (ADD)
    2—NAND gates (ND)
    6—Shift registers (SR)
    1—Single-pulse generator (SPG)
    1—Level switch (S)

Discussion and Implementation

The full-adder module (ADD) is of the type described in Fig. 6-5. All components in that circuit have been combined into the single ADD module. Since both normal and inverted inputs are required for this type of full adder, NAND gates ND1 and ND2 have been provided (see Fig. 6-9) to supply the inverted inputs. The level switch (S) provides inputs to the system and is used to simulate the pair of registers which, in operating equipment, would contain the augend and addend. Each input should be thought of as coming directly from a register.

In the experiment, the two numbers to be added in the full adder will be manually changed. In a normal serial adder, the inputs to the adder would be shifted by the same signal which shifts the sum register.

When signals representing the zeroth-order digits of augend and addend are applied to the ADD module, the zeroth-order sum and carry appear instantly at the output terminals. The sum and carry bits are then admitted to their respective registers by a gating signal from the single-pulse generator (SPG). The temporary carry-storage register (SR1) applies the C and $\overline{C}$ bits to the appropriate terminals of the ADD module, and the circuit is ready for another pair of bits from the level switch. All subsequent sums are processed in the same manner except that the gating signal, in addition to admitting the S and $\overline{S}$ bits to the highest-order shift register (SR2), also gates the previous sums to lower stages of the register (SR3, SR4, etc.). The clear line is provided to clear all registers to the 0 state when it is desired to initiate a new sum.

6-5   *Parallel Addition*

Parallel addition is much faster than serial addition. However, to gain speed, additional equipment is necessary. In parallel addition, a full adder is required for each order of augend and addend. The block diagram in Fig. 6-10 shows the functional arrangement of a parallel adder.

Each order of augend and addend supplies 1 bit to a full adder. These pairs of bits—1 from the augend and 1 from the addend—are combined in the adders to form sums and carries for each order. The carries are then automatically transmitted to the next higher orders. Notice that the final sum and carry for any order do not appear until the carry from

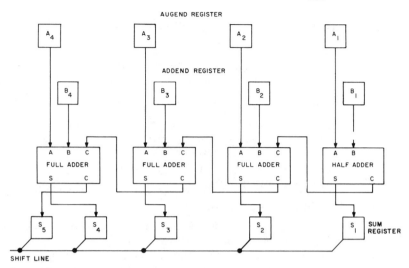

Fig. 6-10   Parallel adder, block diagram.

the previous lower order is received.   The carries must be transmitted, one at a time, from order to order until there are no more carries.   This process of passing the carries along from order to order is called *ripple-through*.   If 0001 (decimal 1) is added to 1111 (decimal 15), the sum will not be available until four carry digits have been generated and have rippled through the logic.   When the carries have rippled completely through the circuit, the correct sum for each order appears at the output terminals of the full adder.   If a carry exists in the highest order, it will appear at the carry output terminal of the highest-order full adder. After all the correct sums have been formed, a gating signal is sent to each stage of the register to gate the sums into the register.   An extra stage in the register is supplied to accept the carry from the highest-order adder, if such a carry exists.   When the sums are admitted to the register, the register contains the sum generated by the addition operation.

The major advantage of parallel addition over serial addition is the speed with which parallel addition is performed.   Parallel addition requires only the time necessary for forming a single sum plus the time necessary for carry propagation, or ripple-through.   Using parallel addition, eight-digit numbers can be added in far less than twice the time it takes to add four-digit numbers.   However, an additional full adder is required for each digit of the sum number.   In the lowest order, no carry input is ever provided.   Since two inputs are all that are required for this order, a half adder can be used in place of a full adder, as shown in Fig. 6-10.

Demonstration 6-4   *Parallel Addition*

Purpose

To demonstrate the construction and operation of a logic circuit that performs parallel addition.

Equipment

   2—Level switches (S)
   1—Single-pulse generator (SPG)
   6—NAND gates (ND)
   3—Full adders (ADD)
   4—Shift registers (SR)

Discussion and Implementation

The same full-adder modules, requiring both assertion and negation inputs, are again used in the parallel adder.   NAND gates ND1 to ND6 supply the inverted inputs for each order of augend and addend.

The two level switches in Fig. 6-11 simulate the augend (S1) and addend (S2) registers and should be thought of as providing these functions.   Two numbers ($A_1B_1C_1$ and $A_2B_2C_2$) will be set up in the two level-switch modules.   When two 3-digit binary numbers have been set up on the two registers (S1 and S2), the final sum and carry outputs appear at the output terminals of the full adder.   While there is a definite time lag while the carry ripples through, this time is insignificant in a manual demonstra-

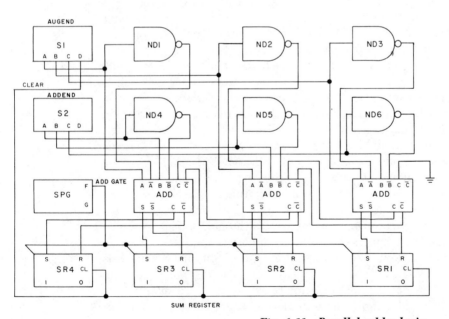

Fig. 6-11   *Parallel-adder logic.*

tion.   A gating signal from SPG then admits the entire sum into the four-stage shift register.   Note that a fourth shift-register stage is provided to accept any carries that might appear in the third stage.   The C input to the zeroth-order adder is grounded to show that no carry ever appears in that order.   Holding this C input to ground disables half of the full adder and forces it to act as a half adder.   The clear line is provided to reset all registers when desired.

6-6   *Accumulation*

A serial adder requires many steps, while a parallel adder requires much gating.   In both systems, the sum produced is the sum of only two binary numbers.   If a third number is to be added to the first two, the original sum must be taken out of the sum register and fed back into an augend register.   This new augend is then combined with the third number to form the sum of all three numbers.   A fourth addend would then require that the sum again be fed back to the augend register, and so on for each additional number.   This process is avoided if addition is performed by accumulation.   Addition by accumulation offers speed advantages over the serial adder while utilizing fewer gates than the parallel adder.

In addition by accumulation, the register containing the sum is called the *accumulator*.   If three or more numbers are to be added by accumulation, the first number is sent directly to the accumulator.   This represents the "sum" of one number.   The second number is then combined with the number in the accumulator to form a new sum.   This sum, however, remains in the accumulator.   Then, when a third number is combined with the number already in the accumulator, the sum of all three numbers is formed.   This sum also remains in the accumulator.   The process can be repeated for more and more numbers and is limited only by the capacity of the accumulator.

To operate properly, an accumulator must perform three distinct functions.   First, each stage of the accumulator must be complemented (changed from 1 to 0 or 0 to 1) every time a 1 is sent to it.   This records an addition in that particular order.   Second, each time a 1 in the addend register complements the corresponding stage of the accumulator from 1 to 0, a carry must be transmitted to the next higher order of the accumulator; this is the familiar carry mechanism.   Third, when any stage of the accumulator is complemented from 1 to 0 by a carry from the previous stage, it, too, must send along a carry to the next higher stage; this represents a secondary carry mechanism.

The first accumulator function is straightforward and requires only that the 1 outputs of the addend register be connected directly to the corresponding stages of the accumulator.   This connection is shown in

Fig. 6-12. The ADD signal does nothing more than gate all the 1s in the addend register into the accumulator, causing the addend to reappear in the accumulator when the accumulator is initially all 0s.

The second function of an accumulator requires that whenever a 1 from the addend register complements a stage of the accumulator from 1 to 0, a carry shall be transmitted to the succeeding stage. In Fig. 6-13, the appropriate gating to perform this function has been added to the configuration of Fig. 6-12. If, after adding, any stage of the addend register is at 1 and the corresponding stage of the accumulator is at 0, then the previous addition must have complemented that stage of the accumulator from 1 to 0. If such a condition exists in any stage, the carry pulse gates a carry into the next stage of the accumulator; if this condition does not exist, no carry will be transmitted.

To perform the third accumulator function, it is necessary to gate through any secondary carries that may have been formed. For a secondary carry to exist, there must be a carry from the previous stage and there must be a 1 already in the stage under consideration. A third set of gates has been supplied in Fig. 6-14 to perform this function. The new row of gates in Fig. 6-14 is only operative if a stage is in the 1 condition and there is a carry from the previous lower order. This is the condition for a secondary carry. Note that the configuration allows for secondary carries to ripple through. After the ADD gating signal is applied,

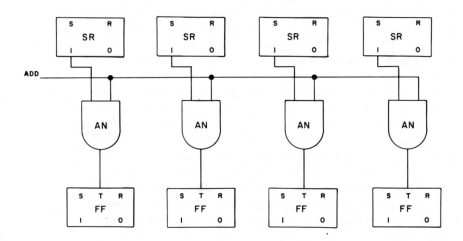

Fig. 6-12   Accumulator transfer.

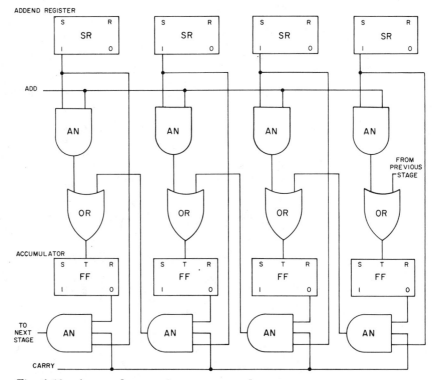

Fig. 6-13 Accumulator, primary carry only.

the carry-gate signal is made a logic 1. It is at this time, while the signal is at a 1, that the primary and secondary carries ripple down the stages. When the gating signal is returned to logic 0, the appropriate flip-flop stages are complemented.

There is almost no limit to the variety of design possibilities for accumulators. Although they are basically parallel devices and therefore relatively faster than serial devices, additional gating can be supplied to make carry propagation even faster and more automatic. Here again, speed and automaticity are purchased at the expense of additional components.

Demonstration 6-5 illustrates two approaches to accumulator design.

Demonstration 6-5 *Accumulators*

Purpose

To demonstrate the operation of an accumulator. Two examples are given to indicate different design approaches.

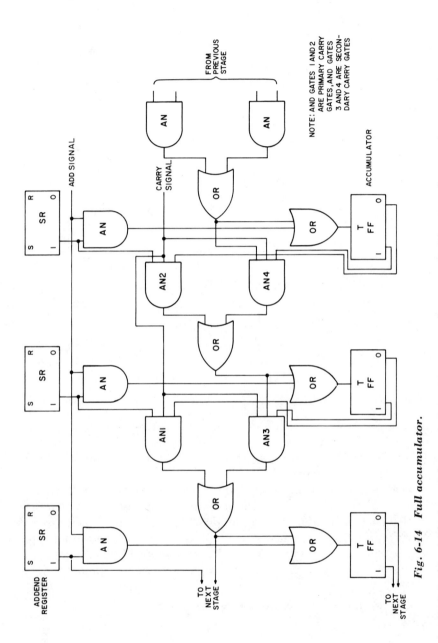

Fig. 6-14 Full accumulator.

Equipment

FIG. 6-15	FIG. 6-16
1—Level switch (S)	1—Level switch (S)
1—Single-pulse	1—Single-pulse
generator (SPG)	generator (SPG)
4—Flip-flops (FF)	3—NAND gates (ND)
6—AND gates (AN)	3—Full adders (ADD)
2—OR gates (OR)	4—Shift registers (SR)
	1—AND gate (AN)

Discussion and Implementation

The accumulator in Fig. 6-15 is identical in operation to the one described in the text. The function of the addend register is performed by the level switch. The unnecessary AND and OR gates have been removed from the first stage since there is no previous carry.

A momentary logic 0 applied to the clear line from channel D of the level switch will clear the accumulator. The next step is to enter a number into the accumulator from the addend register, which in this case is simulated by the level switch. The binary number 011 is entered into the

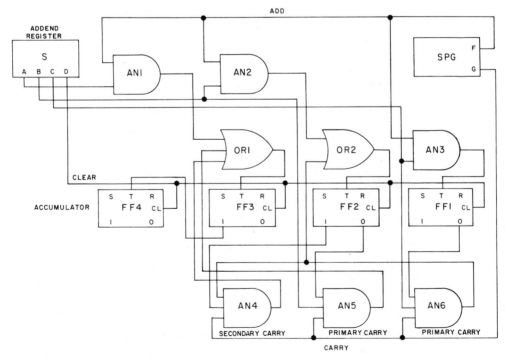

Fig. 6-15   Accumulator logic.

addend register by making channel A a 0 and channels B and C a 1. When the ADD gate is activated by a signal from channel F of the SPG, the resultant pulse will be gated to FF1 through AN3 and to FF2 through gates AN1 and OR2. Thus the accumulator will have in it 0011 due to the toggling of the first two stages. The next operational step is to activate the carry gate with a pulse from channel G of the SPG. This step will not cause a change in the accumulator since the conditions for a carry are not satisfied. Each of gates AN4, AN5, and AN6 have at least one input at logic 0 when the carry-gate pulse arrives, thereby inhibiting any carry operation. To add 001 to the number 0011 stored in the accumulator, the addend register is changed to 001, which activates the AND gate AN3 when SPG channel F is pushed and causes FF1 to toggle. At the end of this step, the accumulator is storing 0010. The addition is not complete until the carry-gate line is activated. When the pulse is applied from channel G of the SPG module, the pulse initially makes a logic 0-to-1 transition. At this time, when the pulse is at logic 1, the output of AN6 will be a logic 1 along with the output of AN4. The 1 output of AN6 gates OR2 to a logic 1, and the 1 output of AN4 gates the output of OR1 to a logic 1. When the carry-gate pulse makes its transition from a logic 1 to 0, this transition will be gated to the toggle inputs of FF2 and FF3. This toggle operation makes the result in the accumulator 0100, thereby completing the addition of the two numbers.

Note that both a primary and a secondary carry were propagated to achieve the result in this example. FF4 in the illustration is used merely to accept an overflow bit from the accumulator, when FF3 goes from the set to reset state.

Other numbers can be added from the addend register until the maximum capacity of the accumulator (1111) is exceeded.

The accumulator illustrated in Fig. 6-16 uses three full adders. In this accumulator, NAND gates ND1 to ND3 are used as inverters to supply negation inputs to the ADD modules. When a three-digit binary number is entered into the level switch, assertion and negation inputs from each order are presented to the ADD modules. A gating signal then admits this number, through the ADD modules, into the previously cleared four-stage register. The outputs of the SR modules are fed directly back to the B and $\bar{B}$ inputs of the ADD modules, so that when a second number is entered into the level switch, it will be combined with the number already in the register to form an accumulated sum. The carry is transmitted from order to order just as in the parallel adder. Another gating signal then admits the accumulated sum into the register. By the same process, subsequent numbers can be entered into the level switch and gated into the accumulator to form larger accumulated sums. Note that the AND gate provides a final shift signal to SR4 to store a carry if one is present from the last order.

This accumulator performs all the required functions for accumulation. All functions are performed in the ADD modules before the accumulated sum is gated into the register. The 1s from the level switch and the carries

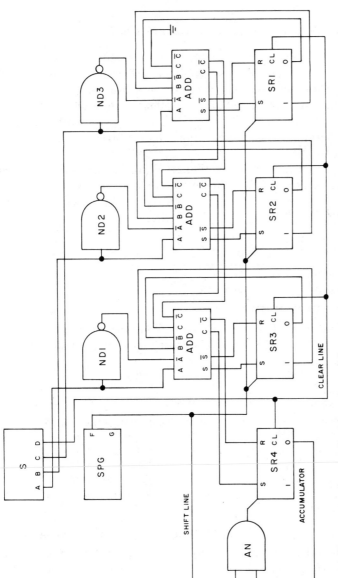

Fig. 6-16 Accumulation using adders.

141

from previous orders, whether primary or secondary, are combined in the ADD modules to form the accumulated sum directly.

6-7   *Logical Subtraction and the Half Subtractor*

Most computers perform subtraction operations by utilizing complement addition.   This process will be described in Sec. 6-9.   Direct subtraction, which is the topic of discussion in this section and in Sec. 6-8, is sometimes used in special digital systems where a subtraction process is required without the need for handling all the possibilities that may arise in a computer.   In such applications, half subtractors or full subtractors can be used.

The rules for logical subtraction are quite similar to those for addition. They were originally given in Chap. 2 and are repeated in Table 6-5.

TABLE 6-5

Y (minuend)	0 0 1 1
Z (subtrahend)	0 1 0 1
D (difference)	0 1 1 0
B (borrow)	0 1 0 0

As an example of the use of these rules in the subtraction of two binary numbers and their decimal equivalents, consider the following:

Decimal			*Binary*		
Minuend		52	110100		
Subtrahend		39	100111		
Difference	(1)	23	010011	Difference	(1)
Borrow	(1)	1	00011	Borrow	(1)
Difference	(2)	13	010101	Difference	(2)
			0010	Borrow	(2)
			011101	Difference	(3)
			010	Borrow	(3)
			001101	Difference	(4)

Here again, when working with pencil and paper, the steps are combined mentally.   Fundamentally, however, the borrow, like the carry, is transmitted from order to order until there are no borrows left.

To form the logic expressions for subtraction, the forms of Table 6-5 can be converted into a truth table (Table 6-6), where the symbols Y, Z, D, and B represent the minuend, subtrahend, difference, and borrow, respectively.

TABLE 6-6 *Truth Table for a Half Subtractor*

Y	Z	D	B
0	0	0	0
0	1	1	1
1	0	1	0
1	1	0	0

From this truth table, the following logic expressions can be derived for the half subtractor:

$$D = \overline{Y} \cdot Z + Y \cdot \overline{Z} \qquad\qquad (6\text{-}9)$$
$$B = \overline{Y} \cdot Z \qquad\qquad (6\text{-}10)$$

Note that the sum expression for a half adder and the difference expression for a half subtractor are identical. The resultant gating circuits to implement the expressions should be quite similar. The borrow term, however, is $\overline{Y} \cdot Z$, in contrast to the $Y \cdot Z$ term derived for the carry in the half adder.

Like the expressions for half addition, the half-subtractor expressions can be manipulated to produce alternative design possibilities. The following derivations are analogous to those in the section on half adders:

$$
\begin{aligned}
D &= Z \cdot \overline{Y} + \overline{Z} \cdot Y & (6\text{-}9)\\
 &= (Z + Y) \cdot (\overline{Z} + \overline{Y}) & (6\text{-}11)\\
 &= (Z + Y) \cdot (\overline{Z \cdot Y}) & (6\text{-}12)\\
B &= \overline{Y} \cdot Z & (6\text{-}10)\\
 &= \overline{Y + \overline{Z}} & (6\text{-}13)\\
B &= \overline{Y} \cdot Z & (6\text{-}10)\\
 &= \overline{Y} \cdot Z + \overline{Z} \cdot Z\\
 &= Z \cdot (\overline{Z} + \overline{Y}) & (6\text{-}14)\\
 &= Z \cdot (\overline{Z \cdot Y}) & (6\text{-}15)
\end{aligned}
$$

Devices that perform these logic operations are called *half subtractors.* The following demonstration describes three possible half-subtractor configurations.

It can be seen that a large number of equivalent half-subtractor expressions are possible and that the following are only representative examples.

Demonstration 6-6   Half Subtractors

Purpose

To illustrate the properties of half subtractors by implementing various half-subtractor configurations. Three examples are given to indicate different design approaches.

Equipment

FIG. 6-17	FIG. 6-18	FIG. 6-19
1—Level switch (S)	1—Level switch (S)	1—Level switch (S)
2—NAND gates (ND)	2—NAND gates (ND)	2—AND gates (AN)
2—AND gates (AN)	2—OR gates (OR)	1—NAND gate (ND)
1—OR gate (OR)	2—AND gates (AN)	1—OR gate (OR)

Discussion and Implementation

The first half subtractor (Fig. 6-17) implements the logic expressions

$$\text{Difference} = \bar{Z} \cdot Y + \bar{Y} \cdot Z \tag{6-9}$$
$$\text{Borrow} = \bar{Y} \cdot Z \tag{6-10}$$

NAND gates ND1 and ND2 supply the inverted inputs $\bar{Y}$ and $\bar{Z}$. These are gated together with the assertion inputs Y and Z in AND gates AN1 and AN2. The outputs of these AND gates are then ORed together in OR1 to form the difference term $\bar{Z} \cdot Y + \bar{Y} \cdot Z$. The borrow term $\bar{Y} \cdot Z$ is taken directly from the output of AN2. Table 6-6 can be verified by having Y and Z assume all possible values.

In Fig. 6-18, the following expressions are implemented directly:

$$\text{Difference} = (Y + Z) \cdot (\bar{Y} + \bar{Z}) \tag{6-11}$$
$$\text{Borrow} = \bar{Y} \cdot Z \tag{6-10}$$

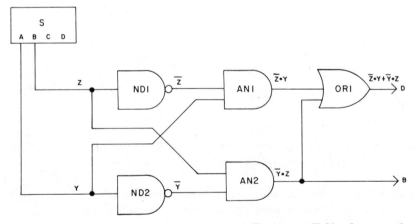

Fig. 6-17   Half subtractor 1.

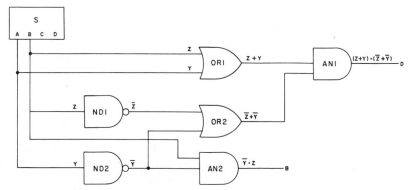

Fig. 6-18   Half subtractor 2.

First, Y and Z are ORed together in OR1 to form $(Y + Z)$.   Next, the inverted inputs $\overline{Y}$ and $\overline{Z}$ are taken from inverters ND1 and ND2 and ORed together in OR2 to form $(\overline{Y} + \overline{Z})$.   These two expressions are then ANDed together in AN1 to form the difference term.   The borrow term is generated directly by ANDing together $\overline{Y}$ and Z in AN2.

The following expressions are implemented by the diagram in Fig. 6-19:

$$\text{Difference} = (Y + Z) \cdot (\overline{Y \cdot Z}) \tag{6-12}$$

$$\text{Borrow} = Z \cdot \overline{Y} = (\overline{Y \cdot Z}) \cdot Z \tag{6-15}$$

Y and Z are ORed together in OR1 to form $(Y + Z)$ and are NANDed together in ND1 to form $(\overline{Y \cdot Z})$.   The outputs of these two gates are then taken into AN1 to form the difference term $(Y + Z) \cdot (\overline{Y \cdot Z})$.   The borrow term is formed by ANDing Z together with $(\overline{Y \cdot Z})$ in AN2.   ND1 in this illustration serves the same purpose as two NAND gates and an OR gate in

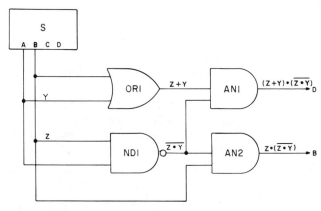

Fig. 6-19   Half subtractor 3.

Fig. 6-18. This version of the half subtractor, therefore, uses two less gates and one less level of gating than half subtractor 2.

Although the three examples require completely different gating, it can be seen that they produce the same truth table. Many other half subtractors are also possible.

6-8 *The Full Subtractor*

The half subtractor, like the half adder, accepts only two inputs. One digit comes from the minuend, and the other from the subtrahend. To perform a complete subtraction, a device must also accept a borrow input from the previous lower order. The full subtractor performs this function.

The rules for full subtraction are similar to those for full addition and are given in Table 6-7.

TABLE 6-7 *Full-subtraction Rules*

Y (minuend input)	0 0 0 0 1 1 1 1
Z (subtrahend input)	0 0 1 1 0 0 1 1
B (borrow input)	0 1 0 1 0 1 0 1
D (difference output)	0 1 1 0 1 0 0 1
B (borrow output)	0 1 1 1 0 0 0 1

The following example, with binary numbers and their decimal equivalents, illustrates the full-subtraction process.

	Decimal	*Binary*
Minuend	36	1 0 0 1 0 0
Subtrahend	−27	− 1 1 0 1 1
Input borrow	1←	1← 1← 0 1← 1←
Output difference	09	0 0 1 0 0 1
Output borrow	01	0 1 1 0 1 1

The borrow in any order augments the subtrahend in the next higher order. This is exactly equivalent to the common subtraction technique, where the borrow is used to reduce the minuend. Augmenting the subtrahend is, in all cases, identically equivalent to reducing the minuend by the same amount. $0 - (1 + 1)$ is the same as $(0 - 1) - 1$. Both are equal to "0 and borrow 1." The full-subtraction process, like that of full addition, is carried out in one step. As soon as the borrow ripples through all orders, the final difference is available.

The algebraic expressions for the difference and borrow of the full-subtraction process can be derived from a truth table. Table 6-7, when converted into a truth table, takes the form of Table 6-8.

TABLE 6-3 *Full-sub-*
traction Truth Table

Input			Output	
Y	Z	B	D	B
0	0	0	0	0
0	0	1	1	1
0	1	0	1	1
0	1	1	0	1
1	0	0	1	0
1	0	1	0	0
1	1	0	0	0
1	1	1	1	1

Like the sum of a full adder, the difference is equal to 1 if one and only one of the Y, Z, B variables is 1 or if all three terms are 1. Symbolically,

$$D = \overline{Y} \cdot \overline{Z} \cdot B + \overline{Y} \cdot Z \cdot \overline{B} + Y \cdot \overline{Z} \cdot \overline{B} + Y \cdot Z \cdot B \qquad (6\text{-}16)$$

The conditions for the borrow term are: If Y is 0, then Z or B or both must be 1; and if Y is 1, then Z and B must both be 1. In other words, to have a borrow, Z and B together must be greater than Y. Symbolically, this is represented as

$$B = \overline{Y} \cdot \overline{Z} \cdot B + \overline{Y} \cdot Z \cdot \overline{B} + \overline{Y} \cdot Z \cdot B + Y \cdot Z \cdot B \qquad (6\text{-}17)$$
$$= \overline{Y} \cdot (\overline{Z} \cdot B + Z \cdot \overline{B} + Z \cdot B) + Y \cdot Z \cdot B \qquad (6\text{-}18)$$
$$= \overline{Y} \cdot (Z + B) + Y \cdot (Z \cdot B) \qquad (6\text{-}19)$$

Full subtractors can be utilized to construct serial and parallel subtractors and subtractor accumulators in a method similar to that used in performing addition using full adders. Since the method of construction is so similar, it will not be described in this text.

Demonstration 6-7 illustrates two possible configurations for a full subtractor.

Demonstration 6-7   *Full Subtractors*

Purpose

To show the properties of full subtractors by implementing full-subtractor configurations. Two examples are given to indicate different design approaches.

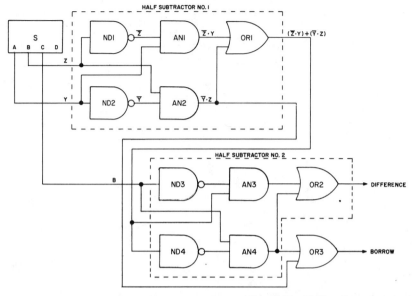

Fig. 6-20   Full subtractor 1.

Equipment

FIG. 6-20	FIG. 6-21
1—Level switch (S)	1—Level switch (S)
4—NAND gates (ND)	5—AND gates (AN)
4—AND gates (AN)	3—NAND gates (ND)
3—OR gates (OR)	2—OR gates (OR)

Discussion and Implementation

In Fig. 6-20, two half subtractors are connected together to form one full subtractor.

The two outputs are

$$\text{Difference} = (\overline{\overline{Z} \cdot Y + \overline{Y} \cdot Z}) \cdot B + (\overline{Z} \cdot Y + \overline{Y} \cdot Z) \cdot \overline{B}$$
$$\text{Borrow} = (\overline{\overline{Z} \cdot Y + \overline{Y} \cdot Z}) \cdot B + \overline{Y} \cdot Z$$

The inputs to the first half subtractor are the minuend and subtrahend digits Y and Z.   The difference formed by this half subtractor, along with the borrow B from the previous lower order, is then connected to the second half subtractor, the output of which becomes the final difference.   The final borrow term is formed by ORing together the borrow terms from the two half subtractors.   Note that borrows can never be generated from both half subtractors at once.   If $Z \cdot \overline{Y}$ exists, then the difference input to half subtractor 2 must be a 1.   In this case, no borrow will be generated by half subtractor 2, regardless of what B is.   If $Z \cdot \overline{Y}$ does not exist, half sub-

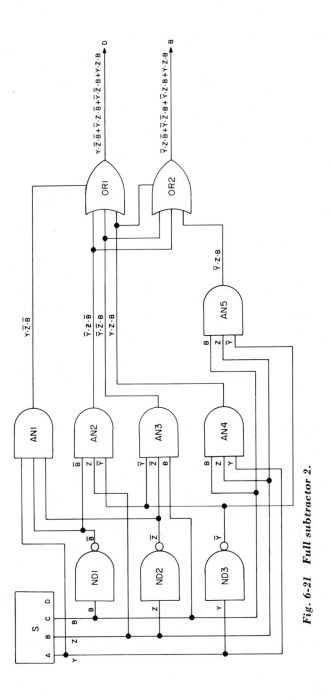

Fig. 6-21 *Full subtractor 2.*

tractor 2 may or may not generate a borrow, depending on the conditions of $Y \cdot \bar{Z}$ and B.

It is left as an exercise to show that the resultant difference expression is equivalent to $\bar{Y} \cdot \bar{Z} \cdot B + \bar{Y} \cdot Z \cdot \bar{B} + Y \cdot \bar{Z} \cdot \bar{B} + Y \cdot Z \cdot B$ and that the borrow expression is equivalent to $\bar{Y} \cdot (Z + B) + Y \cdot Z \cdot B$. By varying the inputs Y, Z, and B through all values, the equivalence of these expressions to Table 6-8 can be verified.

Figure 6-21 directly implements the AND-to-OR expressions

$$\text{Difference} = \bar{Y} \cdot \bar{Z} \cdot B + \bar{Y} \cdot Z \cdot \bar{B} + Y \cdot \bar{Z} \cdot \bar{B} + Y \cdot Z \cdot B \qquad (6\text{-}16)$$
$$\text{Borrow} = \bar{Y} \cdot \bar{Z} \cdot B + \bar{Y} \cdot Z \cdot \bar{B} + \bar{Y} \cdot Z \cdot B + Y \cdot Z \cdot B \qquad (6\text{-}17)$$

NAND gates ND1 to ND3 supply negation terms for the B, Z, and Y inputs, respectively. Each of the required three variable terms is formed by ANDing together the three appropriate inputs in one of the AND gates AN1 to AN5. The difference term is then formed by ORing together the outputs of AN1 to AN4, and the borrow term is formed by ORing together the outputs of AN2 to AN5.

In this case, direct implementation of the AND-to-OR expression reduces not only the number of gates a signal must pass through before appearing at an output but also the total number of gates required. Although an inversion stage is necessary, only three levels of gating are required. This marks another improvement over the six levels of full subtractor 1. Furthermore, the total number of gates has been reduced to 10. If, as is often the case, assertion and negation inputs are already available, even further reduction is possible.

6-9 1s- and 2s-complement Subtraction

The representation of negative numbers can be handled simply in binary notation. A computer can be organized such that 1 bit of each word (groups of bits representing a number) is used to signify whether the number is negative or positive. A 0 preceding the magnitude may signify a positive number, while a 1 preceding the magnitude may signify a negative number. Thus, the binary number 0011 in such a system represents a positive 3, and conversely, 1011 represents a negative 3. This is a rather straightforward concept, but in actuality this simple scheme is not easily implemented in a computer. The rules for addition and subtraction are quite complicated in a sign-plus-magnitude system. To simplify the required operations (which ultimately leads to a reduction in hardware), either the 1s-complement or 2s-complement notation is used in most computers. Each of the schemes has inherent advantages and disadvantages in terms of speed of subtraction, addition of negative numbers, method of representing 0, and ease of multiplication and division. Positive numbers are represented identically in both the 1s- and

2s-complement notation; it is only the negative notations that differ. Once a scheme is selected for a computer, all arithmetic operations are implemented utilizing that method of representing negative numbers.

Up to this point, direct subtraction has been discussed in terms of the basic operation and its logical implementation. In this section, attention will be focused on an entirely different method of subtraction rather than on a new design for implementing it. Furthermore, this method will illustrate the operations involved in adding negative numbers.

Subtraction is normally performed in the decimal system by reducing the minuend by the amount of the subtrahend. For example,

Minuend	Subtrahend	Difference
764	− 598	= 166

If some number, such as 999, is added to the minuend, then the difference, too, will increase by 999:

$$(764 + 999) - 598 = 1{,}763 - 598 = 1{,}165$$

The new difference is now larger by 999 than the old difference. The exact same reasoning is valid if the subtrahend is subtracted from 999:

$$764 + (999 - 598) = 764 + 401 = 1{,}165$$

In this case, however, note that the minuend is added to the term in parentheses. The term in parentheses is equivalent to 401 and is called the 9s *complement* of 598. It is derived simply by subtracting 598 from 999. Note, however, that the formation of a 9s complement never involves borrowing.

Now look at the difference term 1,165. This number is exactly 999, or 1,000 − 1, larger than the difference between 764 and 598. Therefore, if 1,165 is reduced by 1,000 and then increased by 1, the result will be 166, which is exactly the difference between 764 and 598. To accomplish this, the 1 in the third order is brought around and added to the difference as follows:

$$
\begin{array}{r}
1{,}165 \\
+\quad 1 \\
\hline
116 \\
\end{array}
$$

This process, which is called *end-around carrying*, converts the result of 9s-complement addition to the result that would have been obtained from normal subtraction. The following examples illustrate the process of 9s-complement subtraction. In each case, a 1 is subtracted from the most significant digit and added to the least significant digit to correct the answer.

```
  62        62        631        631
 -45      + 54      -456      + 543
 ----     ----      ----      -----
  17       116       175       1,174
            1                     1
          ----                 -----
           17                   175
```

```
        5,642      5,642      6,047      6,047
       -4,187    + 5,812    -  129    + 9,870
       ------    -------    -----    ------
        1,455     11,454     5,918     15,917
                      1                     1
                  ------                ------
                   1,455                 5,918
```

The binary system is especially adaptable to this form of subtraction because in the binary system the 9s complement becomes the 1s complement. To form the 1s complement of a four-digit binary number, the number is subtracted from 1111. Thus the 1s complement of 1011 is formed as follows:

```
  1111
 -1011
 -----
  0100
```

Here again, borrowing is never required. Even more important, the 1s complement of a number turns out to be nothing more than the negation of the original number. All the 1s in the number become 0s, and all the 0s become 1s. This point is of special significance since information is normally gated to the adder from a register. The 1s complement of the number stored in a register can be readily gated from the negation outputs of the flip-flops. Thus, the 1s complement of 11010 is 00101; the 1s complement of 0011 is 1100; and the 1s complement of 101101 is 010010.

As shown in the following examples, 1s-complement addition gives the same results as normal binary subtraction.

```
   101       101       1101       1101      101101      101101
  -011     + 100     -1010     + 0101     -100111     + 011000
  ----     -----     -----     -----      -------     -------
   10       1001      0011      10010      000110      1000101
             1                    1                        1
           -----                -----                  -------
            10                   11                      110
```

To subtract using the 1s-complement approach, the subtrahend is inverted or complemented and added to the minuend. In this case, the equipment need only perform the addition function and, at the end of the operation, an end-around carry to obtain the correct difference. Implementation of the 1s-complement method greatly facilitates logical subtraction and is illustrated in the next demonstration.

Now consider a numbering system where a sign bit is used to determine whether the magnitude of a binary number is positive or negative. Using the 1s-complement system of subtraction by addition and a sign bit, a computer can be designed so that positive and negative numbers could be added and subtracted in any possible combination. This is illustrated in the following examples, where positive numbers have a sign-bit designation of 0 and negative numbers have a sign-bit designation of 1. Note that the sign bits are also added together to determine if an end-around-carry operation should be performed. All negative numbers with a sign-bit designation of 1 have their magnitudes displayed in the 1s-complement form. Thus negative 5 is equivalent to 1010, where the most significant bit identifies the polarity and the last 3 bits are the 1s complement of 5. If the digit on the left is a 1, the number is negative and in the 1s complement; if the digit is a 0, the number can be read directly.

The following are examples of 1s-complement addition:

$+4$	0100	$+2$	0010	-2	1101	$+2$	0010
-2	1101	-4	1011	-4	1011	$+4$	0100
$+2$	10001	-2	1101	-6	11000	$+6$	0110
	1				1		
	0010				1001		
(a)		*(b)*		*(c)*		*(d)*	

It should be noted that there is no distinction between the addition and subtraction process when using complement notation for negative numbers since the resultant sign bit is always correct. In example (a), the computer could have been performing one of two possible operations: one is to add $+4$ to -2, and the other is to subtract $+2$ from $+4$. When adding $+4$ to -2, the -2 is gated to the adder from the assertion outputs of a register storing the 1s complement of $+2$. When subtracting $+2$ from $+4$, the -2 is gated from the negation outputs of a register storing $+2$. Note also that the sign bit is stored in the registers along with the magnitude.

Examples (a) and (c) require an end-around-carry operation before the answer can be obtained. In some instances, this operation is undesirable since it requires more logic and more time to implement the system. Time must be allowed for the end-around carry to ripple through the adder. Therefore, some designers prefer the use of the 2s-complement system of addition and subtraction. In this system, all negative numbers are recorded as in the 1s-complement system except that an additional 1 is added to the magnitude. The 9s-complement and 1s-complement systems both require an end-around carry since each is equivalent to adding 10^n and subtracting 1 (e.g., $10000 - 1$) to the number and then correcting the answer by subtracting 10^n and adding 1. The 2s-complement system is similar to the decimal 10s-complement system, in which 10^n is added and subtracted from the number. A 1s-complement number must be incremented by 1 to transform it to the 2s-complement form. Where negative 5 is equivalent to 1010 in the 1s-complement system, in the 2s-complement system it is equivalent to 1011.

Performing the previous examples proves that an end-around carry is not needed in 2s complement. If a carry occurs, it is ignored. Positive numbers in either system are identical.

The following are examples of 2s-complement addition:

$+4$	0100	$+2$	0010	-2	1110	$+2$	0010
-2	1110	-4	1100	-4	1100	$+4$	0100
$+2$	$\cancel{1}$ 0010	-2	1110	-6	$\cancel{1}$ 1010	$+6$	0110

| | Ignore carry | | | | Ignore carry | | |
| | (*a*) | | (*b*) | | (*c*) | | (*d*) |

Where the digit on the left is a 0, the number is positive and can be read out directly. Where it is a 1, the number is negative and in the 2s-complement system. Furthermore, no end carry is needed. This is a definite advantage over the 1s-complement system, where an end-around-carry operation requires additional time. However, the 2s-complement system has a slight disadvantage when subtracting one number from another since it requires an operation which converts the number stored in a register to the 2s-complement notation. The 1s complement, which is readily available from the reset outputs of the flip-flops, is incremented by 1 to form the 2s complement. Most computers use either the 1s- or 2s-complement systems to perform subtraction, thereby requiring only an adder or an accumulator. When one positive number has to be subtracted from another positive number, the complement of the first number is added to the second. The 1s complement of a number is available simply by gating to the adder the 0 outputs of a register rather than the 1 outputs. Demonstration 6-8 shows a method of performing subtraction in the 1s-complement notation.

Demonstration 6-8   1s-complement Subtraction

Purpose

To demonstrate a circuit which performs binary subtraction by the 1s-complement method.

Equipment

  2—Level switches (S)
  1—Single-pulse generator (SPG)
  6—NAND gates (ND)
  3—Full adders (ADD)
  3—Shift registers (SR)

Discussion and Implementation

This demonstration illustrates subtraction by 1s-complement addition. The circuit in Fig. 6-22 is similar to that used in Demonstration 6-4 for parallel addition with the following exceptions:

1. The inputs to the B and $\bar{B}$ terminals of the ADD modules are reversed. This provides for the admission of the 1s complement, or negation of the subtrahend. In a computer, gating is provided so that assertion or negation signals can be selected.

2. The carry output from the ADD module in the highest stage is fed back to the carry input of the ADD module in the lowest stage. This provides for the end-around-carry mechanism necessary to convert 1s complement results to normal subtraction results.

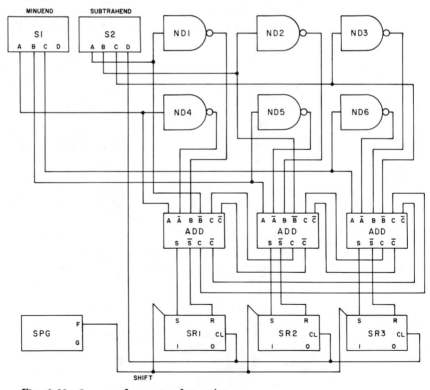

Fig. 6-22   1s-complement subtraction.

NAND gates ND1 to ND6 supply negation inputs for the ADD modules. Assertion and negation inputs from the minuend (S1) and the subtrahend (S2) are sent to the ADD modules so that the minuend is presented directly and the subtrahend is inverted. The minuend and the 1s complement of the subtrahend are then combined in the ADD modules to produce sum and carry terms. Each carry is fed to the next higher stage, as in parallel addition, except for the final carry, which is end-around-carried back to the lowest stage. Note that the carry in this circuit must be propagated through to the highest stage, then back to the lowest stage, and finally back up to the highest stage before the addition is complete. This entails almost twice the circuit delay of the normal parallel adder. A signal from the SPG admits the 1s-complement sum into the register. This adder will only yield correct results when the minuend is larger than the subtrahend since no provision is made to handle negative results by use of a sign bit.

Channel D of S2 is used for the clear line.

6-10 *Logical Multiplication*

The third basic arithmetic operation is multiplication. Multiplication consists of taking one number, the multiplicand, and adding it to itself the number of times indicated by a second number, the multiplier. The result of this repeated addition is called the *product*. For example,

$$36 \times 4 = 144 \quad \text{or} \quad 100100 \times 100 = 10010000$$

$$
\begin{array}{r}
36 \\
36 \\
36 \\
+\ 36 \\
\hline
144
\end{array}
\qquad
\begin{array}{r}
100100 \\
100100 \\
100100 \\
+\ 100100 \\
\hline
10010000
\end{array}
$$

Repeated addition, however, is rarely used due to the difficulty of multiplying large numbers. Instead, the basic combinations of numerals are memorized in the form of multiplication tables, which are then used to form a set of rules for more rapid multiplication. In the binary system, these rules are simple and consist of the following:

Multiplicand
(Y)

		0	1	
Multiplier	0	0	0	Product
(Z)	1	0	1	

These rules are converted to a truth table in Table 6-9.

TABLE 6-9

Y	Z	P
0	0	0
0	1	0
1	0	0
1	1	1

Or, symbolically,

$$P = Y \cdot Z$$

With multiplication, however, implementation of the basic rules is a far cry from complete logical multiplication. A single AND gate performs the $Y \cdot Z$ operation for any one order, but to combine the results from all orders into a final product requires a more complex circuit. It is this combining of results or combining of partial products that presents problems to the computer designer. The following three sections of this chapter and the demonstrations included illustrate three approaches to implementing multiplication. The third approach, utilizing shifting and adding operations, is the one that is most commonly used in computers.

6-11 *Multiplication by Repeated Addition*

One approach to multiplication is to use repeated addition. Although such a process is too time-consuming for pencil-and-paper computation, the high speed of logic circuits makes this approach feasible.

Basically, multiplication by repeated addition can be performed with either of the accumulators presented in Demonstrations 6-5 and 6-6. It is necessary only to enter the multiplicand into the addend register (simulated in the demonstrations by the level switch) and then, using the single-pulse generator (SPG) repeatedly, add it to itself the number of times indicated by the multiplier. After the required number of additions, the accumulated sum is equal to the product of the multiplier and the multiplicand.

The difficulty with this operation is that entry of the multiplier into the system, represented by repeated use of the SPG, is not automatic. However, entry of the multiplier can be made automatic by including a binary counter in the system.

For example, if the SPG in Demonstration 6-6 is replaced by the low-frequency clock (CK), the accumulator will add the multiplicand to itself on every clock pulse. If the clock is, in turn, controlled by a binary counter, only a certain number of clock pulses (the number contained in the counter) will reach the accumulator. By entering the multiplier into the counter, the multiplicand can be added to itself the number of times indicated by the multiplier. This represents multiplication by repeated addition and is illustrated in Demonstration 6-9.

Demonstration 6-9   *Multiplication by Repeated Addition*

Purpose

To demonstrate the process of multiplication by repeated addition and to illustrate how a counter circuit can be used to control operations in a computer.

Equipment

> 2—Level switches (S)
> 1—Single-pulse generator (SPG)
> 1—Low-frequency clock (CK)
> 5—AND gates (AN)
> 4—Shift registers (SR)
> 3—Full adders (ADD)
> 1—NAND gate (ND)
> 3—Flip-flops (FF)

Discussion and Implementation

Figure 6-24 is a block-diagram representation of Fig. 6-23. The two bottom rows of modules in Fig. 6-23 represent the accumulator portion of the circuit and are connected in the same manner as the accumulator in Demonstration 6-6. The only differences are that the gate pulses come from the low-frequency clock (CK), through AND gate AN5, instead of from the SPG, and the negation outputs for the ADD modules are supplied directly from S2 rather than from inverters.

With this accumulator configuration, the number in the multiplicand register (S2) is added to itself each time a clock pulse passes through AN5. Note that channels A and C of S2 are used for assertion inputs to the ADD modules, while channels B and D are used for negation inputs.

The two upper rows of the diagram represent a binary down-counter circuit. Flip-flops FF1 to FF3 are wired so that the output of each 0 terminal goes to the toggle input of the next higher stage in straightforward down-counter fashion. AND gates AN1 to AN3 permit a number from the multiplier register to enter the counter on command from the SPG.

The 0 output of each flip-flop is then connected to NAND gate ND1. Since the output of a NAND gate is a logic 1 unless all three of its inputs are 1s, NAND gate ND1 will be a 1 unless all three flip-flops are in the 0 or reset state. Therefore, if all three flip-flops are cleared, the NAND-gate output will be 0 and so, in turn, will AND gates AN4 and AN5.

Assume now that a three-digit binary number is entered into S1 (the multiplier register). On a gating signal from the SPG, this number will enter the counter and set one or more of the three flip-flops, making the 0 outputs a logic 0. This immediately puts a 1 output on NAND gate ND1, which, in turn, opens AN4 and allows clock pulses to enter the counter. At the same time, the signal from ND1 also opens AN5, allowing clock pulses to reach the accumulator. Each subsequent clock pulse is then sent simultaneously to the counter and to the accumulator. The counter starts counting down, and the accumulator starts accumulating.

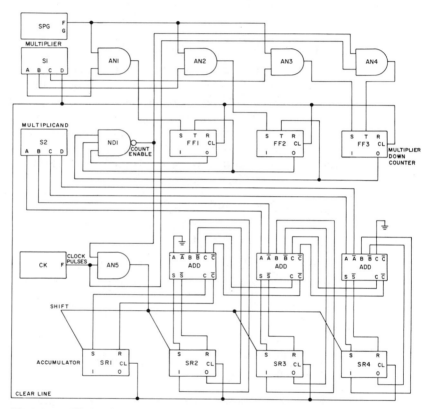

Fig. 6-23 Multiplication by repeated addition.

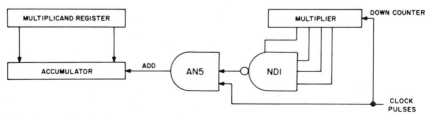

Fig. 6-24 Block diagram of Fig. 6-23.

However, when the counter has counted all the way down to 000, NAND gate ND1 is again closed (output to a logic 0) and the clock pulses are cut off from both the counter and the accumulator. The counter stops counting, and the accumulator stops accumulating. By this time, however, the accumulator has added the multiplicand to itself the exact number of times that the counter counted. This number is equivalent to the multiplier, so the accumulator added the multiplicand to itself the exact number of times indicated by the multiplier. This completes the multiplication by repeated addition.

6-12 *Simultaneous Multiplication*

While the method of repeated addition illustrates the use of counters in computer operations, it is a relatively slow process and only finds application in very special cases. If speed is a prime consideration, multiplication can be performed with special multiplier circuits. One form of multiplier circuit, the simultaneous multiplier, is discussed in this section.

To gain an understanding of simultaneous multiplication, consider first the multiplication of two decimal numbers such as 436 and 32. Such a problem might appear as follows:

$$
\begin{array}{rl}
436 & \text{multiplicand} \\
\times \quad 32 & \text{multiplier} \\
\hline
13{,}952 & \text{product}
\end{array}
$$

Few people, however, can perform this computation as illustrated. Most persons would set the problem up in the following manner:

$$
\begin{array}{r}
436 \\
\times \quad 32 \\
\hline
872 \\
1308 \quad \\
\hline
13{,}952
\end{array}
$$

Even this, however, does not reveal the fundamental steps, most of which are accomplished mentally. The following illustrates all the fundamental steps performed in a multiplication problem:

$$
\begin{array}{rccccc}
 & & 4 & 3 & 6 \\
\times & & & 3 & 2 \\
\hline
 & & (8) & (6) & (12) \\
 & (12) & (9) & (18) \\
\hline
 & \leftarrow (12) & \leftarrow (17) & \leftarrow (24) & \leftarrow (12) \\
(1) & (3) & (9) & (5) & (2) \\
\hline
 & & 13{,}952
\end{array}
$$

In this illustration, each partial product is formed separately and then added to the other partial products in the same order. Carries occur in the addition process and in the multiplication itself.

With binary multiplication, the process is simpler because no carries are ever generated in the multiplication process ($1 \times 1 = 1$ with no carry).

Binary	Decimal

$$
\begin{array}{cccc}
 & 1 & 1 & 1 \\
\times & & 1 & 1 \\
\hline
 & (1) & (1) & (1) \\
(1) & (1) & (1) & \\
\hline
(1) \leftarrow & (10) \leftarrow & (10) & (1) \\
(1) \quad (0) & (1) & (0) & (1) \\
 & 10101 &
\end{array}
\qquad
\begin{array}{r}
7 \\
\times\ 3 \\
\hline
21
\end{array}
$$

Carries are, however, generated when the partial products are summed. In the previous example, the two zeroth-order digits are combined to produce the zeroth-order digit of the product directly. However, to produce the first-order digit of the product, the two zeroth-order digits must be multiplied by the opposite first-order digits and then half-added together. This process can, and in this case does, generate a carry. To produce the second-order digit of the product, this carry must be full-added to the results of the multiplications performed in the next orders, and so on. The process continues with appropriate orders being combined to form partial products and the partial products being full-added with the carries from previous orders to form full products.

Demonstration 6-10 illustrates the simultaneous-multiplication process.

Demonstration 6-10 Simultaneous Multiplication

Purpose

To demonstrate the implementation of simultaneous multiplication.

Equipment

2—Level switches (S)
6—AND gates (AN)
5—NAND gates (ND)
3—Full adders (ADD)

Discussion and Implementation

The circuit presented in Fig. 6-25 will directly multiply any three-digit binary number by any two-digit binary number.

If two binary numbers, $Y_2Y_1Y_0$ and Z_1Z_0, are entered into the multiplicand and multiplier registers (S1 and S2), their product appears immedi-

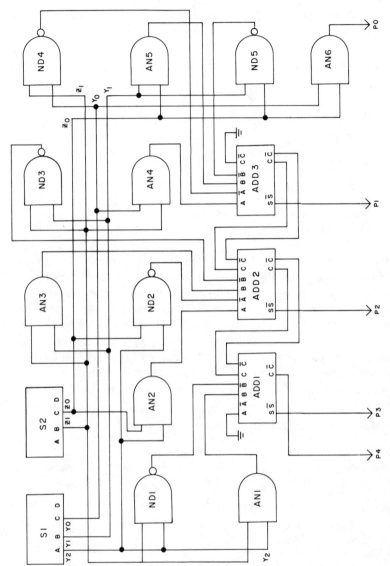

Fig. 6-25 Simultaneous multiplication.

ately at the bottom row of gates. The following example clarifies the gating necessary to produce this product:

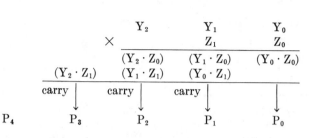

1. Y_0 and Z_0 are ANDed together in AN6 to produce P_0 directly.

2. $Y_1 \cdot Z_0$ and its negation, $\overline{Y_1 \cdot Z_0}$, are formed in AN5 and ND5, respectively. These are then presented at the B and $\overline{B}$ terminals of ADD module 3.

3. $Y_0 \cdot Z_1$ and its negation, $\overline{Y_0 \cdot Z_1}$, are formed in AN4 and ND4, respectively. These are then presented at the A and $\overline{A}$ terminals of ADD module 3.

4. $Y_1 \cdot Z_0$ and $Y_0 \cdot Z_1$ are half-added in ADD module 3, and the carry is sent on to ADD module 2. The sum becomes P_1.

5. $Y_2 \cdot Z_0$ and $Y_1 \cdot Z_1$ and their negations are formed in AN2, AN3, ND2, and ND3 and are presented at the input terminals of ADD module 2. Here they are full-added with the carry from ADD module 3. The sum becomes P_2, and the carry is sent on to ADD module 1.

6. $Y_2 \cdot Z_1$ and its negation are formed in AN1 and ND1 and sent to the B and $\overline{B}$ terminals of ADD module 1. Here $Y_2 \cdot Z_1$ is half-added to the carry from ADD module 2 to produce the term P_3 and a carry, which becomes P_4.

Greater capacity and direct connection of the simultaneous multiplier to a register are, of course, easily obtainable with additional gates. The principle of operation, however, remains the same. It becomes readily apparent that a simultaneous multiplier designed to handle large numbers requires an extremely large number of gates. Here again is an example of the trade-off between speed and increase in hardware.

6-13 *Multiplication by Shifting*

A third method of multiplication, one most frequently encountered in computer design, is that of multiplication by shifting.

In binary multiplication, each partial product either is an exact duplicate of the multiplicand or is all 0s. Those orders of the multiplier which contain 1s produce partial products which are exact duplicates of the multiplicand; those which contain 0s produce partial products which are all 0s.   The following example illustrates this process:

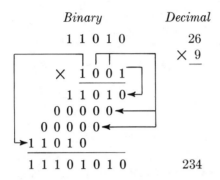

Furthermore, as shown in this example, each new partial product is shifted one digit to the left of the previous partial product.   Multiplication may therefore be accomplished by presenting the multiplicand to an accumulator and entering it only if the zeroth-order digit of the multiplier is a 1.   If the zeroth-order digit of the multiplier is a 0, then the multiplicand is not entered into the accumulator.   Next the multiplicand is shifted one digit to the left.   Then, if the first-order digit is a 1, the multiplicand is again entered, or if it is a 0, it is not entered.   Again the multiplicand is shifted one digit to the left.   This process is continued until the multiplicand has been shifted through the entire multiplier. The number in the accumulator then represents the product of the two numbers.   Figure 6-26 illustrates this process of multiplication by shifting.

In steps *b* and *e*, the multiplier is a 1.   Therefore, the multiplicand is entered into the accumulator.   In steps *c* and *d*, no number is entered into the accumulator since the multiplier is a 0.   After each step, the multiplicand is shifted one digit to the left.   Demonstration 6-11 illustrates multiplication by shifting.

Demonstration 6-11   The Shifting Multiplier

Purpose

To demonstrate the operation of a shifting multiplier.

Equipment

     1—Level switch (S)
     1—Single-pulse generator (SPG)
     8—Shift registers (SR)
     1—AND gate (AN)
     3—Full adders (ADD)
     1—Flip-flop (FF)

Discussion and Implementation

The two bottom rows of modules in Fig. 6-27 again represent the accumulator of Demonstration 6-5.   The top row of modules is connected in typical shift-register fashion, and the multiplicand bits are entered serially from channels A and B of the level switch.   Channel B is used to supply the required negation inputs.   Channel F of the SPG provides the shift signals. In practice, data to the register could be entered in parallel, and negation inputs would be supplied from inverters or directly from flip-flops.

After the multiplicand has been entered into the shift register, the circuit is ready to perform its operation.   Channel G of the SPG provides ADD signals for those orders of the multiplier which contain 1s, and channel F is used for continued shifting of the multiplier.   After each shift operation, the multiplicand is presented to the row of ADD modules and

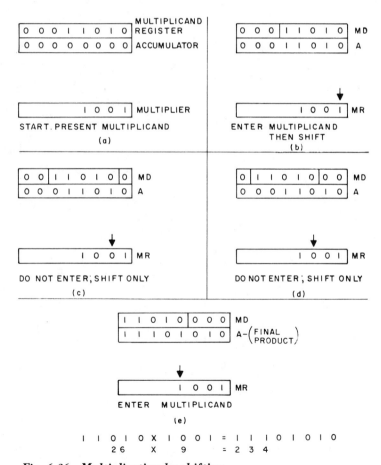

Fig. 6-26 Multiplication by shifting.

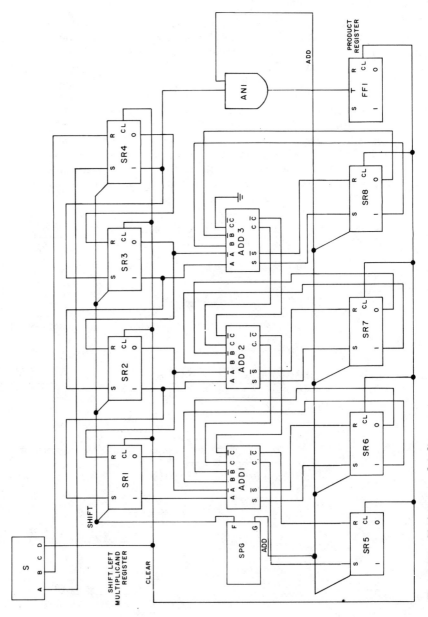

Fig. 6-27 Shifting multiplier.

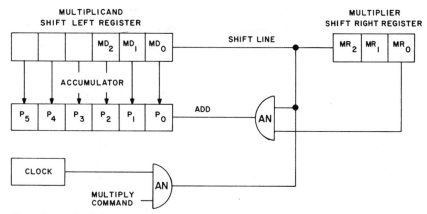

Fig. 6-28   Shifting multiplier block diagram.

combined with the number already in the accumulator to form a new sum
at each stage.   These sums, however, can only enter the accumulator when
an ADD signal is generated.   Therefore, for those orders of the multiplier
containing 0s, the sums are formed but are never admitted to the accumulator.   As the multiplicand is shifted through the entire multiplier, it is
entered only in the proper orders, and when the operation is complete, the
accumulator will contain the product.

In this demonstration, ADD signals are sent out manually from the SPG;
however, a circuit could be designed in which ADD signals come directly
from a multiplier register.   The functional diagram given in Fig. 6-28
illustrates such a circuit.

When the MULTIPLY command is held down, the shift register, containing the multiplicand, shifts to the left and the multiplier register shifts
to the right.   As each order of the multiplier passes through the far-right
stage of its register, it either opens the ADD gate if it is a 1 or leaves it
closed if it is a 0.   In this way, the multiplicand is sent to the accumulator
only for those orders of the multiplier which contain 1s.   In this case, the
clock pulses and the multiplier register perform the same function as the
manually operated SPG of the demonstration.   When the multiplier
register contains all logic 0s, the ADD gate is inhibited.

The circuit diagram for the shifting multiplier is a simplified version of
those used in computers.   An increased number of logic rules are required
to implement logical multiplication which will handle numbers represented
in 1s or 2s complement.   To implement the rules for multiplication in
either of the two systems requires a substantial increase in the amount of
logic to be used with the basic version of the shifting multiplier.

6-14   *Logical Division*

The remaining basic arithmetic operation to be discussed is division.
Division is essentially the opposite of multiplication.   In division, one

number, the divisor, is repeatedly subtracted from another number, the dividend, until no further subtraction is possible. The number of subtractions required to reduce the dividend to 0 is called the *quotient*. For example,

$$144 \div 36 = 4 \qquad\qquad 10010000 \div 100100 = 100$$

144		10010000	
− 36	1	− 100100	
108		1101100	
− 36	2	− 100100	
72		1001000	
− 36	3	− 100100	
36		100100	
− 36	4	− 100100	
0		000000	

Repeated subtraction, such as that illustrated above, could be implemented using an adder which is designed to implement 1s- or 2s-complement subtraction. The dividend would be entered into one of the registers in the arithmetic unit and then the divisor would be subtracted repeatedly. The number of subtractions necessary to reduce the dividend to 0 or to a number less than the divisor would be equivalent to the quotient. As with multiplication by repeated addition, however, this process is slow and is seldom encountered in computer design.

The normal approach to division is that of shifting the divisor. This is quite similar to shifting the multiplier, discussed in the previous section. Where multiplication is performed by repeated addition and shifting, division is almost always performed by repeated subtraction and shifting. To perform division in this manner, the dividend is first entered into a register, as shown in Fig. 6-29.

After the divisor is entered into the three highest stages of the shift register, it is compared with the number in the first three stages of the accumulator. Circuits which perform this comparison operation are discussed in Chap. 9. For the present, however, assume that the divisor can be compared with the three highest stages of the accumulator. If it is less than or equal to those orders of the accumulator, it is subtracted and a 1 is sent to the highest order of the quotient register. If, as in the above example, the divisor is greater than the first three stages of the accumulator, it is shifted one place to the right and a 0 is sent to the quotient register. The process is then continued by shifting the divisor to the right, subtracting, and sending a 1 to the quotient register when the divisor is less than or equal to the appropriate orders of the accumulator

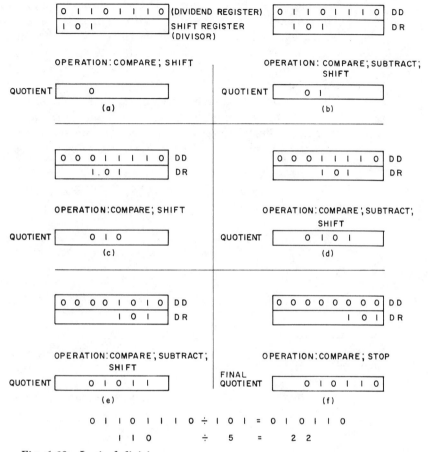

Fig. 6-29   Logical division.

or a 0 when the divisor is greater than the appropriate orders of the accumulator.

In Fig. 6-29, steps *a*, *c*, and *f*, the number in the divisor shift register is larger than the number in the dividend register and a 0 is entered in the quotient.   In steps *b*, *d*, and *e*, the number in the divisor register is smaller than the number in the dividend register; the divisor is then subtracted from the dividend, and a 1 is entered into the quotient.   After each step, the divisor is shifted to the right.

The process in Fig. 6-29 can be modified by using 1s-complement subtraction.   Rather than having to perform a comparison operation to determine whether the dividend is larger than the divisor, a detection of an end-around carry will perform the same function.

In Fig. 6-30*a*, the 1s complement of the divisor is shifted so that its most significant bit is aligned with the most significant bit of the dividend. The 1s complement of the divisor (101) is 010.   Whether a 1 or a 0 should be placed in the quotient register depends on whether the dividend is larger or smaller than the divisor.   If the divisor is added (1s-complement subtraction) to the dividend, an end-around carry would be generated only when the divisor is smaller than the equivalent bits in the dividend. This is a rule of 1s-complement subtraction.   Conversely, no end-around carry will be generated if the positive minuend is smaller than the sub-trahend.   Thus, if no end-around carry is detected when the divisor is subtracted from the dividend in Fig. 6-30*a*, a 0 is entered in the quotient

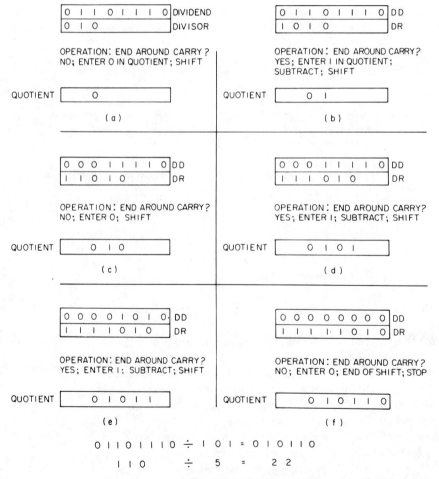

Fig. 6-30   *Division with end-around carry.*

register.   Since a subtraction was not possible in step a, the dividend register is inhibited from changing and will retain the original number in Fig. 6-30b.   The next step is to shift the divisor 1 bit to the right. In step b, the 1s complement of 0101, which is 1010, is shifted in the divisor register.

When the divisor is added to the dividend in step b, an end-around carry is generated.   This means that a 1 should be entered into the quotient and that the dividend should be modified to the resultant of the 1s-complement subtraction.   Thus the modified dividend would be

```
    0 1 1 0 1 1 1 0
    1 0 1 0
  ─────────────────
  1 0 0 0 0 1 1 1 0
  └────────►1           end-around carry
  ─────────────────
    0 0 0 1 1 1 1 0     modified dividend for step c
```

Note that when performing the end-around-carry operation, the 1 is added to the bit which aligns with the least significant bit of the divisor.

In step c, no end-around carry will occur, so a 0 is entered into the quotient and modification of the dividend register is inhibited.   In steps d and e, an end-around carry is generated, requiring a 1 to be entered into the quotient and the dividend to be modified to the result of 1s-complement subtraction.   In step f, no end-around carry is generated, and a 0 is entered into the quotient.

Note that this method of division does not introduce any new basic concepts but that it does utilize a number of the concepts discussed previously.

To implement division for various sign combinations of the divisor and dividend requires special rules.   The rules differ, depending on whether the negative numbers are represented in 1s-complement or 2s-complement notation.   It is beyond the scope of this text to illustrate the mechanization of signed division.

In the previous illustrations, no mention was made as to how a remainder is represented as part of the quotient.   If fractional accuracy is not necessary, the remainder could be ignored.   Usually, the required accuracy demands that fractions be represented.   In a fixed-binary-point system, this means that the dividend must have a number of bits to the right of the binary point to obtain a desired accuracy.   The fractional representation will be accurate to the number of bits to the right of the binary point.   To illustrate this operation, consider the following example, where decimal 52 is divided by 5 and an accuracy of six binary places is desired:

$$
\begin{array}{r}
1\ 0\ 1\ 0.0\ 1\ 1\ 0\ 0\ 1 \\[-2pt]
1\ 0\ 1\,\overline{\left)1\ 1\ 0\ 1\ 0\ 0.0\ 0\ 0\ 0\ 0\ 0\right.}
\end{array}
$$

$$
\begin{aligned}
1\ 0\ 1\ 0.0\ 1\ 1\ 0\ 0\ 1 = \quad & 1 \times 2^3 &=& \quad 8 \\
+\ & 0 \times 2^2 &=& +0 \\
+\ & 1 \times 2^1 &=& +2 \\
+\ & 0 \times 2^0 &=& +0 \\
+\ & 0 \times 2^{-1} &=& +0.0 \\
+\ & 1 \times 2^{-2} &=& +0.25 \\
+\ & 1 \times 2^{-3} &=& +0.125 \\
+\ & 0 \times 2^{-4} &=& +0.0 \\
+\ & 0 \times 2^{-5} &=& +0.0 \\
+\ & 1 \times 2^{-6} &=& \underline{+0.015625} \\
& & & 10.390625
\end{aligned}
$$

The binary quotient is equivalent to decimal 10.390625, which is approximately equal to the decimal answer of 10.4. If further accuracy is required, more orders to the right of the binary point are used. Representation of numbers that are not integers, especially those requiring many significant digits for accuracy, can lead to inefficient computer operation. For this reason, floating-point rather than fixed-point arithmetic is frequently utilized. This is the subject of the next section.

6-15 *Floating-point Arithmetic*

In most computers, binary numbers are represented by groups of bits referred to as *words*. Word size and organization are discussed in Chap. 8. It is desirable, from a cost point of view, to minimize the number of bits required in the computer word. If numbers were represented in fixed-binary-point notation, where each bit position has a certain weight factor (power of 2), a large number of bit positions would be required. Frequently, however, a consistent binary point does not exist in a computer word; that is, the binary point for every word is not always between bit X and bit X + 1.

The burden of determining the location of the binary point in a fixed-point computer is placed upon the programmer. The programmer determines the position of the point by utilizing scale factors. When programming a particular problem, the programmer uses scaling operations which include the shifting of numbers in registers to the left or right in order to align them properly. These scaling operations require the programmer to define the position of the binary point for each number entering the machine. In addition, he must follow the binary point for each computational cycle to ensure that the desired accuracy is maintained. Then he must also predetermine the position of the binary point in the results obtained from the computation. This burden upon the programmer is significantly reduced if the computer is organized to perform arithmetic operations in a floating-point numbering system. On the other hand, the design of such a computer is more complex.

In a floating-point numbering system, each number has three parts which identify its sign and magnitude. One bit is reserved for the sign, in much the same way as was discussed in Sec. 6-9. The magnitude is expressed by two groups of bits, the mantissa and the characteristic, in the same way logarithms are expressed. The mantissa will usually be scaled to be equal to numbers between 2^0 and 2^{-1}. Thus the binary point is always assumed to be to the left of the most significant bit. The bits in the characteristic represent the power of the base 2 by which the mantissa should be multiplied. Thus the magnitude is expressed as some integer multiplied by the radix raised to the power represented by the characteristic (magnitude $= R2^c$), where R equals the radix and c equals the characteristic. The characteristic may be 0 or any integer which is within the maximum number of bits represented by the mantissa. For an example of a floating-point format, consider a word having a mantissa of 7 bits and a characteristic of 4 bits.

In Fig. 6-31, the characteristic is 4 bits long, with 1 bit reserved for sign designation. This sign designation is important since the characteristic must have the ability to represent negative powers of 2 as well as positive powers of 2. Negative characteristics indicate that the binary point should be placed so many bits to the left of the mantissa. The following examples illustrate how numbers are represented in floating point. The sign bit of the mantissa is not given in any of these examples.

(a) 1010000 0001 =   1.010000   = decimal 1.25
(b) 1010000 0100 = 1010.000   = decimal 6
(c) 1010000 1101 =   0.001010000 = decimal 0.15625

In example (a), when the mantissa 0.1010000 is multiplied by the characteristic 0001 (2^1), the result is 1.01, or decimal 1.25. In example

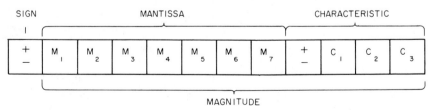

Fig. 6-31 Floating-point format.

(*b*), when the mantissa 0.1010000 is multiplied by the characteristic 0100 (2^4), the result is 1010, or decimal 6. In example (*c*), the characteristic has a negative sign and is in the 1s-complement notation. Thus the number represented is 0.101×2^{-2}, which equals 0.00101. Conversion of binary 0.00101 to decimal notation requires the addition of 2^{-3} (0.125) and 2^{-5} (0.03125), which is equal to decimal 0.15625. From the examples shown, it can be seen that the floating-point system offers a method of representing very large and very small numbers with fewer bit positions than would be necessary in a fixed-binary-point notation. It should be noted that the mantissa always starts with the most significant bit of the magnitude. If the result of a computation has a 0 for that bit position, an automatic scaling operation is performed which increments the characteristic until the most significant bit becomes the first bit in the mantissa.

Frequently, in order to avoid having both positive and negative characteristics, a constant is added to the characteristic. Thus, characteristics of -111 to $+111$ would be changed to $+0001$ to $+1111$ by adding 1000 to each characteristic. The characteristic of 0 in such a system would be equal to 1000, and a negative characteristic of 1 would equal $1000 - 0001$, or 0111. Thus, if the characteristic is negative, it is subtracted from 1000; and if it is positive, it is added to 1000. The computer must be designed to correct these characteristics as a part of the problem solution.

The following are some examples which show how arithmetic operations are manipulated in floating-point notation. To perform addition, a scaling operation is required when the characteristics are not identical. This involves a shifting of the mantissa for the smaller number until the characteristic of the smaller number equals that of the larger number. For example,

$$(0.10100 \times 2^2) + (0.11000 \times 2^3) = \begin{array}{r} 0.01010 \times 2^3 \\ +0.11000 \times 2^3 \\ \hline 1.00010 \times 2^3 \end{array}$$

Then the answer would have to be scaled again to yield an adjusted result of 0.10001×2^4. The same basic operations would be performed for complement subtraction.

When performing multiplication in floating-point arithmetic, the characteristics of the two numbers are added and the mantissas are multiplied. For example,

$$(0.1010 \times 2^{-2}) \times (0.1000 \times 2^4) = \text{unscaled } 0.0101 \times 2^2$$
$$= \text{scaled } \quad 0.1010 \times 2^1$$

A scaling operation is required on the result since the value of the mantissa is not between 2^0 and 2^{-1}. The algebraic addition of the exponents in this example required the addition of a negative number to a positive one.   This addition is easily implemented with complement subtraction.

In floating-point division, the mantissas are divided in normal fashion and the characteristic of the divisor is subtracted from the characteristic of the dividend.   Then the quotient is scaled for proper representation in floating-point notation.   For example,

$$\frac{0.1100 \times 2^2}{0.1000 \times 2^1} = \text{unscaled } 1.1000 \times 2^1 = \text{scaled } 0.1100 \times 2^2$$

Division as well as multiplication can be performed directly in floating-point notation, while addition and subtraction require scaling operations to align the characteristics prior to performing the algebraic addition. Scaling must be performed on any results where the mantissa does not equal less than 2^0 or more than 2^{-1}.

In conclusion, a floating-point computer offers two distinct advantages over one with fixed-point notation.   One advantage is in the handling of those problems where both very large integers and very small fractions are represented.   Floating-point notation offers an efficient means of accommodating the wide range of numbers used in some scientific problems.   The other advantage is that a computer designed for floating-point arithmetic automatically scales and normalizes the mantissa, thus relieving the programmer of having to handle routine scaling.

EXERCISES

6-1. What are the sum and carry for each of the following input conditions to a half adder?

	Augend	*Addend*	*Sum*	*Carry*
(a)	1	0		
(b)	1	1		
(c)	0	1		
(d)	0	0		

6-2. By algebraic manipulation, prove the equivalence of the carry functions given in the three half-adder demonstrations.

6-3. Assuming that signals Y, $\overline{Y}$, Z, and $\overline{Z}$ are available, that is, both the assertion and negation signals for both augend and addend, redraw the diagrams in Figs. 6-1 and 6-2, minimizing the number of logic modules to be used.

6-4. Implement the logic expressions described in Fig. 6-1 using only NAND gates.

6-5. Implement the logic expressions described in Fig. 6-2 using only NOR gates.

6-6. Draw a block diagram for one other half-adder implementation.

6-7. Assume that gate ND1 in Fig. 6-1 is disabled so that its output is always a 0.   Prepare a truth table showing the sum and carry digits for each of the four possible input conditions.

6-8. Add 10011101 to 10110101 and give the resultant sum and carry for each digit that would be generated in a full adder. Verify the sum using the decimal equivalents.

6-9. Describe the signal (1 or 0) at the output of each module in full adder 1 when $Y = 1$, $Z = 0$, and $C = 1$.

6-10. Using the theorems and postulates given in Chap. 3, prove that the sum and carry expressions in Fig. 6-6 are equivalent to those in Fig. 6-5.

6-11. Using the theorems and postulates given in Chap. 3, prove that the sum and carry expressions in Fig. 6-7 are equivalent to those in Fig. 6-5.

6-12. Draw a logic diagram that implements the full-adder functions:

$$\text{Sum} = [(Z + Y) + C] \cdot [\overline{(Z + Y) \cdot (Z \cdot Y + C)} + Z \cdot Y \cdot C]$$
$$\text{Carry} = (Z + Y) \cdot (Z \cdot Y + C)$$

Prove that these terms are equivalent to Eqs. (6-6) and (6-8).

6-13. Construct a block diagram of a full adder using only NAND gates.

6-14. Using the block diagram of Fig. 6-8, draw a timing diagram that reflects the discrete steps required to perform serial addition of two 4-bit numbers 0110 and 0110 contained in the augend and addend registers.

6-15. Draw a timing diagram of the outputs of FF1 to FF4 in Fig. 6-15 if 010, 011, and 100 are placed sequentially in the addend register. Show the outputs before and after each add and carry pulse.

6-16. Draw two other half-subtractor configurations.

6-17. Using the theorems and postulates of Chap. 3, prove the equivalence of the difference and borrow expressions of Figs. 6-20 and 6-21.

6-18. Draw a functional block diagram of a full serial subtractor.

6-19. Draw a functional block diagram of a full parallel subtractor.

6-20. Convert to binary and perform the following subtractions directly, both in the 1s-complement system and in the 2s-complement system:

$$\begin{array}{cccc} 83 & 47 & 8 & -6 \\ -26 & -18 & -26 & -19 \end{array}$$

6-21. Draw a functional block diagram of the logic which will perform 2s-complement subtraction.

6-22. Draw a timing diagram for the shifting-multiplier product register of Fig. 6-27 as 101 is multiplied by 11.

6-23. Prepare a functional block diagram of the logic required to perform division by repeated subtraction.

6-24. Multiply 61.2 by 0.024 and divide by 0.236 using a slide rule. How was the position of the decimal point known?

6-25. Describe the characteristics of floating-point arithmetic.

6-26. What are the decimal equivalents of the following floating-point representations? Negative characteristics are in the 1s-complement form.

	Mantissa	*Characteristic*
(a)	1001011	0111
(b)	1001000	0011
(c)	1100000	1110
(d)	1011000	1101

SEVEN

Memory

7-1 Introduction

The function of the computer memory is to store instructions, data, and partial answers until they are needed by the computer. Within the memory, information must be able to be retained, identified, and retrieved upon command. The computer memory is thus similar to the human memory in possessing the three features of retention, recognition, and recovery of information.

The characteristics of the memory are related to the characteristics of the remainder of the computer. If the arithmetic section were to take 1 second to add two numbers, then it would not be unreasonable to take 1 second to store the result in the computer memory. If, as is typically the case, the arithmetic section were to add these two numbers in approximately one-millionth of a second, the computer memory should be capable of responding to information at this rate. In short, the faster the arithmetic speed, the faster the internal memory should be.

A similar relationship exists for memory capacity. In early computers, a few hundred bits of memory were provided. Now, as larger and more complex problems are attempted, additional memory capacity is needed. A small-size computer will have 100 thousand bits of high-speed storage, while a larger computer installation may require up to 100 billion bits of total storage. Obviously, not all information is required with equal frequency, and much information can be accessible at a slower rate. In this respect, the computer is similar to man's capacity to store information. Certain important facts are remembered and readily available. Other information can be looked up in reference books at home. Still other, more infrequently used information, requires a trip downtown to the library. In a similar manner, a computer is usually organized so that data or instructions required frequently are stored in a moderate-size fast-access main memory, while backup information is stored in large-capacity slower-access external storage.

The important factor is to operate the computer efficiently. The more time spent by the computer waiting for additional data or further instructions from the memory, the more inefficiently the computer is being utilized. This inefficiency is a reflection on the design of the computer system or on the programming of a particular problem.

7-2 *Memory Characteristics*

A computer memory could be designed around any bistable storage device, and a variety of electronic, magnetic, electromechanical, and optical devices have been proposed as memory elements. The value of a memory built of any storage element can be measured in terms of a few important characteristics. These include:

1. *Memory Capacity:* The maximum number of bits which can be stored within the memory. This is usually described as X words, where each word is so many bits long, or X number of characters, where each character is so many bits long.

2. *Memory Access Time:* The average and maximum lengths of time to transfer data in and out of the memory, i.e., to read and write data. To *read a memory* is the process of calling for information from the memory and obtaining it. To *write into a memory* is the process of presenting information to the memory and storing it.

3. *Type of Access; Sequential or Random:* A random-access memory is one in which the time necessary to access any memory location is independent of the last memory location addressed. Sequential access can be compared to listening to a long-playing record, where the time to a specific piece of music is dependent on the portion of the record being played. Random access can be compared to the dialing of a telephone number, where the time to complete the call is independent of the last number called.

4. *Cost per Bit:* The cost per bit of storage is related to the type and size of the memory. It is obvious that this cost is extremely important since a computer may require between 10^5 and 10^{11} bits of storage.

5. *Volatility:* If power to the computer is turned off, are all records in the computer destroyed or will the memory continue to store information? Magnetic elements have the ability to store information indefinitely without applied power.

6. *Permanence:* Can this information in the memory be erased and new information written in the memory? The condition of a flip-flop can be changed, while a card which has a hole punched in it to signify a 1 is not easily modified.

In addition to these characteristics, other important considerations include physical characteristics, power requirements, memory organization required, and any unique properties of the memory.

The ideal memory would be capable of storing up to 10^{12} bits of information for years or until the information is deliberately erased, would be as fast as the arithmetic unit, i.e., access times substantially less than one-millionth of a second, and would cost almost nothing per bit of storage. Unfortunately, this is an ideal memory which is not available. Depending on storage media, the cost per bit ranges from a few dollars to less than one-thousandth of a cent, and the access time ranges from many seconds to less than 10^{-7} second. The computer designer, therefore, uses several media as internal and external storage to balance speed, cost, and bit-capacity trade-offs in a series of memories. Information is then transferred, as required, during a problem from one storage medium to another. The word "memory" is normally used to describe the internal, fast-access storage and not the external, slower-access bulk storage. Some of the major types of bulk storage, such as paper tape, punched cards, and magnetic tape, will be covered in Chap. 10.

7-3 *Types of Memories*

Any bistable device capable of being set in one of its states, maintaining that state, and indicating that state when interrogated can be considered as a possible memory element. However, its feasibility as a memory element must be examined in terms of its speed, cost, and size characteristics. If two memories are of equal speed, the lower-cost memory is preferable since, for a given amount of money, more bits of memory can be provided and the resultant computer will be more powerful. If two memories are of equal cost, the higher-speed memory is preferable since, in a given period of time, the resultant computer can perform more calculations and is therefore more efficient.

The flip-flop described in Chap. 4 could be used for small memories. The flip-flop can be set in one of two conditions; it will maintain this state; and its output can be detected. Since the flip-flop is similar to the gate and registers used in the arithmetic section, its speed of operation is at least as fast as that of the arithmetic section. However, as the number of bits of storage increases, the flip-flop becomes economically impractical.

The cost of a flip-flop is in the range of a few dollars, although there are developments under way to reduce this cost substantially. While this cost is not unreasonable in a few-hundred-bit memory, it becomes significant in a million-bit memory. Therefore it is necessary to use other types of memories which reduce the cost per bit two to five orders of magnitude.

The approach to lower-cost memories has generally followed one of two paths. One method uses an interconnected matrix of individual memory elements in which a bistable device is addressed by simultaneous signals on two or more paths. The element at the intersection of these signals performs a logic AND function. The magnetic-core memory and thin-film magnetic memory are examples of random-access memory design. The second method uses the physical motion of a continuous recording surface relative to a read-write device. A magnetic drum, disk, or tape is an example of a sequential-access memory. In a random-access memory, the data to be stored go directly to a previously assigned location and remain there until read out. In a sequential-access memory, there is usually physical motion of the stored data. Although many memory elements can be used in either random-access or sequential memories, they usually have advantages in one type of organization. There are other approaches to memory design, including electronic and acoustic shift registers, optical devices, and low-temperature superconductive memories. Most computers today are designed to operate with one or more of the magnetic memories. In the following sections, a discussion of a random-access magnetic-core memory and several types of sequential-access memories will illustrate some of the general considerations in memory organization, access, and addressing.

7-4   *Magnetic-core Memory*

The most common type of high-speed computer memory is a coincident-current ferrite-core memory. Memories with capacities up to several million bits and access times substantially less than one-millionth of a second have been built in this way.

A magnetic core is a tiny doughnut-shaped object made of ferromagnetic material. It can be magnetized easily and, unless deliberately changed, will retain its magnetism indefinitely. If a wire is passed through the core and a sufficiently large current sent through it, the core becomes magnetized. The direction of the current determines the polarity of the magnetic field, and the core can be considered as being magnetized in the clockwise or counterclockwise (positive or negative) direction. A positive core has a value of 1, and a negative core has a value of 0. (See Fig. 7-1.) Since each core can be magnetized in either the 1 or the 0 polarity state, each core can store 1 bit. The time required to switch a core from one state to another is dependent on the core

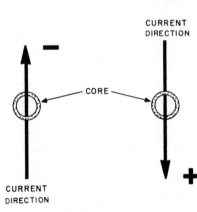

CURRENT DIRECTION

CORE

CURRENT DIRECTION

Fig. 7-1   Magnetic core.

material and is related to its size since a smaller core requires smaller currents to change its state. Cores measuring several thousandths of an inch in diameter are used to provide fast switching speeds.

A magnetic core is similar to a flip-flop, and an array of cores arranged in sequence can provide functions similar to a flip-flop register. A flip-flop is set or reset by applying pulses to the appropriate input. A core is set by application of a current pulse in one direction and is reset by a similar current pulse applied in the opposite direction. The core, because of its magnetic characteristics, does not require power normally and only dissipates power while being switched from one state to another. Unlike the flip-flop, the core memory is nonvolatile. If power is removed or lost, the magnetic cores retain stored information indefinitely.

It is possible to build a core memory by using one write wire through each core. However, this would require 100 circuits capable of supplying current for 100 bits of memory and would involve almost as much electronics as 100 flip-flops. It is therefore desirable to reduce the overall number of wires into the entire core array.

If two wires are passed through a core and half the amount of current necessary to magnetize the core is sent through each wire in the proper direction, the core will become magnetized. The cores are strung on screens or planes, with one core on each intersection, so that when current is sent through one horizontal and one vertical wire, only one of the cores is magnetized. No other core is magnetized because only the selected core receives the full magnetization current. A core has a very sharp and well-defined threshold. One-half of the magnetization current will never switch the core, while the full current will always switch it. By passing current through any pair of wires, one can control the magnetism of any of the cores. (See Fig. 7-2.) The core memory depends on the coincidence of two half currents in the proper direction to set the core in the logic-1 state. Two half currents applied in the opposite direction will reset the core to the logic-0 state. A core with two half currents is essentially an AND circuit, requiring that half currents be applied to both X and Y lines in the same direction to change the state of the core. It is this feature which causes the core memory to be called a *coincident-current memory*. In this way, 100 cores can be addressed by a 10-by-10 matrix, or 20 wires rather than 100. Similarly, 4,096 cores can be addressed by a 64-by-64 matrix, or 128 wires rather than 4,096. The number of wires required to address all bits of a core memory increases as the square root of the increased number of addresses.

A disadvantage of the magnetic core is that it does not provide a static indication of its state, i.e., whether it is set or reset. To obtain an indication of the condition of the core, the state of the core must be switched. For this purpose, a common sense line is connected through each core in

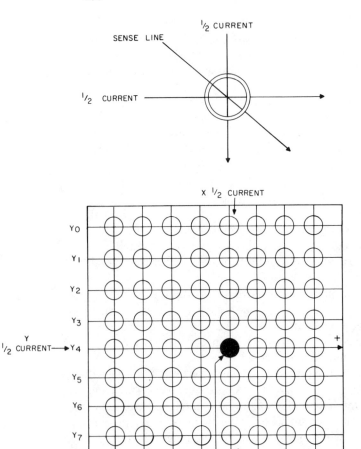

Fig. 7-2 *Coincident-current core memory.*

a plane and performs an OR function for the plane. When it is desired
to read the state of a core, reverse half currents are applied to the appropriate X and Y lines in order to reset the core to 0. If there is a change
in the core, this change is detected on the common sense line, indicating
that at least one core in the plane has switched and was previously in the
1 state. If there is no change, no core in the plane changed its state, and
therefore, the selected core must have been in the 0 state. Reading the
information in the core destroys the information, and it must be subsequently rewritten if it is desired to continue to store it.

Planes can be organized with four, three, or two wires through each
core. The remainder of this section will describe a four-wire system.

A memory must be able to be addressed so that the proper information is read or written in the correct location. In the example given in Fig. 7-2, the address of the core which is written is X4, Y4. The memory can be designed so that each address corresponds to one core and information is read into the memory 1 bit at a time. The computer normally handles information in a group of bits called a *word*. If, for example, the computer is designed around a 24-bit word (i.e., it always handles 24 bits at a time), then a series of 24 cores are identified by a specific location. Twenty-four memory planes, similar to the plane shown in Fig. 7-2, are used.

Every plane has common X and Y addresses but unique sense and inhibit lines. When location X4, Y4 is specified on a WRITE cycle, currents are supplied on the X and Y lines. Bit 1 is written in plane 1 by means of the plane-1 inhibit line, bit 2 in plane 2 by means of the plane-2 inhibit line, etc. During the READ cycle, individual sense lines, one on each plane, detect the various bits. This subject will be expanded in Sec. 7-5.

Demonstration 7-1   Coincident-current-address Logic

Purpose

To demonstrate the principle of a core-memory address-register and decoding matrix.

Equipment

1—Level switch (S)
1—Single-pulse generator (SPG)
4—Shift registers (SR)
4—NAND gates (ND)
8—AND gates (AN)

Discussion and Implementation

The address of a particular bit or group of bits within a coincident-current memory is specified in terms of an X, Y location. This address, which is stored in a register, is decoded, and appropriate X and Y control lines are driven with currents of the correct magnitude and direction. Since the core acts as an AND gate, only the core or cores whose X and Y lines are energized by specially designed current drivers will change state. For purposes of this demonstration, an AND gate will be assumed to have the correct properties to drive a core. See Fig. 7-3.

This demonstration uses a 4-by-4 matrix to define 16 addresses. A similar demonstration could be developed for any size array, although for larger memories, more registers and gates would be required.

The level switch and its inverted outputs are used to provide set and reset inputs to a four-stage register. Two stages of the register are used to

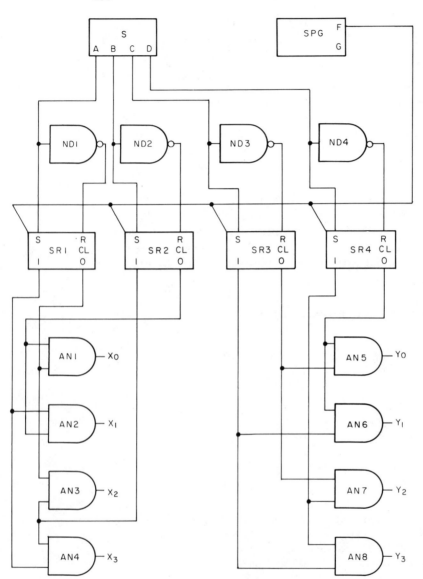

Fig. 7-3   Coincident-current-address register.

identify the X coordinate and provide inputs to four decoding AND gates. For any condition of SR1 and SR2, one and only one X gate is in the logic-1 state, while the remainder of the X gates are in the logic-0 state.   The other two stages of the register are used to identify the Y coordinate and provide inputs to another four decoding AND gates, one of which will be activated.

Every time the single-pulse generator produces an output, the condition of the level-switch channels is shifted into the four-stage register and one X- and one Y-gate output become logic 1s. They will remain in the 1 state until another number is shifted into the register. For example, if the level-switch channels are all at 0, then all stages of the register will be reset when the single-pulse generator provides an output. X_0 and Y_0 then become logic 1s. If the A and B channels of the level switch are changed to 1s, nothing will happen until another pulse is applied. At that time, SR1 and SR2 will be set, while SR3 and SR4 will remain reset. X_3 and Y_0 gates will now be in the 1 condition.

If the output of the two gates were to provide a current of the proper characteristics when switching to the 1 state, then only the core at the intersection of the selected X and Y lines would detect a coincident current and have data read into it.

7-5 Core-memory Organization

A memory must be able to be addressed by memory location, and the information to be written or read in the memory must be able to be identified. In a random-access core memory, many memory organization and addressing schemes are possible. Figure 7-4 shows the block diagram of one approach.

The memory address register stores the address of the bit or word (group of bits) which is being acted on. The address register is divided

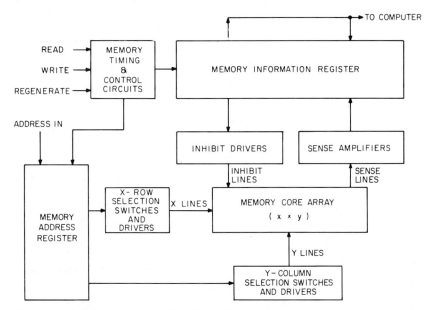

Fig. 7-4   Memory, organization block diagram.

into an X-address and a Y-address portion. The X-address information selects one X line and provides a current of the proper amount and polarity. The Y-address information is decoded, and output current of the proper amplitude and polarity is provided on one Y line. The core memory is built in a three-dimensional array—X by Y in one plane and as many planes high as there are bits per word. Only one core in any plane is selected at any time. Each X and Y line is wired in series through a common row in each plane of the memory core array so that all planes can be addressed by common X, Y signals. A common sense line goes through all bits in a plane and indicates when a change occurs in any one of the bits. An inhibit line also is common to all cores in a given plane. A memory information register, used to store the information to be written into the memory or the information which has been read out of the memory, serves as a buffer between the computer and the memory. This register is as long as the core array is deep, i.e., as many bits as there are per word. In addition, memory timing and control circuits are used to supply READ, WRITE, RESTORE, and other signals to control the memory.

During the WRITE cycle, the memory address register specifies some location, e.g., X27, Y18. The data in the memory information register are then written into that location. Assuming that the memory is designed for a 1-bit word, only one core corresponds to that location, and a 1 or a 0 is transferred to the memory from the information register. With a 24-bit word, a series of 24 cores are identified by that location, and a 24-bit binary number is transferred to the memory.

When a memory location is specified, one X line and one Y line are selected. The lines selected are determined by decoding the contents of the memory address register. The X line and Y line selected will be in the same physical position on each plane. Each plane represents a fixed bit position in the word; i.e., plane 1 has a 2^0 value, plane 2 has a 2^1 value, etc. The X and Y currents change the state of the individual memory cores by supplying drive current in accordance with the control signals and the data in the information register. When it is desired to write into the memory, the appropriate address is decoded. In each plane, this signal must be gated against the data in the information register to determine if a 1 is to be read into that core-memory bit. This gating could be done in the selection switches, but it is usually done in the memory cores themselves. The data in the information register are used to control the inhibit drivers which operate in conjunction with the write-current drivers to transfer data to the specified address location. A $+ I/2$ current is supplied on the selected X line, and a $+ I/2$ current is supplied on the selected Y line. If it is desired to write a 1 into the particular plane because there is a 1 in the information register in that bit position, write half currents combine at the selected X-and-Y junction to switch the selected core with the full magnetizing current. If there is a 0 in the information register, a negative current equal to $I/2$ is supplied on the inhibit line. At the selected core, the resultant current is the sum of the three inputs: $+I/2$, $+I/2$, and $-I/2$. This is equivalent to a select half current and is not sufficient to read a 1 into the core. Before writing a 1 in the memory, the selected address must be a 0. This is accomplished by reading the contents of the memory prior to writing.

In the READ cycle, the memory is addressed and the information in the specified address is transferred to the information register. This is accomplished by resetting the core or cores to 0 by one of a number of methods and detecting any change on the sense line. Magnetic cores are destructive readout devices; i.e., when reading out of them, the information is destroyed in the memory and must be restored. Reading is essentially a two-phase operation: read and restore; i.e., the information is read out of the memory into the information register, and the identical information is written back into the specified location.

To read a memory, an address is specified in the memory address register and negative half currents are read on the proper X and Y lines. The read half currents combine at the X-and-Y-line intersection to change the cores to 0 in each plane where they are 1. If a core is already in the 0 state, it is impossible to change it to a 0. A sense winding, common to all cores in a single memory plane, detects any change of state and provides an output signal to the associated sense amplifier.

Each bit of the selected word is amplified in the sense amplifiers and sets the corresponding flip-flop in the memory information register. This completes the READ portion of the memory cycle. The information is then written back into the memory by writing a 1 into each bit of the particular memory location if there is a 1 in the information register and inhibiting if there is a 0. This step completes the RESTORE phase of the memory cycle.

The organization just described is but one of many possible organizations. Instead of four wires through every core, three- or even two-wire schemes have been used. In some cases, instead of the information being requested at memory location XY, the memory is organized to be addressed by content; i.e., look for information of the following type and read it out. However, in all cases, there are similarities to the previous organization.

The memory can be addressed sequentially by connecting the memory address register as a counter. In this manner, the memory, starting at address 0, will increase the address by 1 every time a count pulse is supplied. When desired, the register can be reset to address 0 and the information unloaded from memory in the same sequence in which it was loaded. The memory can also be addressed in any order by specifying the desired address in the address register.

Since the computer can select any set of X and Y drivers within the same amount of time, addressing is defined to be random access. For example, the content of one memory location can be obtained in the same amount of time as that of another location. Random access has a distinct advantage over serial-access memories, such as drums and disks. These require that the read-write heads be positioned at a particular location on the recording media before the information can be read or written, and this results in a substantially higher average access time.

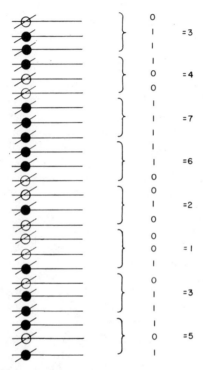

Cores are controlled in two ways. By selecting a specific pair of wires, a core can be selected. By controlling the direction of the current flow, the direction of core magnetization can be selected.

An example will show how the octal number 34762135 can be stored in magnetic-core memory. Information is stored in memory in bit increments called *words*. In this case, the word is represented by eight octal positions. Inside the computer, magnetized cores represent the number, with a column of 3 cores for each octal numeral (24 cores total). The positions of the column are designated the binary values 1, 2, and 4, respectively, as illustrated in Fig. 7-5. Therefore,

Fig. 7-5 Twenty-four-bit storage in octal code.

Octal 3 = 2 + 1	Octal 2 = 2
Octal 4 = 4	Octal 1 = 1
Octal 7 = 4 + 2 + 1	Octal 3 = 2 + 1
Octal 6 = 4 + 2	Octal 5 = 4 + 1

In Fig. 7-5, the positively magnetized cores are indicated in black. All other cores are unshaded, indicating that they are 0. This particular memory would have to have a minimum of 24 core planes since the number stored is 24 bits long.

7-6 *Sequential-access Memories*

While a random-access memory could be built in any size, the cost per bit is somewhat high. In a large memory, the memory cost would become excessive and dominate the cost of the computer. Therefore, above 10^5 to 10^7 bits of storage, it is necessary to develop lower-cost high-bit-capacity memories. For this application, magnetic tapes, drums, and disks offer many advantages.

In a core memory, addressing is accomplished by selecting matrix coordinates and reading information into the device at the intersection of the activated lines. In a sequential-access magnetic memory, a magnetic storage medium is physically moved relative to a recording and reading device. The storage medium possesses magnetic properties similar to the core memory and can be magnetized permanently by application of a current pulse on or near the surface of the medium. In a core memory, each core is capable of storing 1 bit. In a tape, drum, or disk memory, the recording surface is continuous and bits are stored quite close together.

A description of magnetic tape indicates some of the general considerations involved in the design of sequential-access memories. Magnetic tape is usually made of a base material such as Mylar which has been coated with iron oxide or other magnetic material. The general properties and operation of the tape are quite similar to those of tapes used on a home tape recorder. The magnetic characteristic of a region of the tape is changed by running the tape past a magnetic recording head. A small area on the tape can be magnetized in one direction to store a 1 and in the other direction for a 0. The tape can then be moved to another position, and another bit can be stored. The number of bits that can be stored are related to the bit density, i.e., how close the two areas can become before the signals cannot be discriminated. In order to read the tape, the magnetization on these areas must be detected. This is accomplished by passing the tape over a reading head, which detects the information by sensing the signal induced by the magnetized coating.

Tapes are available in widths of approximately $\frac{1}{2}$ to 3 inches. More than one magnetic head is normally used, and a number of tracks are placed across the tape. This allows the density of data on the tape to be increased and, for a given number of bits of storage, the access time to be reduced. A $\frac{1}{2}$-inch tape can have up to 15 recording tracks, while a 1-inch tape can have up to 30 recording tracks or bit positions. At least one of the tracks is used to store timing pulses. Lengths of tape may vary from a few hundred to many thousand feet.

To obtain a specific piece of information, the track on which it was placed and its recording timing signal must be known.   For example, a command could be given to the address register to get the information on track 3, which is 1,000 timing pulses from the start of the tape.

The access time for magnetic tape is dependent on the position of the desired information relative to the current position of the tape since the tape must be moved so that the desired portion is under the recording-reading head.   The maximum access time is the time to run from one end of the tape to the other, i.e., the total length of the tape divided by its velocity.

If a tape is 1,000 feet long and moved with a velocity of 75 inches/second, the maximum access time can be calculated as

$$\text{Max time} = \frac{1,000 \text{ ft} \times 12 \text{ in./ft}}{75 \text{ in./sec}} = 160 \text{ sec}$$

The number of bits that can be stored on a piece of tape depends on the bit packing density (how close consecutive bits of data can be placed or how many bits per inch), the number of tracks, and the length of the tape.   Assuming the above tape had 10 tracks and a packing density of 300 bits per inch, the total number of bits that could be stored is

$$\begin{aligned} \text{Total storage} &= (10 \text{ tracks})(300 \text{ bits/in.})(12 \text{ in./ft})(1,000 \text{ ft}) \\ &= 36 \text{ million bits} \end{aligned}$$

Since the tape travels at high speeds, spaces between groups of data (records) are necessary to provide for the starting and stopping of the tape movement.   This time gap must be long enough to allow the tape to come to a full stop at the end of one group of data and then start without losing information on the succeeding group of data.   To do this, a space, or gap, must precede each group.   These gaps reduce the total number of bits that can be stored.   Even so, magnetic tapes afford a means of storing tremendous amounts of information in a very small area.

A third factor of interest is the number of bits that are accessible in a given time period.   This can be calculated by multiplying the packing density by the tape speed.   In the previous example, this is equal to

$$75 \text{ in./sec} \times 300 \text{ bits/in.} = 22,500 \text{ bits/sec per track}$$

or 225,000 bits/second if all tracks are written on simultaneously.

Information is usually handled as words or characters (groups of bits) rather than as bits, and the preceding answers might be given as so many words of storage or so many words per second.

It can be seen that tape offers the advantage of a very low-cost mass storage, with the disadvantage of very long access times.   For this reason, it is usually used as external storage.   It will be discussed further in

Chap. 10.   Two other approaches to magnetic serial-access memories are aimed at offering other cost–access-time trade-offs and filling in the speed and cost area between magnetic tape and magnetic cores.

Figure 7-6 shows a magnetic drum, which consists of a circular cylinder upon which has been deposited a magnetic material.   The drum is machined to precise tolerances in order to maintain flatness on its surface. A number of reading-recording heads are mounted near the surface of the drum.   These heads magnetize small areas of the drum and store 1s and 0s in a manner similar to that of magnetic tape.   The drum is mounted on a shaft, and a motor drives the shaft at angular velocities up to a few thousand rpm.   As the drum rotates, different areas of the drum pass under the recording heads and allow data to be stored.   A timing track provides a means of locating information on the drum.

It would be possible to use only one writing head and to select different tracks by physical movement of the head across the drum.   Since physical motion is slower than electronic switching, a trade-off exists between the number of heads and the access time, and usually a large number of heads, as many as a hundred, are used on a drum.   Due to the cost of the electronics, drums usually have read and write circuitry shared by many heads, with the correct channel selected by switching means.   As with magnetic tape, in order to locate a specific piece of data, both the track and the timing pulse or address must be specified.

The drum can be organized in a serial or a parallel manner.   Data can be sequentially written on one track, and then the next track filled.   The

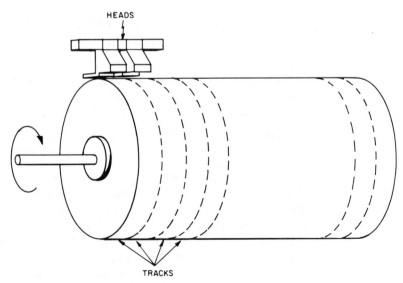

Fig. 7-6   Magnetic-drum memory.

drum can also be organized in a parallel fashion, with a group of bits written simultaneously on different tracks. The organization scheme and physical characteristics depend on the desired properties of the memory.

The size and organization of the drum are dependent on the number of bits of storage required and the access time. Typical drums are in the range of 6 inches to 4 feet in diameter and 4 inches to 5 feet in length. For a given-size drum, the greater the angular velocity, the shorter the access time. However, the greater the velocity, the more difficult it is to reach the maximum bit density. The bit density is also dependent on the separation distance between the head and the surface of the drum. It is desired to have the head as close to the surface of the drum as possible without introducing wear on the drum, and head-to-surface spacings are on the order of 0.001 inch.

The access time, bit capacity, and bit handling capacity of a drum can be calculated in a manner similar to that used in calculating these characteristics for magnetic tape. Given a drum with a rotational speed of 1,000 rpm, the access time for one revolution is

$$1 \text{ min}/1,000 \text{ rev} \times 60 \text{ sec/min} = 60 \times 10^{-3} \text{ sec}$$

This time would increase if mechanical switching of heads were required to select the track.

Given a bit packing density of 200 bits per inch, a drum diameter of 24 inches, and 1,000 tracks across the drum, the total number of bits that could be stored is

$$\text{Total storage} = (1,000 \text{ tracks})(200 \text{ bits/in.})\pi \times (24 \text{ in.})$$
$$\approx 15 \text{ million bits}$$

Timing tracks which are required for addressing must be subtracted from the total-storage number to obtain the number of data bits that can be stored.

The maximum bit rate can be calculated as follows:

$$1,000 \text{ rpm} \times 1 \text{ min}/60 \text{ sec} \times \pi(24 \text{ in.}) \times 200 \text{ bits/in.}$$
$$\approx 250,000 \text{ bits/sec per channel}$$

As with the calculations for magnetic tape, the bit-rate calculation is based on one channel of information. With more than one channel, the maximum bit rate is increased by the number of channels minus the time lost in switching from one channel to another.

The magnetic disk is also widely used as a computer memory. A circular disk 1 to 4 feet in diameter is coated with a magnetic material. This disk can be mounted on a horizontal shaft and rotated beneath a reading-writing head. By using the rotational motion of the disk beneath the head and the radial movement of the head, every portion of the disk can be brought under the head. By using two heads, areas on both sides of the disk can be magnetized, in either the 1 or the 0 direction. A number of concentric tracks are defined on each disk with a given number of bits per track. A single disk has very many similarities to a magnetic drum.

In normal operation, many disks are stacked in a disk file mounted on a motor-driven shaft. (See Fig. 7-7.) Between 5 and 50 disks are rotated at speeds from a few hundred to a few thousand rpm. One head could be used to control the entire disk array by physically moving the head to the selected disk and then inward to the specified track on the disk. In order to minimize the effect of mechanical motion on access time, one or more heads are used per disk. An individual fixed-position head for each track on the disk offers substantial speed advantages but increases the cost of the disk significantly; thus a compromise is made between speed and cost. The number of heads per memory depends on the specific memory requirements, and a typical disk has two to eight heads for the 200 to 500 tracks.

The access time, number of bits, and read-write speeds per disk are dependent on the same factors that influence tape and drums, i.e., bit density per track, number of tracks, disk radius, and rotational speed. Memory characteristics also depend on the number of disks, the physical

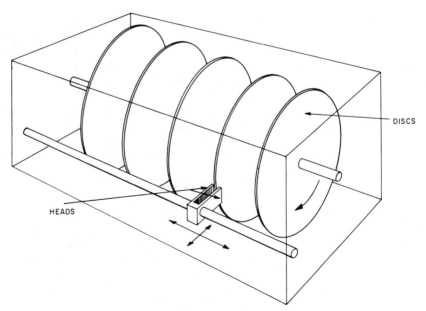

Fig. 7-7 Magnetic-disk memory.

motion of the heads, the mechanical relationship between heads, and the specific organization of the memory.

A file of 50 disks may store a few million bits to two billion bits, have an access time of ten to fifty thousandths of a second, and have a read-write speed of one to a hundred million bits per second. Obviously, there are trade-offs between these various factors, and actual characteristics depend on the specific disk file. A disk file offers more storage capacity than a drum at an access time significantly lower than that for tape.

Demonstration 7-2   Serial-access-address Logic

Purpose

To demonstrate the address logic for a serial-access memory.

Equipment

1—Level switch (S)
1—Single-pulse generator (SPG)
8—Shift registers (SR)
3—Flip-flops (FF)
4—AND gates (AN)
1—OR gate (OR)
2—NAND gates (ND)

Discussion and Implementation

This experiment simulates a magnetic serial-access memory by shift registers SR1 to SR8. In a tape, drum, or disk memory, there is physical motion of the magnetic surface relative to a read-write head. In a shift register, the information is shifted from one stage to another. In both schemes, the relative address or the location of the data must be known at all times in order to obtain the correct information. In a magnetic memory, this is usually accomplished by writing timing pulses in one channel of the memory and counting them. In this demonstration, this operation is accomplished by counting the shift pulses in a three-stage counter, FF1 to FF3.

To begin the demonstration, the counter is cleared to 000 by setting level-switch channel D momentarily to a logic 0. The WRITE signal is made a 1, which enables AND gate AN1. The desired information is read into the register by alternately putting level-switch channel A to a 1 or a 0 and then activating the single-pulse generator. This shifts the information into the register and increases the count in the flip-flops by 1 each time a shift pulse is generated. When the desired information is written into the register, the write switch, channel B, is changed to 0. This inhibits further writing action into the memory and enables AND gate AN2, allowing the information in the register to recirculate. Upon application of further

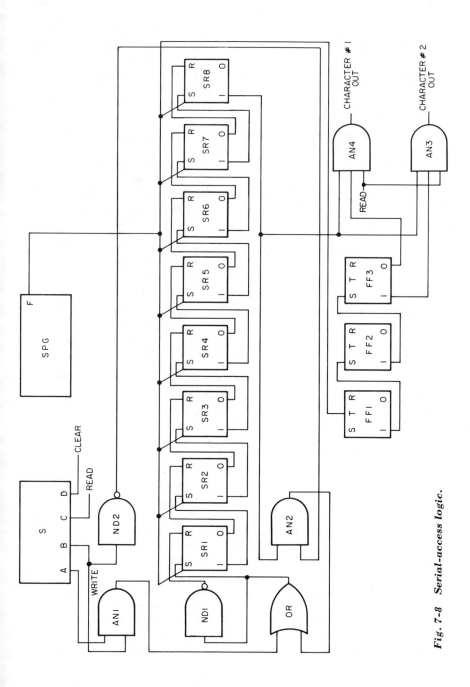

Fig. 7-8 Serial-access logic.

shift pulses, the information in SR8 is shifted back into SR1. The information will continue to recirculate until initiation of further writing action.

To read the information from the register, the address of the desired information should be specified. This is normally accomplished by comparing the contents of a memory address register with the contents of the counter and opening a gate when the proper count is reached. The operation of such a comparator will be discussed in Chap. 9. In this demonstration, a particular address is permanently connected to AND gates AN3 and AN4.

Usually, information is stored by groups of bits sometimes referred to as *characters*. For this demonstration, assume that each character is 4 bits long; thus, the eight-stage shift register is capable of storing two characters. To enter the 8 bits of data into the register requires eight shift pulses. These shift signals are also connected to FF1 of the three-stage counter, which will count from 0 through to 7 and then back to 0 on the eighth shift signal. Upon completing the WRITE phase, SR5 to SR8 contain a 4-bit character, which can be addressed by sensing the fact that FF3 is in the reset state. As the information is recirculated through the register by application of shift pulses, the counter is incremented while the data in the shift register are shifted to the right. After 4 recirculating shift bits are applied, the data in SR1 to SR4 are shifted into SR5 to SR8 and FF3 is in the set state. Thus, when FF3 is set, the second 4-bit character can be read out of the shift register. This is accomplished by gating into AN3 the 1 output of FF3 with the READ signal and the 1 output of SR8. Readout will occur at the output of AN3 so long as FF3 is in the set state, which will be for the duration of the four shift signals. This will sequentially shift the bits of character 2 to SR8 and subsequently out to AN3.

EXERCISES

7-1. Define memory capacity, access time, and type of access.

7-2. What factors influence memory access time? Why is access time important?

7-3. Why do computers frequently have more than one memory?

7-4. If it is desired to store 1,024 words, each 16 bits long, in a coincident-circuit memory, how many cores are required? How many X and Y address lines are needed? How many stages are there in the address register?

7-5. Compare magnetic tape, core, drum, and disk in terms of access time. How would the times be calculated?

7-6. What is the bit capacity, access time, and maximum bit rate for a tape which has a bit density of 150 bits/inch, is 20 channels across and 1,500 feet long, and has a speed of 60 inches/second?

7-7. Construct the address-logic scheme for an 8-bit shift register which has four 2-bit characters rather than two 4-bit characters as illustrated in Fig. 7-8.

EIGHT

Word Organization

8-1 *Introduction*

The computer handles data in a variety of formats. Within the computer, data and instructions must be able to be identified by some method of coding. As information is presented to the outside world, another code may be required to separate the data into groups easily handled by the input-output equipment. Finally, as the programmer interfaces with the computer, a language must be adopted which can be used easily by both. Input-output and programming languages are discussed in Chaps. 10 and 12. This chapter discusses how information is coded within the computer.

A computer word is a series of digits that is handled as a unit in the computer. Both data and instructions are stored in the computer as numbers and are processed in some type of word format. Without some form of word organization, it would be impossible for the computer to separate one number from another or one instruction from another.

A word can be organized in a variety of ways. *Word size* is the number of bits per word. *Word format* signifies the arrangement of bits within the word. There are many possible combinations of the arrangement and number of bits within a computer word; and in a computer, a number of word organizations may be used. The bits can be arranged as a series of coded groups called *characters*, expressed in binary, binary-coded decimal, octal, or a special coded alphabet called the *alphanumeric code*. A description of the word size, format, and memory capacity provides one method of measuring the capability of the computer and describing its capacity for handling data.

The computer word must include, as a minimum, a command or instruction of what to do and the memory address of the information upon which the command is to be performed or the information itself. The memory address of the next instruction to be performed may be specified in the word if it is not the next memory address in sequence after the current instruction.

It is important to note that instructions as well as data are stored within the computer in the form of numbers. This is the stored-program concept of a computer. If instructions were permanently wired into the computer, the computer would always behave in an identical manner. For example, in order to solve a specific problem, the computer could be wired to read six numbers from a punched card, add the first four numbers, subtract the fifth number, and divide the total by the sixth number. The next time it was desired to read a similar punched card, the same sequence would be performed automatically. However, to modify this sequence of commands, the computer interconnections would have to be modified. By storing instructions in the memory, instructions and memory addresses can be selected, acted upon, and modified by other instructions in the same way that data are operated on and modified. Instruction words are brought from the memory; they are decoded; and the specific instruction is performed. If the programmer desires to perform addition, the address of an ADD instruction is specified. Normally, instructions are performed sequentially; e.g., after performing the instructions at memory location N, the computer performs the instruction at memory location $N + 1$. By using a variety of addressing techniques, however, this sequence can be modified and any address selected. It is therefore possible, by programming means, to repeat instructions as frequently as required and in any sequence.

Commands can be given conditionally; e.g., compare A to B, and if $A > B$, do this. Thus the next action can be chosen based on the last action completed. This allows the operator to specify a series of instructions whose exact sequence may not be known prior to the problem solution. All these characteristics provide the stored-program computer with a great amount of flexibility.

The computer word, therefore, is handled by the control unit as an instruction or command and by the arithmetic unit as a number. Thus the command "Add the data in memory locations X_1Y_1 and X_2Y_2" would require the control unit to provide control signals for an ADD command and would require the arithmetic unit to treat the data in memory locations X_1Y_1 and X_2Y_2 as numbers to be added.

8-2 *Word Format*

The computer can be designed around a variety of word sizes, formats, and codes. Word length can be fixed or variable. Data and instructions can be combined in one word or handled as separate words. A discussion of some of the possible word formats will serve as a foundation for subsequent chapters on computer organization and programming.

A computer can be organized to operate with one word, containing both data and instruction, or two words, one for instructions and another for

data. With a single-word format, one part of each word always signifies
the command. With separate words, the only method of distinguishing
between an instruction and data may be by the location of the word
within the memory. The same memory location may store data at one
time and instructions at another time, with the programmer being
responsible for identifying which is which.

Figure 8-1 shows three possible word formats. The first is a word 24
bits long, and the others are each 20 bits long. Figure 8-1A shows a
single-word format. This word is divided into three parts: an operation
code or instruction, a memory address, and the operand, or number to
be operated on. The operation code specifies a certain command from
the computer command repertoire, that is, an operation the computer
can perform. In the example, the operation code is represented by the
first 3 binary bits of the word. This automatically limits the maximum
possible number of different commands which the computer can execute
to eight (2^3). Typical commands would include arithmetic and logic
commands, such as add, multiply, place in A register, store in memory,
shift B register right, compare A with B, read magnetic tape into the
memory, turn on the card reader. An actual computer can perform
many more commands, and the operation code would require more bits.

The memory address identifies a physical location in the memory
capable of storing one word. In Fig. 8-1A, bits 4 to 10 signify the memory-
address location. With this configuration, which reserves 7 bits for the
memory address, 2^7 (128) different words can be stored in the computer

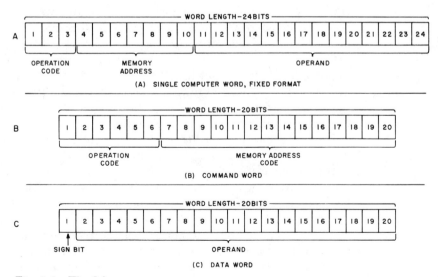

Fig. 8-1 Word formats.

memory. The memory address can be used to specify the address of the next instruction to be performed or the address where the data being processed should be stored. The operand, or data portion of the word, is given by bits 11 to 24. This would allow data words up to 14 bits or 13 bits plus sign to be handled by the computer. Normally, data are stored in the memory and withdrawn when the appropriate memory address is specified. Using a series of such words, data can be inserted into the memory, withdrawn at the proper time, and operated on, and the results can be reinserted into the memory for future use.

Figure 8-1*B* and *C* show examples of a 20-bit fixed-word format in which separate data words and command words are used in conjunction with one another. The words are distinguished from one another by their location in the memory, i.e., memory address, although the same memory location may store data at one time and instructions at another. The command word contains instruction data, and the data word contains the number to be operated upon. Double-word format provides a flexibility in the machine that is not attainable with the single-word format because it allows greater command-data capability and minimizes word ineffi-ciencies. With a single-word format, the machine must handle individu-ally all sections of the word. If a series of commands are to be applied to an operand, the operand portion of the word is redundant in each case and some of the word capacity is unused. Furthermore, a single word must be quite long to provide sufficient bits for operation code, memory address, and operand. Two separate word formats, for command and data, allow the computer to handle sequences and programs much more efficiently by combining common instructions or data. As an example, a single command word might be used to load many words sequentially into the internal memory from an input device. Twenty data words might be read into a computer along with one command word. The command word would not have to be repeated as part of every word, as in the case of a single-word format. With a two-word format, more of the word capacity is used, and a minimum of control information is required to insert a sizable amount of input data.

The command word in Fig. 8-1*B* has a 6-bit operation code. A com-puter using this word format is capable of executing up to 2^6, or 64, dif-ferent command functions. The 14 bits of memory address indicate a memory capacity of up to 2^{14}, or 16,384, words. The data word in Fig. 8-1*C* is represented by a 20-bit binary number. A sign bit indicates whether the number represented by the remaining 19 bits is positive or negative. If a sign bit of 0 represents a positive numerical value, then a 1 would indicate a negative value. Negative numbers could be repre-sented not only in the sign-magnitude code but also in the 1s- or 2s-complement notation. The example is of a fixed-word format in which all words are of the same length. Although the number contained in a data word may be less than 20 bits, it is always represented by the full 20-bit format. For example, a positive binary number of 11, or decimal 3, would be represented by a 0 sign bit, 17 zeros, and binary 11: 0000000-0000000000011.

The example just presented was based on a binary word format. A word can also be organized around octal, binary-coded decimal, alphanumeric, or any other code. As an example, the 12-bit word 100101101001 would be read directly if a binary word is used. If the computer is designed around an octal word, it is equivalent to octal 4551. If the computer is designed around a binary-coded decimal word, then the word is broken into groups of 4 bits and is equivalent to decimal 969. An alphanumeric code is one in which all the letters of the alphabet, the 10 decimal digits, and a variety of the most common symbols are represented by a code of 6 or more bits. In a more common alphanumeric code, the first 6 bits of the 12-bit word are equivalent to the letter N, while the last 6 are equivalent to the letter R. Thus a 12-bit word can be interpreted in a variety of ways, depending on the code used.

In addition to a fixed-word format, it is also possible to organize a computer around a variable word length. As the name implies, variable word length allows for change in word length depending on the needs of the problem. A number of computers, particularly those designed for business applications, use a variable word length to provide efficiency in the arrangement of data.

With this format, the word variation is extremely flexible and system memory capacity can be expanded by efficiency. An end-of-word bit or end-of-word mark can be used to signify where one word ends and another starts. In a variable-word-length format, 5 bits can be used for each decimal character 0 to 9. In this case, the most significant bit could be used to represent the end-of-word bit. For example, if the number 831 is the data word, it would be represented as shown in Fig. 8-2. The use of the word mark provides a simple identification of word beginning and end. This identification can also be accomplished by using a special code between words or by changing the position of this information with respect to other data. In many cases, the memory capacity can be utilized more efficiently by the use of a variable-word format. Where it took 20 bits to store the decimal number 3 using a fixed-word format, it

Fig. 8-2   *Variable-length word.*

would take only 5 bits using the variable-word format.　On the other hand, variable word length results in more complicated control and memory-address logic.　In a 48-bit fixed-word organization, 48 bits of memory are always addressed by the same memory location.　In a variable-word-length organization, each group of bits must be addressed independently, and this may result in more memory addresses.　The actual choice of fixed word versus variable word depends on the particular problems the computer will experience.

To summarize, the computer handles both data and instructions. This information is organized into separate groups called *words*.　These words may be in any code, of any length, and of any format.　The choice is dependent on the desired properties of the computer.　For example, if the computer has 50 different commands and 32,000 memory locations, the word must have at least 6 bits for the operation code ($2^6 = 64$) and 15 bits for the memory address ($2^{15} = 32,768$).　In addition, word length and format are dependent on the required precision of calculations, the desired input-output characteristics, and the desired cost of the computer (the longer the word length, the more hardware required to build the computer, the more bits of memory required for each instruction, and the more expensive the machine).　The computer may be designed around fixed word lengths X bits long or variable word lengths.　Data and instruction information may be combined in one word, or separate data and instruction words may be used.

The remainder of this chapter will consider fixed-word formats using separate command and data words in order to illustrate some of the considerations involved in word organization.

8-3　*Data Words*

The organization of the data word is principally determined by four factors: (1) the code to be used, (2) the range and precision of numbers to be processed, (3) how answers are to be scaled so that the decimal or binary point is in the proper place, and (4) how negative numbers are to be handled.　In addition, it is preferable that the data word and the instruction word be the same length, although the format can vary significantly.

The data word can be handled in binary, octal, binary-coded decimal, or any other code.　However, since arithmetic is to be performed with these words, the rules outlined in Chap. 6 apply.　Binary or octal words are normally used, and most other word formats usually will be converted to binary prior to performing arithmetic operations.

Range of numbers refers to the extreme values that numbers may assume.　If it is desired to process numbers between 10^{-5} and 10^{+5}, the

word format would have to provide a range of 10^{10}. *Precision* refers to
the number of bits required during a series of calculations to guarantee a
certain amount of significance to the result.   For example, if it is desired
to multiply A by B, divide the product by C, and obtain a result to three
significant figures, A, B, and C will have to be stated to at least four significant figures.   The reason is that errors due to rounding off a figure can
accumulate.   In problems involving many steps, initial numbers may
have to be given to a great amount of precision for the final answer to
have proper significance.

A significant factor is the scaling of intermediate and final answers to a
problem.   In a simple addition performed with pencil and paper, the
numbers are usually scaled by placing all decimal points under one another
and performing the addition.   Overflow, i.e., the generation of a number
with a more significant digit then any digit being added, is also handled
easily.   Multiplication by pencil and paper involves more work in scaling
the answer but no major problem with overflow.   Scaling and overflow
present problems in a computer and are handled in two ways.   Figure
8-3A shows a fixed-point data-word format.   The word is organized so
that the first bit gives the sign and the next 23 bits give the magnitude of
the number.   If the sign is negative, the magnitude could be given as an
absolute number or in the 1s-complement or 2s-complement notation.
The programmer must decide where in the word the point is to be located.
For example, he may decide that the binary point should be located
between positions 17 and 18, with everything to the right of the point
(bits 18 to 24) being fractional and everything to the left of the point
(bits 2 to 17) being an integer.   In this case, it is the responsibility of the
programmer to scale the result correctly and place the point in the proper
place.   He must also guarantee that the computer does not overflow.
Since a 24-bit word is used, any word greater than 24 bits long must not

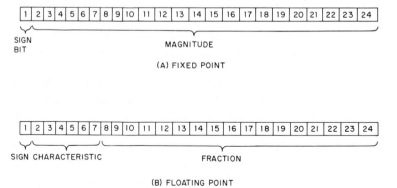

Fig. 8-3 Data words.

be allowed to occur, or if it is allowed to occur, it must be taken care of specifically. Scaling on some problems is relatively easy. On many problems, however, it is difficult to predict proper scaling and the answer may be erroneous or precision may be lost. To minimize this problem, a floating-point format is frequently used which provides automatic scaling. Floating-point arithmetic was discussed in Sec. 6-15. A floating-point number is represented by a characteristic and a mantissa, i.e., a fraction times a power of 10 (decimal), 2 (binary), 8 (octal), or other matrix. Thus, in a decimal system,

$$1{,}472 = 0.1472 \times 10^4$$
$$-31.2 = -0.312 \times 10^2$$
$$0.0364 = 0.364 \times 10^{-1}$$

Similarly, in the binary system,

$$1101 = 0.1101 \times 2^4$$
$$-1.1101 = -0.11101 \times 2^1$$
$$0.01101 = 0.1101 \times 2^{-1}$$

Generally, when using floating point, all numbers are normalized so that the point is to the left of the most significant digit. In Fig. 8-3*B*, a 24-bit floating-point data-word format is shown. Bit 1 is the sign bit of the data word. Bits 2 to 7 represent the power of 2 which the number is multiplied by. Bits 8 to 24 represent the fraction. Rather than having both positive and negative characteristics, the characteristics are usually kept positive by adding a constant to them. In the example given in Fig. 8-3*B*, 32 (2^5) might be added to the characteristic. Thus a characteristic of 111111 to 000000 would represent a characteristic of 2^{31} to 2^{-32}. Use of floating-point numbers simplifies multiplication and division problems but complicates additions and subtractions since the two numbers must be properly lined up by making the characteristics identical.

It is possible to increase the precision of the data by using two memory locations and performing double-precision arithmetic. Double-precision arithmetic, while being more accurate, will be slower. With a normal 24-bit data word, 48 bits of data can be stored in two successive 24-bit memory locations or as two floating-point words. Use of double-precision words requires that instructions be written which allow the computer to act on these two parts of the data word independently, thereby requiring more logic within the arithmetic and control sections or more commands by the programmer.

One question that must be decided prior to establishing a data-word format is how to handle negative numbers. A negative number can be represented by a sign bit plus the magnitude of the negative number, or it can be represented in the 1s-complement or 2s-complement format.

Each of these approaches, both of which are widely used in computer design, influences the design of the arithmetic unit.

8-4 *Instruction Words*

The instruction word must, as a minimum, contain an operation code, i.e., what to do, and at least one memory address. It usually contains more information. It can be of any length and have any format. Almost universally, however, the length of the instruction word is identical to that of the data word, although its format is substantially different.

Computers have been organized around a quadruple-, triple-, double-, and single-addressing scheme. The choice has an effect on the word size and the number of words required to perform a given operation.

Figure 8-4*A* shows an example of a quadruple-address word. Bits 1 to 6 give an operation code which tells the computer which operation to perform. The remainder of the word is divided into four memory addresses, A, B, C, and D, each 12 bits long, i.e., specifying 2^{12}, or 4,096, memory addresses. An instruction word might specify the operation code for ADD and four memory addresses A, B, C, and D. This would be interpreted by the computer as "Add the data word at memory location A to the data word at memory location B, store the result at memory location C, and go to memory location D for the next instruction word."

Figure 8-4*B* shows a triple-address word. For purpose of illustration,

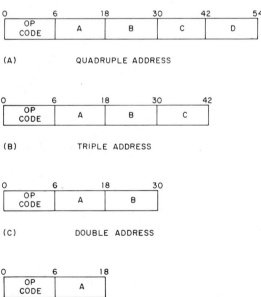

(A)   QUADRUPLE ADDRESS

(B)   TRIPLE ADDRESS

(C)   DOUBLE ADDRESS

Fig. 8-4 Instruction words.

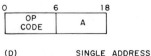

(D)   SINGLE ADDRESS

the same number of operation codes and the same number of memory-address bits are used.   A command might be given to add the data word at memory location A to the data word at memory location B and store the result in memory location C.   The computer would automatically go to the next sequential memory location for the next instruction.   This automatic sequential addressing of instructions can be interrupted by one of a number of schemes, which will be discussed.   It is also possible to use one of the three memory addresses to specify the next instruction address and to store one of the data words or the result in some arithmetic register.

Figure 8-4*C* shows a double-address word.   Here the command might be given to add the data word at memory location A to the data word at memory location B.   The sum is then automatically stored in the arithmetic unit unless a second instruction word is given to store the data word.   The next instruction word is then taken sequentially from the memory if it is not interrupted by a different method of addressing.

Figure 8-4*D* shows a single-address word.   Here only one memory address is specified.   To perform the same operation, three instruction words would be required: (1) to store the data word in memory location A in the accumulator, (2) to add the data word in memory location B to the accumulator, and (3) to store the new data word in the accumulator in memory location C.   Until the third command is given, the answer is stored in the arithmetic unit; i.e., the accumulator temporarily stores the resultant data.

It is apparent that as the number of memory addresses used in the instruction word increases, the word length becomes larger, but fewer commands are required, in many cases, to perform a given operation.

Figure 8-5 shows a single-address-word format.   Bits 4 to 9 specify the operations code.   The 64 (2^6) possible operation codes include (1) arithmetic commands (add, subtract, multiply, divide), (2) load and store commands (load data into or store the contents of some specific register), (3) shifting commands (shift information into, out of, or within a specific register), (4) conditional commands (skip this command if certain condi-

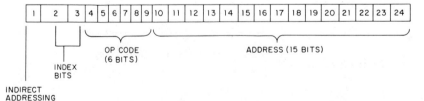

Fig. 8-5   Single-address instruction word.

tions are fulfilled), (5) input-output commands, (6) logic commands, and
(7) control commands. Bits 10 to 24 specify a 15-bit memory location
($2^{15} = 32,768$ addresses). This normally specifies the address of the data
word. The remaining 3 bits are used for indexing and indirect addressing.

Instruction addresses are normally selected sequentially from the
memory; e.g., the computer selects the instruction at memory location
N, then performs the instruction at memory location $N + 1$, then at
$N + 2$, etc. However, the programmer must have a method of initiating
and breaking this cycle. Indexing and indirect addressing are two of
many schemes available for accomplishing this. In *indexing*, the address
of the next instruction word is incremented by some amount specified in
an index register. If the index register contains the number 10 and if the
index register was specified in the instruction word, the next instruction
would be 10 memory locations higher than the last instruction instead of
the next sequential one. *Indirect addressing* indicates that the memory
address specified in the instruction word is the address of a new instruction,
rather than a data word. Thus the program, at any time, could address
any memory location for the next instruction. Both of these addressing
schemes will be discussed in Chap. 9; they are mentioned here to show
that the instruction word may include information other than operation
code and memory address and that a requirement for one or more index
registers, indirect addressing, base addressing, and other addressing modes
have an effect on the word size and organization.

In summary, within the computer, data are organized around groups
of bits called *words*. Both instructions (what to do) and data (the number
to be handled) must be described. Data and instructions may be handled
in a combined word or as separate words. These words may be of fixed
or variable length, of any length, and of any format. A decision about
word length and format is, however, dependent on decisions about the
rest of the computer. Many computers use separate data and instruction
words of a fixed word length between 12 and 60 bits long. These words
have a variety of organizations and use binary, octal, binary-coded decimal,
and alphanumeric coding. Specific word formats will be discussed in the
chapters on computer organization and programming.

EXERCISES

8-1. Define word size, word format, and word coding.

8-2. Why are instructions stored in the memory?

8-3. What will be the minimum size of a single fixed word in a computer which has
100 operation codes and 60,000 memory addresses and is required to handle

data in the range of 2^{-9} to 2^{12}?   What are the reasons for separate data and instruction words?

8-4. Solve the following problems.   Repeat, using floating-point notation.

(a) $\dfrac{111.01 \times 1.10}{0.11}$ (b) $\begin{array}{r} \bar{1}.111 \\ + \ 0.011 \\ + \ 0.01 \end{array}$ (c) $\dfrac{1111.11}{0.0011}$

8-5. Describe the difference between an instruction word having triple addressing and one using single addressing.   Discuss their relative advantages.

NINE

The Control Element

9-1 *Function of Control Unit*

The control unit accepts instructions from either the input element or the memory element and generates the timing signals necessary to implement these instructions. Each computer can execute a designated number of instructions, referred to as the computer *command repertoire* or *instruction complement*. The gating and timing signals required to implement each of these commands are designed into and are supplied from the control unit. In terms of hardware, the control unit constitutes a significant portion of all the gating elements in the computer. Although the classical block diagram for a computer (Fig. 1-1) distinctly shows five separate blocks interconnected by arrows, in actuality the various elements of a computer are not physically isolated from each other. Furthermore, the gating required to interconnect the various elements to one another (illustrated by the arrows in Fig. 1-1) is provided as part of the control unit. Thus, the control unit by its very nature has gating elements throughout each portion of the computer.

Sections 9-2 to 9-4 discuss the primary functions of the control element, while the remainder of the chapter illustrates the gating required to implement specific control functions.

Prior to solving a particular problem on a stored-program computer, a program must be entered into the internal computer-memory element. The program entered into the memory element contains instruction words as well as the data words which are to be operated on by the instructions. Word format was discussed in Chap. 8; programming will be discussed in Chap. 12. The instructions of the program must be implemented sequentially in order to attain a solution to the problem. Every instruction and data word for a particular program is stored in a specific location (address) in the memory. In order to solve the problem properly, the computer must fetch from the memory the first instruction word in the program. The computer then executes this instruction. When the computer has completed the operations specified by the first instruction, it must then sequentially fetch and execute succeeding instructions stored in the memory. The most elementary computer organization is designed around this two-cycle operation. Many large, high-speed computers use various methods of instruction look-ahead in order to minimize the dependence in every instruction on memory access time. However, the control unit must always be designed to perform its two primary functions of addressing the memory to obtain the next instruction and then executing this instruction.

9-2   *The Program Counter*

The control element must provide a method which will properly sequence the fetching of instructions stored in the memory, decode the instructions, and generate gating signals that will execute those instructions. The first task can be implemented by use of a binary counter. It should be noted that this counter is not required when a computer is designed around a multiple-address-word format in which one of the addresses specifies the location of the next instruction. The contents of the binary counter, commonly referred to as the *program* or *instruction counter*, contain the effective address of the next instruction word to be executed. If a program is written such that the address of the first instruction word is in location 0 of the memory, the program counter will fetch the contents of that memory location when the computer is initially started. This is guaranteed since all registers and counters in the computer are cleared prior to starting any operations. Thus all the flip-flops of the program counter are in the reset state and indicate the command "Fetch the instruction word stored in location 0." The program counter is gated in the memory address register so that when a fetch command is given, the memory element will select the instruction word specified by the program counter. After the first fetch operation is performed, the program counter is automatically incremented by 1. The number in the counter would then indicate the address of the next instruction in the program. The program counter, incremented by 1 as each instruction is fetched, sequentially addresses the instruction words of the program stored in the memory. An obvious requirement in such a system is that each program must be written such that the instruction words are loaded in sequential locations in the memory.

There are two common methods of interrupting this sequential addressing of memory locations and jumping to a new location. One method is by the use of one or more index registers. When an index bit is specified, the contents of a special register called an *index register* are added to the contents of the program counter to obtain the next effective address. Thus, if the number decimal 37 is stored in the index register and the index register is specified in the instruction word, the next instruction is taken from the memory location which is 37 higher than the last instruction. A second method of performing nonsequential addressing is by the use of indirect addressing. When an indirect-addressing bit is specified in the instruction word, the memory location specified is the address of the next instruction and not the address of the data. By use of either of these two methods, the program counter can be set to any location and will obtain further instructions from sequential memory locations until a jump instruction to a new nonsequential location is specified.

When an instruction word is fetched from the memory, the control unit must decode the operation-code portion of the word and generate signals that will execute the desired operation. In addition, the word specified by the address portion of the instruction must be obtained from the memory. For example, an instruction word may state "Store the contents of memory location XXX in the A register." This instruction cannot be executed instantaneously but instead is implemented step by step according to the timing signals developed by the control unit.

In the example given, control signals developed from decoding the operation code may in turn:

1. Send the memory-address portion of the instruction word to the memory address register.

2. Take the data word specified by the address from the memory information register and enter it into the A register located in the arithmetic unit.

3. Fetch the next instruction word specified by the number in the program counter.

This is a relatively simple execution cycle. The number of logic steps and timing signals necessary to implement the many different operation codes varies, depending on which operation is being executed.

9-3   *Computer Timing*

From a review of the steps required to implement the demonstrations in the latter part of Chap. 6, it is evident that the steps have to be performed in a specific sequence in order to achieve valid results. Most of these operations are performed manually by generating pulses from an SPG module. In a computer, pulses are developed automatically by use of a clock and a clock matrix. The pulses are gated with logic levels which are developed from decoding the operation-code portion of the instruction word. The resultant pulses from these gating operations are the signals which execute the instruction. It usually requires many pulses to execute an operation code, and these pulses must be timed in such a way as to ensure that the required steps are performed in a proper sequence. Thus many command lines and timing pulses are distributed from the control unit to the various elements in the computer. Each command line performs a discrete operation, and the selection of command lines is prescribed by the operation codes.

The block diagram in Fig. 9-1 illustrates the logic required to activate the various command lines. When an instruction word is fetched from the memory, the bits defining the operation-code portion of the word are transferred into the operation-code register. The information in the register is decoded, causing one of the decode gates to put out a logic level, which in turn selects a number of command lines. If the operation-code register were 6 bits long, there could be as many as 64 (2^6) selection lines going from the decode gates to the gating networks. The decode gates in Fig. 9-1 would then be wired in a manner similar to the decoder in Fig. 5-3, with the difference that this decoder would be wired for straight binary rather than binary-coded decimal. Each selection line corresponds to one of the instructions that a computer can execute, and a particular selection line is activated only when the corresponding instruction is stored in the operation-code register.

To illustrate how the timing-command lines are controlled, consider the instruction "Add the number stored in the memory location (specified by the address portion of the instruction word) to the number in the A register of the arithmetic unit." A specific binary number would be

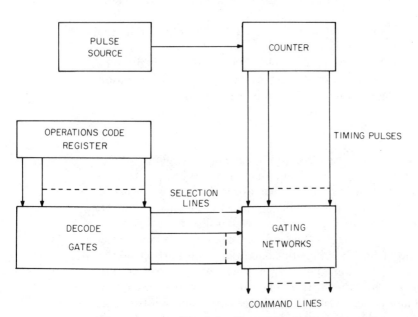

Fig. 9-1   Generation of command lines.

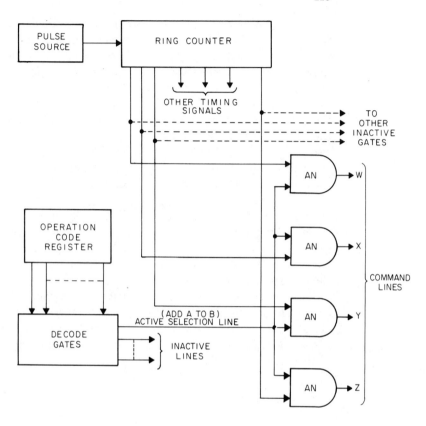

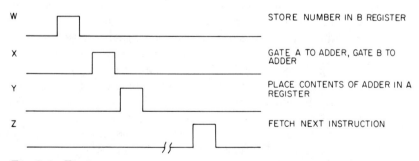

Fig. 9-2   Timing sequence.

assigned to this particular operation code. Whenever this number is stored in the operation-code register of Fig. 9-2, it is decoded. As a result of the decoding operation, only one selection line will be active, i.e., the one which will select the proper command lines for implementing the instruction. After the proper line is selected, the timing pulses generated by the ring counter (refer to Chap. 4 for ring-counter operation) sequence the gates in the gating network. Only those gates having inputs from the active selection line will respond to the timing signals. Thus, in this case, only command lines W, X, Y, and Z will have output signals. All other command lines will be inhibited. Timing signal W is used to read the contents of memory location XXX into the B register. On the leading edge of command line X, the contents of the A register and B register are both gated to the adder. While this signal is up, the two numbers are added together. On the trailing edge of command line Y, the resultant sum is gated to the A register. The last timing signal for this operation is a signal (Z) that indicates that this operation is complete and commands the computer to fetch the next instruction.

This description is merely illustrative; many methods are possible for generating timing signals. Any approach must perform the function of decoding the operation-code portion of the instruction word and generating and distributing control signals and timing pulses based on the content of the operation code.

9-4 The Transfer Bus

Another principal function of the control unit is to provide the gating structures necessary for transferring information to and from the various registers within the computer. In one operation, a particular register may be the source of data to be transferred, while in another operation, the same register may be the destination of the transferred data. The data in any one register can be shifted to any one of a number of other registers. For instance, different operation codes may call for the data in the A register to be shifted to the B register, the adder, the memory information register, or an output channel. One means of fulfilling this requirement would be to gate directly from the output of each register to the input of all the other registers. However, such a scheme may prove to be impractical due to the large number of gates required to implement it. Another method of fulfilling the transfer requirements is by the use of transfer buses.

A transfer bus is a system of prewired gating structures that provide controlled paths for the transfer of data within a computer. The signals which control the transfers are the command lines which are generated in the timing-control circuits in Fig. 9-1. A command line will select and gate the data from a source register onto the bus, and during the time these data are on the bus, another command line will gate the data to a destination register.

Figure 9-3 is a block diagram illustrating how the various registers in a computer can be connected to and from the transfer bus. This diagram serves to illustrate how data from any one register connected to the bus may be transferred to another register.

Figure 9-4 is a typical gating structure which implements 1 bit of the transfer bus in Fig. 9-3. If the computer were organized around a 24-bit word, 24 of these gating structures would be required to make up the entire bus. Only one source command line and one destination command line are active at any time. However, one of each must be active simultaneously. For example, if the operation-code register were storing the instruction "Transfer the data in the memory information register to the A register," the following conditions would exist on the transfer bus:

1. Command line 1 would be a logic 1.
2. Command lines 2 to 5 would be logic 0s.
3. The outputs of AN1 and the OR gate would be a logic 1 or 0, depending on the state of the flip-flop in the memory information register, which is connected to the input of AN1.
4. Command line 8 would be a logic 1.
5. Command lines 6, 7, and 9 to 11 would be logic 0s.
6. The output of AN8 would be a logic 1 or 0, corresponding to that bit in the memory information register.

One can readily see the advantage of a transfer bus over a scheme of direct gating to and from each register. Where it might take 30 to 40 gating elements for direct gating, the transfer bus shown in Fig. 9-4 performs the same function with 12. For a 24-bit machine, a saving of 400 to 500 gates is realized for the complete transfer bus.

When a computer is organized around a large transfer bus, as illustrated in Fig. 9-4, it is somewhat limited in that simultaneous transfers cannot be performed. In order to shorten the execution times required to implement various commands, machines are organized utilizing some direct transfers in addition to multiple transfer buses, thus allowing for simultaneous transfers. Here again, the designer must make compromises between higher speeds of operation and the cost of additional hardware.

9-5 Recognition Gates

A control circuit which finds wide application is the recognition gate. A recognition gate is used to recognize only one number or logic condition

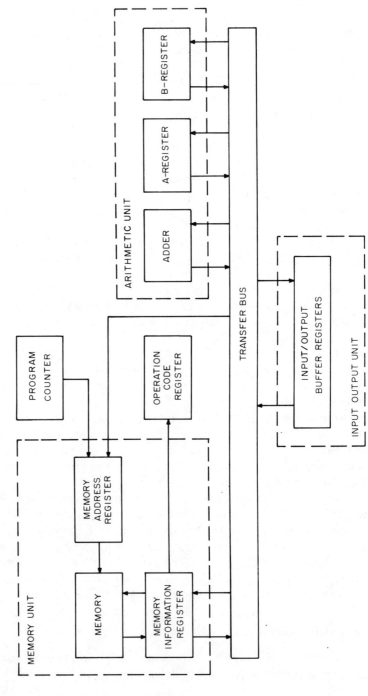

Fig. 9-3 Transfer-bus configuration.

216

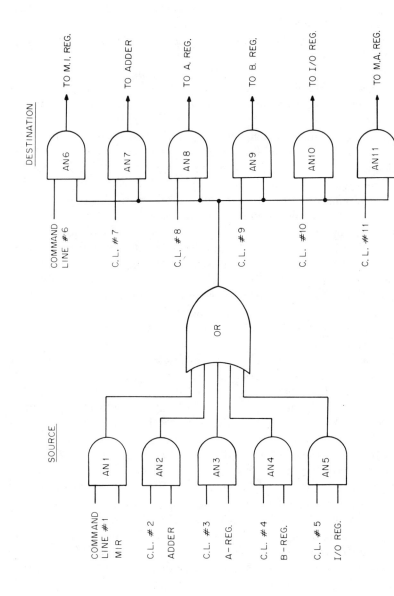

Fig. 9-4   One bit of transfer bus in Fig. 9-3.

and emit a signal only if that condition is present.   Any type of gate can be connected as a recognition gate.

The gates described in the decoder in Fig. 5-2 are really recognition gates.   The gate that decodes 0110 into 6 only emits a 1 if it recognizes the number 0110.   At all other times, it remains 0.   If a certain number (0010, for example) indicates an address in a memory device, the gate that allows signals to enter that particular portion of the memory is set to recognize only the number 0010.   Only if this address is present will the gate open, permitting signals to flow into or out of this portion of the memory.

The same principle is used in sending orders to various sections of the computer.   If the command 0011 means "Store contents of adder in the A Register," a recognition gate is set to recognize 0011.   This selection gate will activate the necessary command lines.   This type of recognition gate is functionally illustrated in the decode-gate block in Fig. 9-1. Recognition gates are also used for internal control in the arithmetic unit. The comparators used in division circuits are an example of internal control.   Another example is the recognition of the end-around carry in 1s-complement addition.   In 1s-complement addition, when the carry is 1, a recognition gate permits the end-around-carry operation to be performed.   When the carry is 0, the recognition gate closes and blocks the end-around-carry operation.   A careful review of the demonstrations given in Chap. 6 reveals that most represent applications where recognition gates can be used.

Timing and counting controls represent another area where recognition gates are used.   In Demonstration 5-1, the 8-4-2-1 BCD counter, the AND gate recognizes when the count is at 1001 and conditions the counter to revert to 0000 on the next count.   This signal could also be sent to other areas of the machine.   In this way, certain operations can be controlled by every tenth count.   Furthermore, recognition gates can be used to recognize each individual counter representation.   When the counter is set at 0001, this count is recognized and a signal to perform some operation is sent out.   When the counter is set at 0010, another gate recognizes this count and sends out a signal to perform some other operation.   When the third count, 0011, is reached, a third recognition gate opens and a third operation is performed.   In this way, operations can be sequenced so that they occur in some specified order.

Demonstration 9-1 illustrates one circuit using recognition gates. However, a wide variety of applications is possible.   The demonstration, therefore, should be thought of as merely representative and not as the only way (or even the most frequent way) in which recognition gates are used.

Demonstration 9-1   Recognition Gates

Purpose

To demonstrate one possible application of recognition gates.

Equipment

2—Level switches (S)
1—Single-pulse generator (SPG)
4—NAND gates (ND)
2—AND gates (AN)
1—NOR gate (NR)
4—Shift registers (SR)

Discussion and Implementation

The recognition gating in Fig. 9-5 is made up of NR1 and AN1. Only when the number 0010 is in the level switch S1 will the recognition gate emit a logic-1 signal from AN1, allowing the signals from the SPG to pass through AN2 to the shift line of the register. For all other numbers, the output of AN1 will be logic 0; therefore, AN2 will be inhibited.

If AN1 is 1, then AN2 is open and allows gating signals from the SPG to place the number in S2 into the four-stage register made up of SR1 to SR4. If these four shift-register modules represent the data to be stored in the 0010 address location in a memory, numbers will be admitted to this portion of the memory only when the 0010 address appears at S1. Note that no CLEAR signal is required. When a new number enters the register, the previous number is erased automatically.

9-6   Comparators

Another fundamental circuit used in control operations is the comparator. Although special cases of comparator circuits appear more frequently than does the comparator circuit itself, it is the comparator and the principle of comparison which are fundamental to their operation. Basically, the comparator receives two numerical inputs from elsewhere in the system and compares them to see which is greater. If A is greater than B, the comparator emits one signal; if B is greater than A, it emits a different signal; if A and B are equal, either a third signal or one of the first two is emitted. Thus comparators are assembled which can determine the correct condition in the following three cases:

1. $A \geq B$ or $A < B$
2. $A \leq B$ or $A > B$
3. $A > B$, $A < B$, or $A = B$

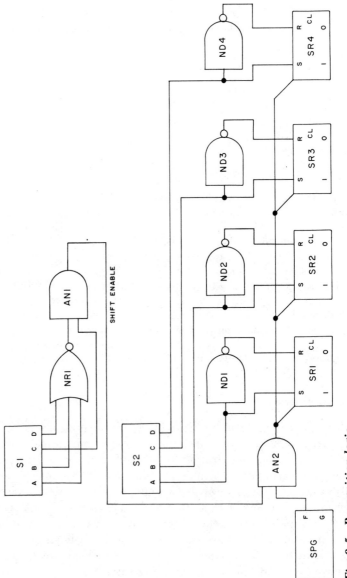

Fig. 9-5 Recognition logic.

In the first case, one sequence of operations can be triggered if A ≥ B (A is greater than or equal to B) and a second sequence triggered if A < B (A is less than B).   The second and third cases produce different sequences of operation.   A fourth case may be desired in which one output is produced if A = B and a second output is produced if A ≠ B.

One obvious application for a comparator is in binary division.   If the three digits of the divisor are greater than the first three digits of the dividend, the SHIFT-RIGHT operation is triggered; if they are less than or equal to the first three digits of the dividend, the SUBTRACT operation is triggered.

Comparison can be performed in either the serial or the parallel mode. Both methods are implemented in Demonstrations 9-2 and 9-3.   In a serial comparison, the two highest-order digits are compared.   If they are unequal, a decision is made immediately; if they are equal, the next highest-order digits are compared.   This procedure continues until a decision is made or until it is determined that the two numbers are equal. In a parallel comparator, all digits are compared simultaneously and a decision is reached in a single operation.

Demonstration 9-2   *The Serial Comparator*

Purpose

To demonstrate the construction and operation of a serial comparator.

Equipment

1—Level switch (S)
2—NAND gates (ND)
2—AND gates (AN)
1—NOR gate (NR)

Discussion and Implementation

In comparing two binary numbers, the two highest-order digits are compared first.   If one of these is larger than the other, the corresponding number is also the larger; if the digits are equal, the next higher order is compared.   The process is continued until an order is found in which one digit is greater than the other.   This immediately identifies the greater of the two numbers.   If no such order is discovered, the numbers must be equal.   For example, compare the following number pairs:

(a)   1 0 0 1 0 1 1 0 1
     (0) 1 0 1 1 1 1 0 0
(b)   1 1 1 0 1 0 1 1 0
      1 1 1 0 1 1 0 1 0
(c)   1 1 0 1 0 1 1 1 0
      1 1 0 1 0 1 1 1 0

For pair (*a*), the second number is really an eight-digit number. Since the first number is a nine-digit number, it is automatically greater. When the two eighth-order digits are compared, the comparator would assume that the eighth-order digit of the second number was 0 and it would indicate that the first number was greater. Note, however, that correct alignment is required prior to comparison.

For pair (*b*), it is necessary to proceed all the way down to the third order before finding two unequal digits. The third-order comparison, however, reveals that the second number is the greater.

For pair (*c*), all orders are equal. This, of course, means that the numbers themselves must also be equal.

The basic building block of this comparator is the exclusive OR circuit shown in Fig. 9-6. An exclusive OR circuit is one which produces an output when one and only one of two input signals is in the 1 state. This is performed by gates AN1, AN2, and NR1. However, the output of NR1 produces the inverted exclusive OR circuit; thus its output will be a logic 0 if one and only one of the two signals to be compared is in the logic-1 state. Replacing NR1 with an OR gate would make a true exclusive OR gate. The outputs of AN1 and AN2 are NORed together in NR1 to produce the term $\overline{A \cdot \overline{B} + \overline{A} \cdot B}$. By algebraic manipulation, this term reduces to $A \cdot B + \overline{A} \cdot \overline{B}$. All four possible combinations of A and B are, therefore, represented at the three gates AN1, AN2, and NR1. These are listed in Table 9-1.

TABLE 9-1

A B	Resultant term	Gate location	Meaning
1 1	$A \cdot B$	NR1	$A = B$
1 0	$A \cdot \overline{B}$	AN1	$A > B$
0 1	$\overline{A} \cdot B$	AN2	$A < B$
0 0	$\overline{A} \cdot \overline{B}$	NR1	$A = B$

Therefore, if the output of NR1 is a logic 1, A and B are both 1 or both

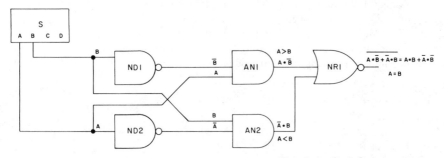

Fig. 9-6   Serial comparator.

0; that is, they are equal. If AN1 is a 1, A = 1 and B = 0; that is, A is greater than B. If AN2 is a 1, A = 0 and B = 1; that is, B is greater than A.

To make a comparison, the two numbers to be compared would be read into registers A and B, starting with the most significant digits. The two numbers would have to be aligned correctly. In a computer, this would be done by reading the two numbers into a shift register, then shifting into the comparator, one pair of bits at a time. In the demonstration, the numbers are set manually into the comparator from a level switch.

As long as NR1 is a 1, the two bits being compared are equal and the next most significant bit should be shifted into the comparator. As soon as AN1 or AN2 becomes a 1, A > B or A < B, and the comparison can be stopped by inhibiting further shifting. If, however, NR1 remains a 1 throughout the comparison process, the two numbers are identical.

Demonstration 9-3   The Parallel Comparator

Purpose

To demonstrate a comparator that operates on two 2-bit numbers in the parallel mode.

Equipment

2—Level switches (S)
6—NAND gates (ND)
1—NOR gate (NR)

Discussion and Implementation

The major disadvantage with serial comparison is one of decision time. In order to compare two 10-bit numbers, time must be allowed to shift a 10-digit number into the comparator and make 10 sequential decisions. Frequently, this requires more time than is desired in a computer, and parallel comparison is utilized.

In a parallel comparator, the numbers to be compared are placed in registers and all digits are compared in independent comparator stages. If any two digits differ, all lower-order stages of the comparator are forced into the correct state. A difference in the first high-order digit overrides a difference in subsequent low-order digits. Thus, the decision time is only the time necessary for the decision to ripple down or propagate through all stages or circuits of the comparator, and it is substantially lower than that of a serial comparator.

In Fig. 9-7, two 2-bit numbers are compared in a parallel comparator. Both the number and its complement are needed to make the comparison. It can be seen that the gating for the least significant digit is identical to that of the serial comparator.

To achieve parallel operation, one 2-digit number is entered into the A channels of the two level switches, with the high-order digit in S1 and the second digit in S2.   The complement of this number is then entered into the B channels.   Another two-digit number is entered into the C channels of the two level switches, again with the highest-order digit in S1 and the second digit in S2.   The complement of this number is then entered in the D channels.

Let Y_1, Y_0 stand for the first two-digit number, and let Z_1, Z_0 stand for the second.   The two level switches then read Y_1, $\overline{Y}_1$, Z_1, $\overline{Z}_1$ and Y_0, $\overline{Y}_0$, Z_0, $\overline{Z}_0$.   The most significant digits are then gated together. Y_1 and $\overline{Z}_1$ are NANDed together in ND1; Z_1 and $\overline{Y}_1$ are NANDed in ND2.   Both outputs of these gates are 1s if Y_1 and Z_1 are identical, i.e., both 0s or both 1s. When Y_1 and Z_1 are alike, each gate receives a 1 and a 0 input and each output is a 1.   If, however, Y_1 and Z_1 are different, one is 1 and the other is 0. One NAND gate receives two 0 inputs, and the other receives two 1 inputs. The two 1 inputs represent the only combination that can make one output of the NAND gates a 0.   For example, if $Y_1 = 1$ and $Z_1 = 0$, the inputs to ND1 are both 1, while the inputs to ND2 are both 0.   The output of ND1, in this case a logic 0, will cause the outputs of ND4 and ND6 to be 1s. ND6, therefore, indicates that Y_1 is 1 and Z_1 is 0, or that Y_1, Y_0 is greater than Z_1, Z_0.   Had the opposite example been chosen ($Z_1 = 1$ and $Y_1 = 0$), then ND5 would be 1, indicating that Z_1, Z_0 was greater than Y_1, Y_0.

NAND gates ND3 and ND4 perform exactly the same function for the two lower-order digits.   These gates, however, are inhibited if NAND gates ND1 and ND2 have already determined that one number is larger than the other.   Gates ND5, ND6, and NR1 are the outputs of the comparator. When ND6 is 1, $Y > Z$.   When ND5 is 1, $Y < Z$.

The NOR gate NR1 is 1 when both of its inputs are 0.   This gate, therefore, can only be a 1 if, after each order has been compared, ND5 and ND6 still do not indicate that one number is larger than the other.   NOR gate NR1 must then indicate when the two numbers are equal.

The same scheme can be carried on to higher orders for comparing larger numbers.   Each new order requires two additional NAND gates.   Nevertheless, the principle of comparing the two highest-order digits first and then moving down to lower orders as the higher orders are determined to be equal, remains the same, and the output stage is identical to a serial-comparator stage.

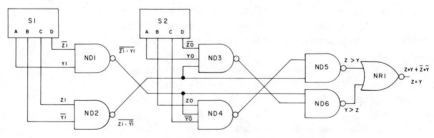

Fig. 9-7   Parallel comparator.

9-7 *Parity Generators*

One special case of the recognition gate which deserves consideration is the parity generator.   Parity generators find frequent use in computers in detecting problems associated with errors.   To illustrate this application, it is first necessary to expand the discussion of errors and error detection which was introduced in Chap. 5.

Chapter 5 described the 7-4-2-1-0 code as being error-detecting.   If there is a single error made in transferring a binary-coded decimal character in the 7-4-2-1-0 code, that error can be detected since every number is represented by two and only two 1s.   A single error will always result in a false representation that can immediately be detected as erroneous since it will change the number of 1s to something other than two.   This property does not exist for the 8-4-2-1 code, which was based on the binary number system, and this property does not exist for binary numbers themselves.   If the binary number 11010110 (decimal 214) is being processed and the 1 in the sixth order is inadvertently dropped, the number becomes 10010110 (decimal 150).   The results of this error could be substantial, e.g., a significant payroll mistake or an inventory error. Therefore, in some cases, every effort must be made within the computer to enable it to detect and correct errors.   This is especially true of input information the computer receives from other devices.   Here the possibility of errors is greater.   Thus many error-detecting codes are utilized when data are transferred to and from a computer.

One technique used to avoid such errors is the generation of parity bits. If a number (such as 11010110) contains an odd number of 1s, it has odd parity; if it has an even number of 1s, it has even parity.   The number 10010110 has even parity.   Circuits can be built which will generate a 1 or a 0, depending on whether the number presented to its input has an odd or an even number of bits in the 1 state.   Thus, a parity generator, which is designed for even parity, will count the number of 1s in the word and will generate a 1 if the total number is odd; otherwise, it will generate a 0.

This bit is added on the end of the original number to produce a new number which is 1 bit longer.   When the new, longer number is used elsewhere in the computer, its parity is checked for correctness.   If its parity is incorrect, a 1 has either been added to or dropped from the original number and it is now erroneous.   For example, if the number 10010110 is presented to an even-parity generator, the generator will produce a 0 bit, representing even parity, and add it to the end of the original number. That number now becomes 100101100, where the digit on the far right is the parity bit.   If a bit is accidentally changed in the processing of the number to produce a different number (such as 100001100), the parity bit is erroneous since parity is now odd. Either odd or even parity can be used for a word. The parity generator can be designed using a counter that counts the number of 1s in a word, or a recognition gate can be used whose output is controlled by the condition of all input bits in a parallel parity generator. In either case, by adding a parity bit to a word and then later checking its parity for correctness, 1-bit errors can be detected.

The parity bit, however, is of no use if two simultaneous errors are made, and it will not reveal the location of the error when only 1 bit is changed. If a 1 is dropped at the same time that another bit changes from 0 to 1, the parity remains the same. A single parity bit is, therefore, useless in the face of two or more errors, and other techniques must be used if the results of the occasional double errors are to be sufficiently serious or if error correction is necessary.

Additional parity bits, however, can deal with additional errors. For example, consider the 8-bit number 01001101. Now generate a parity bit for the seventh, fifth, third, and first orders only.

```
01001101
| | | |
0 0 1 0  = odd = 1
```

Generate another parity bit for the seventh, sixth, third, and second orders only.

```
01001101
||  ||
01  11   = odd = 1
```

Generate a third parity bit for the seventh, sixth, fifth, and fourth orders only.

```
01001101
||||
0100     = odd = 1
```

Finally, generate a parity bit for the entire number.

```
01001101 = even = 0
```

The number, complete with parity bits, now looks like this:

```
01001101      1110
   ↑            ↑
Number        Parity
              bits
```

By processing the parity bits as well as the data, the correctness of the data can be guaranteed at any step. If one error is made in transmitting the number, the following number might be the result:

01000101

Now generate a set of four new parity bits, in the same way as above, for this number:

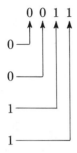

01000101   0 0 1 1

Compare the two sets of parity bits:

First set of parity bits	1	1	1	0
Second set of parity bits	0	0	1	1
Comparison bits	D	D	S	D

where S = same and D = different.

   Since the first bits in the two sets differ, the parity for the entire number must be wrong.   But, since the next bits of the two sets are the same, the four high-order bits must be all right.   The next two bits place error in either the second or third order, and finally, since the last two bits also differ, the error is identified as being in the third order.   This scheme has not only detected an error, but it has actually identified the error.   Such a scheme is called *error correcting*, since feedback methods can provide automatic correction of any detected error.

   Assume now that two errors are made in the transmission of **01001101**. The erroneous number might then appear as 01010101.   Parity checking on this number is accomplished as previously described, and the word with original parity is

   01010101 1110

Generating a new parity for the erroneous number, according to the previous criteria, yields 0000.   Comparison then yields the following results:

Original parity bits	1	1	1	0
New parity bits	0	0	0	0
Comparison bits	D	D	D	S

where S = same and D = different.

The S in the first comparison bit means that the parity for the entire word is all right. The D's in other comparison bits, however, indicate that errors have been made. An error is thus identified, but it cannot be located. When the number of errors increases, the error-correcting property is lost but the error-detecting property is retained. In some cases, even three errors at a time can be detected.

Parity generation and parity checking of the type described in this section are normally accomplished at the boundaries between separate computer elements. This allows the computer to check itself when accepting numbers from an external element to the input unit. In this way, processing through the equipment is monitored to ensure that no errors have been made along the way.

Not all computers use parity bits internally, although many use parity bits on input-output equipment. The use of parity bits is dependent on the probability of error in the computer and on the effect of an error. Certainly, the guidance computer of a missile or submarine should be protected against errors, and errors, when detected, should be corrected either automatically or by requesting that the data be retransmitted.

Demonstration 9-4   4-bit Even-parity Generator

Purpose

To demonstrate a parity generator which produces a 1 bit whenever its 4-bit input has an odd number of 1s.

Equipment

    1—Level switch (S)
    6—NAND gates (ND)
    6—AND gates (AN)
    2—OR gates (OR)
    1—NOR gate (NR)

Discussion and Implementation

The level switch in Fig. 9-8 provides the normal inputs to the parity generator; the NAND gates provide the inverted inputs. The two highest-order bits and their negations are gated in AND gates AN1 and AN2, respectively. The outputs of AN1 and AN2 are connected to OR1. The output of OR1 is a 1 only if both highest-order bits are 1s or both are 0s. The two lowest-order bits are taken to AND gates AN3 and AN4. The outputs of those gates are then ORed together in OR2. OR2 also puts out a 1 only if the two lowest-order bits are either both 1s or both 0s. The outputs of OR gates OR1 and OR2 are then taken to AN5, and their negations, formed in NAND gates ND5 and ND6, are taken to AN6. If both the low-order and the high-order digits have even parity, the whole number has even parity and a 1 bit is generated at AND gate AN5. If, on the other

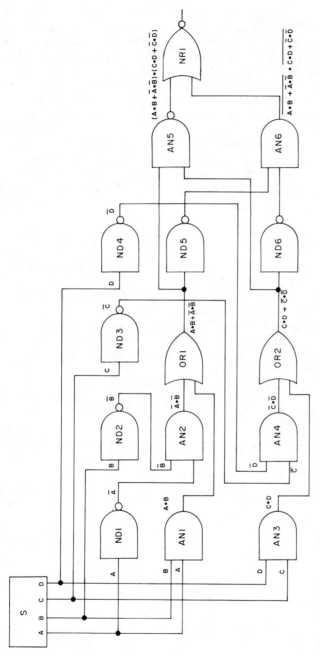

Fig. 9-8 Even–parity generator.

hand, both pairs of digits have odd parity, the whole number still has even parity and a 1 bit is generated at AND gate AN6.   Only if one pair of digits has even parity and the other pair has odd parity will the entire number be odd, and only then will both AN5 and AN6 be 0.   AN5 and AN6 can therefore be NORed together in NR1 to produce the parity bit for the whole number.   The output of NR1 will be a logic 1 only if an odd number of 1s are in the word.   The addition of this generated parity bit to the word will always cause the modified word to have an even number of logic 1s.

A parity bit may also be generated by use of a binary counter which counts the number of 1s in the word as it is shifted serially from a register. If the lowest-order stage of the counter is a logic 1 after the word is cycled through, this means that the word has an odd number of bits.   This method of generating parity is much slower than the parallel method illustrated in Fig. 9-8.

EXERCISES

9-1. Describe the function of the program counter.   When are instructions not taken from sequential locations?

9-2. In Fig. 9-2, what is the purpose of the operation-code register?

9-3. In Fig. 9-3, describe the control signals required to gate information from the A register to the B register.

9-4. Given a six-stage shift register, draw a recognition gate which recognizes the number 100110 and inhibits further gating.   Assume that no gate can have more than four inputs.

9-5. Repeat Demonstration 9-2, comparing 10111010 with 10111011.

9-6. Redraw Fig. 9-6 so that one output is a logic 1 only if $A \geq B$ and a second output is a logic 1 only if $A < B$.

9-7. Prepare a block diagram of a parallel comparator which compares two 6-digit numbers.   Assume both assertion and negation inputs are available.

9-8. Draw a parallel 4-bit odd-parity generator.

9-9. Repeat Exercise 9-8 using a serial counter.

TEN

Input-Output Equipment

10-1 *Introduction*

The user must be able to communicate with the computer. Prepared data must be coded properly and then entered into the computer. Similarly, results obtained from the computer must be recorded, displayed, and/or entered into another machine. This transfer of data is accomplished by means of input and output equipment.

The input-output sections of the computer serve as a buffer and translator to match the central processor to the speed and data format of a wide variety of external peripheral equipment. Peripheral equipment is used to perform two general functions. One function is to communicate directly with the operator. Examples of devices which perform this function include a typewriter, display unit, cards, and character-recognition device, as inputs to the computer, and a printer, display, plotter, and audio device, as outputs from the computer. The second function is to provide external bulk storage for storing data and programs. Examples of devices which perform this function include magnetic tape, disks, drums, punched cards, and paper tape.

It is possible for the operator to enter information directly into the computer by means of a keying device similar to a typewriter. The output information could be typed out. While this is effective and is used as one of the means of interfacing with the computer, it is slow, and other devices have been developed. The central processor, an extremely fast device, is very inefficient when input data are entered via a manual keying operation from a single terminal. To use the central processor efficiently, large amounts of raw data should be prepared in advance and entered into the computer rapidly or a large number of terminals should have simultaneous access to the computer. The first organization is defined as *batch processing*, while the second is referred to as *time sharing*. The preparation of data is a relatively slow operation involving problem solving by programmers, translation of the solving process into machine language, and the preparation of data for entry into the computer. The process of preparing data may involve many people, especially in a large computer installation which may have many independent groups programming different problems. Thus *off-line equipment* is normally used to prepare data. Devices which are under the direct control of the central processor are called *on-line equipment*. These devices are designed to read data into or out of the central processor upon command and are considered part of the computer system. Peripheral equipment is off-line when it is operated independent of and prior to the actual data processing. For example, a card punch is off-line if the operator prepares the cards and then later brings them, or the same data transferred to magnetic tape, to a computer for processing. A console keyboard connected to the computer is on-line equipment since the output of the keyboard is presented to the computer in real time. By means of off-line equipment, data and programs can be prepared by many operators, and then a number of programs, which have been transferred onto a storage medium such as magnetic tape, can be entered into the computer. This batch processing saves computer time since the computer receives programs sequentially at a fast rate and does not have to wait for operator decisions. The same principle can be applied in the output area, where the results of many programs can be written on magnetic tape. Later the tape can be played back at a slower rate and the data transferred to cards, printer, or other media, depending on the requirements of the user.

The flow diagram of Fig. 10-1 illustrates some of the operations involved in preparing data for entry to the central processor and some of the forms of output data.

The amount and type of input-output equipment are dependent on the application of the computer and the desired input-output format. For example, output data may be presented as numbers, graphs, or spoken words, and a permanent or temporary record may be kept of the data. The output devices will differ substantially in their speed, format, and cost. A device may present data in words, in characters, in bits, or in its own special code. The input-output section may have to translate the words of the computer to the code of the device. If parity bits are used, the input-output section may have to check and assign parity. The design of the input-output section is also dependent on the number of peripheral devices, the number of separate channels required, the logic provided with these peripheral devices, and any requirements for intermediate storage. Frequently, an input to the computer is from another machine. This is the case in a large computational system where more than one computer is required to handle all the input data. Other sources may be from analog devices which convert analog signals to digital form for processing by the computer. A computer will normally be designed to interface with a wide variety of peripheral equipment,

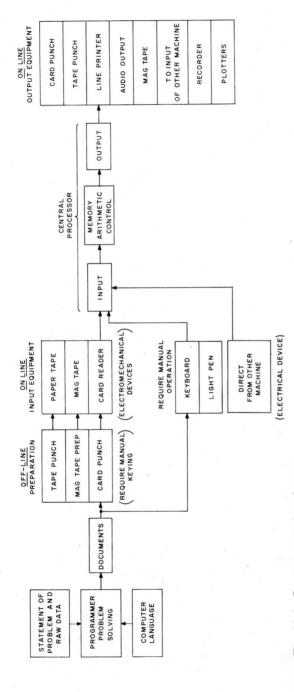

Fig. 10-1 Input-output equipment.

although the typical computer installation will include only a limited number of these devices.

This chapter briefly describes some of the principal types of input-output devices and the flow of data from these devices through the input-output subsystem. It then indicates how batch processing and time sharing affect the organization of the input-output area.

10-2 *Input-Output Equipment*

The following five devices are widely used in computer installations to provide a communication means between the computer and the operator. While all can be used as on-line equipment, they are also widely used in off-line applications.

A paramount feature of off-line operation is that the entire program can be prepared remote from the central processor, so that highly efficient machine operation is possible and independence of data preparation and computer operation is achieved. However, to enter data into a computer at high speed requires a storage medium. This storage medium must be capable of accepting data at a slow rate, for example, from a card-punching operation. When ready, its content must be read into the central processor at high speeds under control of electromechanical input equipment. Three such media are discussed: punched cards, punched paper tape, and magnetic tape. Once prepared, each of these storage media provides permanent records which can be read into the computer's memory at a later date. Two other input-output devices are also described: typewriters and printers.

Typewriter. A special typewriter is normally a part of the operator's console or control panel and is widely used as an input keyboard for remote time-sharing stations. Consoles are also available using push buttons instead of a typewriter as an input device in order to decrease the cost of the terminal. A typewriter has the advantage that it is a familiar and easy-to-use device. It is, however, quite slow, especially when used as a manual input device.

Although the familiar keyboard, which includes the letters of the alphabet, the numerals 0 to 9, and special symbols, is most frequently used, special keyboards have been developed for specific applications, e.g., airline reservations, the stock market, and information-retrieval systems. Each typed character is coded into a special 6-bit alphanumeric code. A seventh bit is frequently added to indicate parity. The input information is typed, and contacts in the selection mechanism transmit pulses to the computer that define the character being printed and any special machine instructions, e.g., uppercase, space, and carriage return. When the computer wishes to type out information, the process is reversed and alphanumeric codes are sent to the typewriter. These are decoded, and the proper character is selected and printed.

While the keyboard can be located physically close to the computer, it frequently is a few hundred feet or many hundreds of miles away. Data are transmitted using wires, telephone lines, radio links, or other methods of communication. When data are transmitted from a remote location, a parity check is usually performed on each character to check the integrity of data transmission.

Punched Cards. The coding of information on punched cards is directly equivalent to the 1 and 0 binary notations used by the computer. There are a number of punched-card systems possible. The example shown in Fig. 10-2 is a standard card using the Hollerith code. A punched-card tabulator using this code was developed by Dr. Herman Hollerith in 1890 for the Bureau of the Census. This card is $3\frac{1}{4}$ by $7\frac{7}{8}$ inches and has 80 columns with 12 rows per column. A card can store a maximum of 80 characters. Ten bit positions are numbered, with bit positions 11 and 12 unnumbered at the top of the card. Each bit position may represent a 1 or a 0, depending on whether or not the position is punched. The 12 rows offer a combination of 2^{12}, or 4,096, coded characters. The alphanumeric code (Hollerith code) used with this card is limited to the 47 characters common to a typewriter keyboard. Numeric characters 0 to 9 are designated by a single punched hole on the 0 to 9 bit positions on the card. Other characters are represented by punching combinations of up to 3 bit positions per column. Table 10-1 lists the 47 characters and their corresponding codes.

An 80-column scale is written between rows 0 and 1 and below row 9 for the aid of the operator. Thus, the letter A is stored in column 3 by punching a hole in bit positions 12 and 1. In column 39, the number 9 is

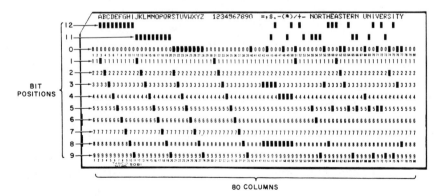

Fig. 10-2   Punched card.

TABLE 10-1

Character	Code	Character	Code	Character	Code	Character	Code	Character	Code
0	0	A	12, 1	J	11, 1	S	0, 2	,	0, 3, 8
1	1	B	12, 2	K	11, 2	T	0, 3	&	11, 3, 8
2	2	C	12, 3	L	11, 3	U	0, 4	.	12, 3, 8
3	3	D	12, 4	M	11, 4	V	0, 5	−	4, 8
4	4	E	12, 5	N	11, 5	W	0, 6	(	0, 4, 8
5	5	F	12, 6	O	11, 6	X	0, 7	*	11, 4, 8
6	6	G	12, 7	P	11, 7	Y	0, 8	)	12, 4, 8
7	7	H	12, 8	Q	11, 8	Z	0, 9	/	0, 1
8	8	I	12, 9	R	11, 9	=	3, 8	+	12
9	9								−	11

stored by punching a hole in bit position 9. In column 46, the point symbol (.) is stored by punching a hole in bit positions 12, 3, and 8.

The 80 columns can be used to represent any data. When used by a payroll department, for example, columns 1 to 9 might be used for the employee's social security number, columns 10 to 14 for his employment date, columns 15 to 19 for his date of birth, columns 20 to 38 for his name, columns 39 to 45 for his salary, and so on. Another application would assign completely different meanings to the various columns.

There is a variety of equipment available for punching, sorting, and reading cards. The manual preparation of cards is accomplished by the use of key punches, consisting of a keyboard with control and punching mechanisms. Cards can be punched automatically by the computer at a rate of 100 to 500 cards per minute. This rate is substantially slower if the information is being manually entered on the card by an operator. A proficient operator can punch information from documents onto the cards at a rate of about 10,000 characters per hour, or about two cards per minute. When the cards are punched initially, a verifier may be used to check the correctness of the card. This operation calls for a duplicate keying operation. If an error is detected while the operator is verifying, the keyboard can be locked automatically, indicating to the operator that an error has been made.

Punched-card readers are used as input devices to the processor. There are a number of readers available which operate at various speeds. Mechanical readers use brush contacts which develop signals as they detect holes in the card that slides over them. When a hole is detected, a brush makes contact to the other side of the card until an unbroken portion of the card goes by. Cards can be read in this manner at speeds of a few hundred per minute. Higher reading speeds are attainable by using photoelectric techniques. These readers have photoelectric cells positioned over the card so that a light source on the other side of the card activates the cell when a hole on the card allows the light to pass through. Even when using photoelectric cells, card speeds are substantially slower than magnetic tape for comparable information transfer.

Cards can be sorted easily, and a number of card systems have been developed. These will sort the cards according to any criteria selected. For instance, in a data-processing application, columns 20 and 21 may indicate the billing date of a customer. All cards can be sorted by examining these two columns. A sort can be set so that the cards of all customers billed on the first 10 days of the month are divided into 10 separate groups while the remainder are placed in an eleventh group.

Since the cards are punched in the Hollerith code and not in the word format of the computer, either the peripheral device or the input and output sections of the computer must perform a translation process.

Punched cards offer a number of advantages. They are inexpensive, easy to sort, and easy to decode. If it is desired to modify the data on a particular card, it is easy to replace the card with a new one. However, cards have the disadvantages that they are bulky and difficult to store, they are exactly 80 characters long and therefore may provide too much or too little capacity to store the data on a particular item, and they are much slower than magnetic tape. Despite these disadvantages, card readers and punches are among the most widely used input-output equipment.

Punched Paper Tape. Punched paper tape provides a relatively inexpensive method of preparing input information. The tape consists of thin paper or Mylar tape into which holes are punched. A hole represents a 1, and no hole represents a 0. Various widths of tape are possible, with a different number of bits across the tape. The tape can be in reels or in strips. A reel may contain as much as a 1,000 feet of paper tape. Figure 10-3 shows a seven-level tape with seven bit positions across the width of the tape. Each row across the tape represents one character of information. The tape is $7/8$ inch wide and can record 10 characters per inch. Other tapes having five, six, and eight bit positions, or channels, are commercially available. A sprocket hole on the seven-level tape is used to register the tape properly on the punch while it is going through the perforator and is also used to develop timing signals for data transfer when the tape is being read.

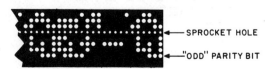

*Fig. 10-3   Seven-level punched paper
tape.*

The seven bit positions on the tape can be used to implement an alphanumeric code.   Only six of the bit positions are needed to implement the code.   The seventh bit is used as a parity bit.

A tape-perforator unit can be attached to specially designed typewriters. As the operator depresses a key on the keyboard, the corresponding 6-bit coded character is punched on the tape along with a parity bit.   As with punched cards, verifiers can be used to check the correctness of the information transferred to the tape.   The paper-tape unit can be operated off-line or can be controlled directly by the central processor.   The tape is read by sensing the presence or absence of punched holes.   Tape can be punched at speeds of about 100 characters per second and read at a few hundred characters per second.

Punched tape is inexpensive and requires substantially less storage space than cards.   It also can store variable amounts of data.   However, it has the disadvantage that, unlike a card, it is difficult to modify any portions of the data or the sequence of data.   The entire reel of tape must be treated as a whole, and the data pertinent to a problem must be found by reading the entire reel of paper tape sequentially.

Magnetic Tape.   Magnetic tape, which was discussed in Chap. 7, is one of the most commonly used input-output media.   A computer may be connected to one or more tape transports.   Each tape transport consists of a few thousand feet of thin Mylar tape coated with a magnetic material and wound between two reels and of read-write heads with electronics and control logic.   Depending on its input-output organization, it is possible for the computer to interface with two tapes at once, reading data from one tape while writing on another.

There are many possible formats for arranging information on a tape, with different tape widths, numbers of channels, and lengths.   Figure 10-4 shows an example of one arrangement.   Information is usually recorded in blocks called *records*, with each record having one or more words.   Since the tape travels at high speeds, time gaps between records

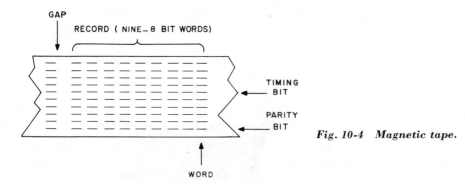

Fig. 10-4   Magnetic tape.

are necessary to start and stop the tape movement physically. The time gap must be long enough to allow the tape to come to a full stop at the end of a record and then start without losing information on the succeeding record. To do this, a space or gap must precede each record. The record shown in Fig. 10-4 contains nine 8-bit words. Two additional bits are used as timing and parity bits. The record is a variable-length block of data, which can be of any length up to some maximum length set by the equipment design. Thus the next block of data may be 36 words long with an interrecord gap at its beginning and end.

Magnetic tapes are usually prepared from other media, such as punched cards or paper tape, although keyboard devices are available which directly key information to magnetic tapes. The cards and paper tapes are verified before the data are transferred from them to the tape. The data on the tape can be erased, allowing portions of the data to be modified or the entire tape to be reused. Tape transports are used in both off-line and on-line applications to prepare data remotely as well as to interface directly with the computer.

Magnetic tape allows large amounts of data to be stored in a small volume. A reel of $\frac{1}{2}$-inch tape, 12 inches across, can contain 2,400 feet of tape and can store many millions of characters. Tape is an extremely fast input-output medium, with transfer rates from 20,000 characters/second to ten times that. Because data can be stored in variable blocks, there is no limitation of file size. Tape is widely used in information-retrieval systems, where data pertaining to a large number of subjects or accounts are filed on tape. The entire tape may be read, and specific data on each account may be made available; or the tape may be searched to make available only data pertaining to one subject or account. Thus, tape is used where fast access is required to large amounts of data. It has three disadvantages: a tape transport is more expensive than a punched-card or paper-tape system; it is impossible to sort data visually; and it is a sequential-access memory.

Printers. The printer is widely used as an output device because printing is easily read. Coded signals in the word format of the computer are translated and printed as normal English characters. The computer can be connected to many printers, and all can be actuated with the same message; or the computer can select one at any given time. The output from the computer can be printed out directly, or the data can be written on tape or other storage medium and subsequently printed.

A line printer will have the capacity to print so many characters per line, 120 to 130 print positions being typical, and so many lines per minute. An impact printer will print a few hundred to about a thousand lines per minute. In one scheme, printing is accomplished by having print hammers drive paper against a continuously rotating drum which has been engraved with the letters of the alphabet, the decimal digits, and other special symbols.   Each symbol is repeated many times across the cylindrical drum.   As each line of characters passes the print hammers, the hammers are activated by the printer control logic, which is based on a 6-bit code defining each letter.   The hammers drive the paper against the drum and print all like characters at one time.   When the drum has rotated to the next character, the 6-bit code for that character is decoded and the appropriate hammers are activated.   After a full revolution of the drum, the complete line is printed and the paper is moved to the next line.

A nonimpact printer will allow even higher print speeds to be achieved, up to several thousand lines per minute.   Here the information to be printed is displayed electronically and is then transferred to paper by photographic process or other technique.

A printer is widely used where large amounts of output data are required in a visual format.   It is more expensive than a typewriter but is significantly faster.

10-3   *Other Input-Output Devices*

The devices described in the last section are used because of the speed with which they interact with the computer and the relative cost in performing this function.   Data are stored as punched holes, printed symbols, or magnetized areas and then converted to a format for processing by the computer.   These devices are the most common peripheral equipment, and almost every computer has been designed to interface with them.

Another class of device has been developed whose purpose is to interface better with the operator, i.e., make the computer easier to use.   In some cases, the user would like to be able to write, draw pictures, or talk directly with the computer and be able to receive outputs as pictures, graphs, or spoken words.   The user would also like to be able to have a terminal on his desk and communicate with a remote computer using his natural language.   This section describes a few of the devices designed to provide greater information transfer between the operator and the computer.   Some of these devices have been available for a number of years, while others are still in the early stages of development.

Input Devices.   A normal typewriter has the disadvantage that a mistake requires that the entire message be retyped.   In addition, a typewritten message is not always the best or fastest method of display for the operator.   A number of schemes have been developed which use a cathode-ray tube, similar to a television picture tube, together with a keyboard as an input-output terminal.   The face of the tube is divided into a number of points, e.g., a grid 1,024 by 1,024 points. An electron beam is deflected to trace a series of strokes between a number of these points. This electron beam hits a phosphore coating on the face of the tube, causing it to glow and thereby writing a character on the screen. The character will fade within a very short time; therefore, the character is rewritten many times per second under the control of either the computer or the buffer storage.

The message is typed by the operator and stored on the display tube. The amount of data that can be stored varies, depending on the characteristics of the display. One system stores up to 768 characters in an array of 32 characters per line and 24 lines. Another system stores 52 lines with 74 characters per line. The operator can clear the entire message or erase any character or any line by a simple typed instruction. When the entire message is complete, displayed, and verified by the operator, a button is pushed and the entire message, usually in a serial mode, is sent to a remote computer. Each character of the message is coded by the display station into a binary code, e.g., a 6-bit alphanumeric code plus a parity bit. Thus, to send 768 characters, a total of 5,376 bits of data must be sent to the computer. The computer will be connected to many such display stations and will sequence through them looking for a message. It can be seen that a large amount of input data can be supplied to the computer.

This same terminal will be used as an output device, with the characters written under the control of the computer. The computer can also present data in chart or graphical form by preparing a digital equivalent of the data. The electron beam is deflected the proper amount under the control of the computer, and a graph is displayed on the face of the cathode-ray tube.

The cathode-ray tube is also used as a means of presenting data in graphical or pictorial form to the computer. The computer can present stored information as a display on the cathode-ray tube. The operator can draw on the face of the tube by using a light pen in conjunction with appropriate control signals and computer subprograms. The light pen contains a photocell which generates a signal when the section of the tube face where it is pointed is intensified by the electron beam. The computer relates this signal to the point which is intensified at the time of the response. The operator can draw, delete, or modify displayed data through appropriate programming. In this way, the operator and the computer jointly produce drawings or graphs. The computer can complete and check these drawings according to preprogrammed criteria, store this information, and produce other drawings for examination by the operator. Graphic input and output systems are in the early stages of development. The reader is referred to any article on the subject of computer graphics for more information on this excellent method of man-machine interface.

Another type of input equipment is an optical or magnetic character-recognition device. One application of such a device is in correcting multiple-choice tests. An answer sheet has a number of boxes corresponding to various possible choices. For each question, one choice is blackened in, using a pencil. This answer sheet can be corrected manually. However, in many cases, optical character-recognition equipment is used. If a special pencil is provided, the marked areas can be detected by examining the various portions of the paper for their magnetic characteristics. If a normal pencil is used, the marked areas can be detected by their reflectivity, using an optical scanner. In both cases, the number of correct answers can be tabulated by noting the areas with markings in the proper places. This principle has been applied to provide information on sales records, inventory status, and shipping records for a variety of applications.

These applications are based upon providing information in a binary format; i.e., every point either is filled in or is not filled in. It is desirable to be able to supply written inputs in a decimal form, i.e., to have the numbers 0 to 9 written or printed and then identified directly by a peripheral device. This generally requires that each number be unique (e.g., a poorly written 7 should never look like a 2) and that the translating mechanism know where to look for each digit. One application of such a system is in banking, where an identification number is printed on each check in a constant position. These numbers, written in magnetic ink, are highly stylized. A character-recognition device can then examine every digit and determine its value.

Much work is being done on developing equipment which directly reads handwritten or printed data. Here the problem is substantially more difficult since the variation in handwriting and positioning of letters makes the generation of translation rules extremely difficult. The development of a peripheral device which possesses more of the human capability in reading would be a significant technical advance.

Output Devices. Frequently, the output of a computer is a series of numbers which represents the relationship of two or more variables. Rather than listing these numbers in tabular form, it is desirable to present the same information as a graph. A *digital plotter* is an output device which presents data in graphical form. The X axis can be defined as one variable, and the Y axis as a second. When the computer lists a value of X and a value of Y, a point is plotted at the proper intersection. The next values of X and Y generate another point. The values of the X and Y axes can be scaled to allow all data to be plotted within the graph. When the final values of X and Y are given, all points can be connected or the plotter can draw the nearest straight line or smooth curve to the points. If a third variable, Z, is given, the plotter can generate a family of curves for constant values of Z. Since some information is most meaningful to the operator in graphical form, the digital plotter is widely used as a peripheral device.

Another output means, which is extremely impressive where used, is an *audio-output device*. A number of computer systems, including that used by the New York Stock Exchange, have utilized "talking computers." The basic operation of an audio-output device is to store a digital equivalent of a syllable on a disk or other storage medium and then, where required, to translate this digital number back to its analog equivalent.

Speech can be characterized in a variety of ways. One method would be to speak each word and examine the value of the amplitude of the sound or its voltage equivalent at frequent intervals. These analog values could be digitized, and the numerical equivalents stored. When it is desired to reconstruct a word, the number could generate an analog equivalent. In order to minimize the amount of digital data that must be stored, other conversion schemes have been developed which examine sound from an amplitude, frequency, and pitch point of view and store this information. When it is desired to prepare an audio equivalent to output data, the digital equivalent is identified, produced, and converted to an audio signal.

10-4 *Peripheral Storage*

Chapter 7 discussed storage elements used as part of the computer memory. The main memory must provide storage for large amounts of data at access times which are comparable to the speed of the arithmetic section. In addition, external storage of data and programs is provided in slower-speed on-line and off-line peripheral devices. These devices, though slower, are less expensive per bit of storage and provide large amounts of storage.

Disks and drums are used to provide fast-access external storage. A disk package can provide up to 800 million bits of storage at transfer rates of 400,000 characters per second. In addition, the access time to any bit of data can be substantially lower than with magnetic tape. However, the cost of each bit of storage is higher than with magnetic tape.

Magnetic tape is the most widely used type of peripheral storage, due to its relatively low cost, extremely large storage capacity, and fast input-output transfer speed. A tape transport can store 300 million bits of data and transfer data at 30,000 characters per second.

Finally, both punched cards and paper tape are also widely used to provide peripheral storage. While they each have the disadvantages listed previously, they are inexpensive where limited amounts of external storage are required. Most computer systems use one or both of these storage media.

10-5 *Input-Output Organization*

The function of the input-output section of the computer is to transfer data to and from a variety of peripheral devices. Data must be entered into the computer, and results must be supplied from the computer at speeds which are compatible with the computer data-transfer-handling capability. These data are usually stored in the computer memory, although in some cases, they can be stored in a specific arithmetic register. These peripheral devices are much slower than the central processor and usually operate asynchronously with respect to it. Data, however, can be transferred between the peripheral device and the central processor either synchronously or asynchronously. Thus, a principal function of the input-output section is to match the speed of the central processor to that of the peripheral device. Other functions would normally include data buffering, data-format conversion, and parity generation and checking.

The organization of the input-output section is dependent on the requirements of the specific computer system. These requirements include the number and types of devices to be addressed, the number to be addressed simultaneously, the input-output data rate, and any special logic and control signals required. Data can be sent to a single peripheral device in either a serial or a parallel format. When more than one device is to be connected, either separate signals can be sent to each device or control logic can be supplied in order to identify the address of the specific peripheral device which is to receive the common information. In addition, signals can be sent on either separate input and output lines or common input-output lines with an additional bit of information sent to indicate whether the information is being sent to or received from the peripheral device. The choice between serial and parallel is based on standard criteria. Parallel transfer is faster but requires more logic and wiring to implement it.

For example, if the computer is to address four peripheral devices with 24 bits of parallel data, a number of alternatives are possible. Twenty-four separate wires can be connected to the input and output logic of each device. This corresponds to $24 \times 4 \times 2$, or 192, wires. The other extreme would be to connect the same 24 wires to all four devices. Two additional bits would be required to identify which device is to be addressed, and one bit would be required to identify whether data are being sent to or received from the central processor. This approach would use 27 wires but would require more logic in the input-output section and in the peripheral equipment in order to decode the address. These groups of wires are called *input-output channels*. Separate channels are required if the computer is designed to interface with more than one device simultaneously. Thus, if the computer is designed to read from one magnetic tape unit and write on another at the same time, the two tape units cannot be on the same channel.

Another major consideration is how to match the speed of the central processor to the peripheral device. The two units can be operated synchronously during data transfer. When data from the main memory are to be written on magnetic tape, all other program activities can be inhibited until the data transfer is completed. This, in effect, slows down the central processor to the speed of the peripheral device and operates the units synchronously. When data are to be read into the memory from magnetic tape, other functions of the computer are inhibited and the data are transferred at the reading speed of the tape unit. This INTERRUPT signal is supplied when the central processor and peripheral device are ready for transfer. This is the simplest method of data transfer, but the computer is not being used as efficiently as it might be. A second method of organization allows the central processor and the peripheral unit to run asynchronously by means of buffered channels. A portion of the data to be transferred to the peripheral device is read from the main memory into buffer storage. This is done at the speed of the central processor. While data are being read out of the buffer, the central processor continues with arithmetic operations at its normal processing rate. The process is reversed during the input operation. A busy signal will be sent from the peripheral device until it is ready for additional data transfer, and the computer will continue with its normal operations. When the busy signal disappears, the central processor can again access the peripheral device. To address a specific device on an output line, a number of steps are required. The appropriate channel must be selected. It is then interrogated to determine that it is not busy. Next, the appropriate device is addressed to determine that it, too, is not in use. The data are then transferred from the central processor via the output lines. Normally, these data are stored in the buffered output section of the central processor until the device has indicated that it has received the data. There are a number of methods of providing data buffering. Separate registers can be supplied either in the input-output section or external to the computer. Buffering can also be provided by dividing the memory into sections and, while data are being transferred from one section, allowing other sections to be used by the central processor.

The input-output sections also perform functions with respect to parity generation and word-format conversion. If parity is used, data sent from the peripheral devices must be checked for correct parity. Parity may be generated for output data from the computer. This is usually necessary in cases where the peripheral device is located remotely and data must be sent over long distances. Computer words must also be formed from the input characters supplied by the peripheral device. Similarly, in the output section, computer words may be broken down into characters, bytes, or bits.

The input-output section contains buffer registers, conversion logic, and control logic. The following example describes one method of reading information from a tape unit into the central processor. Both input buffering and parity generation are included in the example.

Figure 10-5 illustrates a method of accepting data from a seven-channel tape for insertion into the computer memory. The computer word (fixed-word format) contains 18 bits and is arranged on tape in three rows of 6 bits each. Preceding each word is a 6-bit address character which directs the word to a specific physical location in the computer memory. A seventh bit is used as a parity bit for the 6 bits of information in each row across the tape. A time-mark signal, which precedes each word, is sent to a counter which is part of the control unit.

This counter generates timing signals T_1 to T_5. As information enters the input section, the 6-bit blocks are entered sequentially into appropriate registers by the timing signals T_1 to T_4. The first 6 bits from the tape make up the memory address. Signal T_1 shifts the address into the memory address register. The next 6 bits are shifted into register 1 by timing signal T_2. The rest of the word is shifted into registers 2 and 3 by timing signals T_3 and T_4. If no error has been detected by the parity detector, timing signal T_5 allows the information in the registers to be transferred to the memory location specified by the code in the address register. In asynchronous operation, data would not be read out of the buffer word registers until the central processor unit was ready for it. As each 6 bits of information are received, they are sent to a parity generator, which generates a parity bit. This bit is compared with the parity bit on the tape for correctness. If the two parity bits differ, the data will not be entered and an appropriate signal will be sent to the operator or noted on the program, indicating that the data are questionable. Frequently, instead of addressing a specific memory location on the tape, a block of data is read from the tape into the memory, starting at a specific memory location.

The input section may also contain conversion logic. Data may be received in binary-coded decimal or alphanumeric code and may be converted to binary notation in the word format of the computer.

This process is reversed at the output section, where data from the

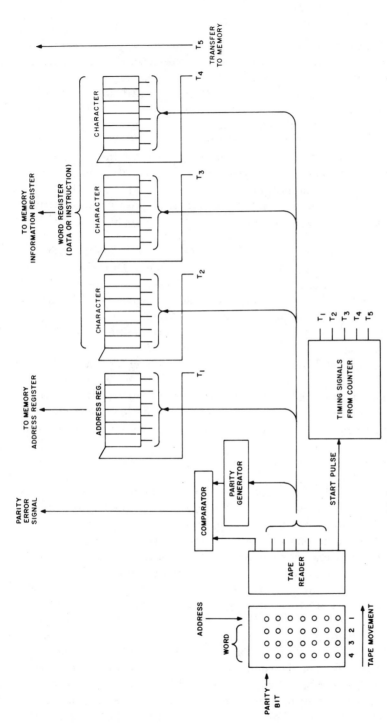

Fig. 10-5 Input data transfer, tape to memory.

247

memory are transferred to the output equipment. Here again, timing signals are used to match the difference in speeds of the central processor and the slower output equipment. Data are read from the central processor into buffer registers. Parity is generated on each word, and the data are read from these registers onto tape at the write speed of the tape unit. While the data are being written, the central processor can continue processing arithmetic information.

The input-output sections are normally designed to interface with a variety of slow-speed peripheral devices. Usually, it is desired to make each of these devices appear identical to the central processor by buffering them and converting their data format to a standard notation, either by means of separate data channels or by conversion logic located in the input-output sections, outside of the computer, or in the peripheral device itself. A system of control signals must be designed into the computer to allow these devices to be addressed. During the design of the computer, a priority system must also be set up. This establishes in what order devices are to be addressed and in what order INTERRUPT and busy signals are to be assigned.

Significant amounts of logic capability can be designed into the input-output section. One scheme allows the memory to be addressed directly by the peripheral device through appropriate buffering and logic without requiring special program-control signals from the central-processor unit. This transfer is normally performed in one memory-cycle time. Another approach allows one channel to process several slow-speed devices by buffering each device. Each of these features can be designed into the computer.

A computer designed to allow sharing of the central processor and input-output areas by several operators at the same time will have a different input-output organization than a computer designed to solve several problems sequentially. *Batch processing* refers to the approach to problem solution which enters programs into the computer sequentially, one or a batch at a time, for the computer to execute one at a time. Here a number of operators may prepare their programs simultaneously in off-line equipment. When the programs are prepared, as will be described in Chap. 12, they are then written on cards, paper tape, or other media. These programs are then entered into the computer, and the computer acts on each series of instructions sequentially. The computer operates on one program until all instructions are completed and then operates on the next program. The results of each program are supplied via an output medium from the computer. They can then be transferred off-line to another peripheral device specified by the operator. All information could be written on cards, and the cards read sequentially by the computer. In general, however, it is desired to operate the computer as efficiently as possible. Since a card reader is substantially slower than the central processor, the central processor would spend most of its time idle. Thus it is desired to use the fastest input-output peripheral device possible. This frequently means that a tape unit or a disk unit is used to enter data; often, one or more small computers are used to prepare programs for a larger machine. Program preparation and language translation are described in Chap. 12.

Most computers developed to date are organized for batch processing and require the development of extremely fast peripheral devices. Batch processing has the advantage of minimum cost but may introduce substantial delays between the time the operator has written his program on cards and the time the answer is available. This is especially true in a large computer complex where many people are waiting for time on the same computer, and many hours or even days may elapse before a program can be run and the results obtained.

Computer systems have been developed which allow a number of users at remote locations to share the computer simultaneously in real time. These systems vary from those which allow several operators to use part or all of the same computer to those which allow several operators to share the same data and programs within a computer. The term "time sharing" is used to cover these classes of organizations. Here the computer sequentially steps through all input channels. When it discovers a channel that is activated, it acts on these data, either for a specific period of time or according to a preprogrammed priority system. A supervisory program keeps track of the current status of each program and prevents program interference. Priorities can be assigned on the basis of first come, first served; on a round robin basis; or on the basis of the relative importance of each terminal. In this way, the computer sequentially executes a number of programs for short periods of time. From the viewpoint of the operator, the computer belongs to him alone since the delays are very short. Typical delays until an operator is serviced are less than 5 seconds. The actual characteristics depend on the specific properties of the computer, the number of input terminals, the sequencing logic, and the priority controls.

Time sharing requires low-cost remote terminals since many terminals are required. The terminals should be easy to use but do not require high speeds since speed is limited by the response time of the operator. Most terminals are special keyboards or typewriters or cathode-ray displays, although many input devices can be used. Generally, input and output data are presented on the same lines, with a special bit indicating the direction of information flow. The cost of the communication link from the terminal to the computer is also very important. All input-output devices should be fully buffered so that the computer does not have to wait for a specific peripheral device to be ready but can operate on other data during this interval. A system designed for time sharing has

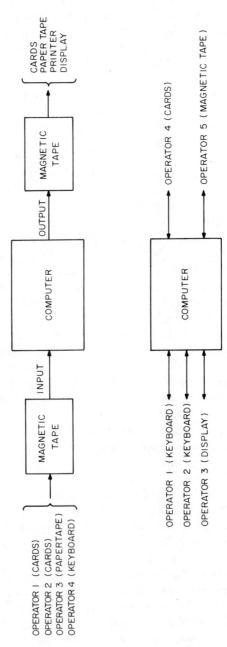

Fig. 10-6 Batch processing and time sharing, input and output.

a substantially different organization than one designed for batch processing, especially in the input-output area and in memory organization. The computer must be designed so that the data and programs of one operator are protected from accidental or deliberate reading or modification by another operator. This is called *memory protection*, and it can be obtained by dividing the memory into sections and making certain sections private to one operator or by other memory-protect schemes. The program normally will be relocated in a different section of the memory each time it is being executed. Memory address registers keep track of the location of any specific program at any time.

Figure 10-6 is a simplified block diagram showing an organization for batch processing and one for time sharing. In batch processing, a number of input and output channels may be provided, instead of the one shown in the diagram. The computer will complete one set of instructions before reading another. In time sharing, the computer steps from one channel to another, executing all or part of a program. If a program is not completed, the computer stores the intermediate information until it is time to continue that program. In both systems, the operator can request output data in a number of formats. Thus operator 1 in both cases could request a printout of his problem solution as well as request it in the same format as the data were entered. Generally, a computer designed for time sharing will also be used for batch processing.

The next chapter will describe the organization of the computer in greater detail.

EXERCISES

10-1. What is the difference between on-line and off-line equipment?

10-2. What are some of the characteristics of peripheral devices? How are they specified?

10-3. Using the punched-card format of Fig. 10-2, how would you code your name and telephone number?

10-4. What are the differences between paper tape and magnetic tape?

10-5. Obtain detailed data on any specific computer. What peripheral devices are available? What are some of the input-output characteristics and specifications?

10-6. Select one of the following types of peripheral devices. Review the literature on the device and write a description of its operation.

    (a)   Display station
    (b)   Audio-output device
    (c)   Character-recognition device
    (d)   Plotter

10-7. Describe batch processing and time sharing as they affect the input-output area.

ELEVEN

Computer Organization

11-1 *General Design Considerations*

A computer is essentially an information-processing device which accepts input data, manipulates the data by combining, modifying, or performing arithmetic operations, and produces a result at the output. A computer can be designed to solve a specific class of problems very efficiently or to solve a wider variety of problems with a more extensive series of instructions and a greater number of programs. A special-purpose computer can be designed in those cases where it is desired to optimize the computer performance for very specific objectives, e.g., as a guidance computer on a rocket. Most early computers were special-purpose machines. In general, however, designing a computer organized around a particular user's requirements is an expensive endeavor due to the high cost of initial design plus the fact that the machine normally will be manufactured in small quantity.

As the application for computers expanded, companies began to market general-purpose computers designed to fulfill a major portion of the various users' requirements. The introduction of the general-purpose computer allowed a company to fabricate many similar machines and utilize more efficient manufacturing techniques. The cost of such systems was effectively reduced due to one-time design costs, common documentation, and common programming aides. However, to meet the diverse needs of a number of users, a general-purpose computer is usually designed to have a much larger command repertoire plus a greater variety of software.

Computers designed for business purposes have generally differed from those designed to solve scientific problems. The major difficulty in making scientific and business computers identical is the difference in the type and volume of data to be processed. As a rule, business problems usually require large amounts of data to be processed with a minimum amount of mathematical computation and are limited by input-output data transfer rates. A scientific problem generally requires a large number of mathematical operations to be performed on a relatively small

amount of data and is limited by the speed of the central processor. In
addition, more flexibility may have to be designed into a scientific
machine since problem areas are less well defined. The differences in
user requirements have also led to the development of separate programming languages oriented toward either business or scientific applications.
These languages are discussed further in Chap. 12.

Although a given problem can be solved on almost any computer, the
cost of program conversion and required processing time may prove
inefficient and expensive. Just as a computer is much more efficient in
solving most problems than is an operator with an adding machine, so
one computer may be more efficient than another computer in solving a
given problem. It should be noted, however, that efforts are being made
to develop universal computer languages and hardware that will more
efficiently meet the needs of both scientific and business applications. In
recent years, the distinctions between business and scientific machines
have tended to lessen as more powerful and universal computers have
been developed.

A general-purpose computer system consists of a central processor and
a number of peripheral devices. The central processor includes the elements illustrated in Fig. 11-1, while the peripheral devices could be any
of those discussed in Chap. 10. If the peripheral device is under the
control of the central processor, it is considered to be an on-line device.
Traditionally, computer systems have been organized such that the programs to be processed are prepared on off-line equipment and subsequently
transferred onto high-speed magnetic tape or punched cards. The independent programs are then written sequentially, and the entire batch is
processed one program at a time. This batch processing improves the
utilization of the central processor since it handles the programs of many
users who can be working independently of one another in defining their
programs. However, this system has the disadvantage that the user is
isolated from the central processor and must wait for a turn to run his

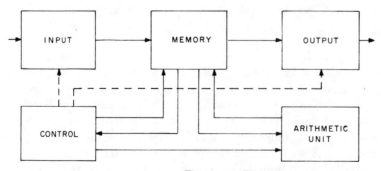

Fig. 11-1   Elements of a computer.

program.   If a mistake is made in writing the original program, it may
not be found until the central processor runs the program and produces
erroneous results.   Then the output is returned to the user for analysis
and correction, and he must rewrite his program and submit a modified
program for processing.   If the demand for computer time is excessive,
it may be hours or even days before the programmer can obtain results.
For these reasons, another approach to organization, commonly referred
to as *time sharing*, has been developed.   In a time-sharing system, each
user has an on-line terminal device which is connected to the central
processor.   The computer, in a preset order, follows the instructions from
each input for a short period of time.   Since the response of the central
processor is much faster than the response time of any operator or of the
peripheral equipment, each user effectively has immediate response from
the processor and is unaware and unconcerned about the other users'
demands.   Time-sharing systems are discussed further in the last section
of this chapter.

Some systems applications require the computer to respond almost
instantaneously to input signals monitored by the machine.   The output
of such a system may be used to control a manufacturing process, correct
the trajectory of a guided missile, monitor and control the traffic pattern
of a large airport, or respond to the actions of future astronauts on a
simulated space mission.   Some savings banks have central-processor
and mass-memory systems which store the entire updated history of each
account.   Information on the accounts is made accessible to each teller
via terminal equipment, and any teller can update an account when
desired.   There are also similar airline reservation systems which produce,
on demand, information to reservation agents on departure times and
available space on flights as far as a year in advance.   These types of
installations are referred to as *real-time computer systems*.   A real-time
(on-line) computer receives its input data at the time the data are generated, processes these data, and presents an output which is used immediately.   The speed of the computer is determined by external factors
since the computer operates synchronously with another system.

A computer can be designed as a special-purpose or general-purpose
machine.   It can be intended primarily for scientific or for business
applications.   It can be developed for batch-processing operations or
can possess time-sharing capability.   It can be part of a real-time or a
non-real-time system.   The intended applications for the computer, its
required instruction complement, the number and types of peripheral
devices, the required software, and many other factors influence the
design of the computer.   This chapter will discuss characteristics affecting
the organization of the central processor and will show the organization
of one machine.

One of the more evident differences between the various computers offered in the market is the word format used in each machine. A fixed-word-format single-address machine intended for scientific application will differ substantially in organization from a business machine which has a variable word format and provisions for multiple addressing. The choice of word format depends on the desired properties of the computer, its instruction complement, and the types of problems the computer will be solving.

Another consideration in the design of a computer is the capability of expanding the basic system to meet the future requirements of the user. This entails adding components to an existing computer installation with a minimum of time and effort. These components may be additional peripheral devices, additional memory capacity, or other options offered for expansion of the primary elements of the computer. This expansion feature is important since the user at first may only require a basic system. Rather than having to replace the entire computer as his requirements expand, he can simply add to what he already has. In this way, the user does not have to pay for parts of a system which are not required initially.

Other important considerations in the design and organization of a computer are its anticipated costs, its required speed, its memory and input-output characteristics, and the programming effort that will be required to use it. The programming costs for operating a computer system will sometimes exceed the cost of the hardware. All manufacturers offer their customers software **support** as a means of reducing these programming costs.

11-2 *Elements of a Computer*

Although no two computers are identical in their organization, there is a certain amount of commonality among them. The basic logic building blocks described throughout this text are used in all computer systems. The five basic elements illustrated in Fig. 11-1 make up the central processor. However, the organization of these elements may differ substantially from one machine to the next, depending on the desired properties of the computer, even though the general function of each element is similar. This section will expand on some of the special system functions which may be performed by each element, in order to give an insight as to why computer organizations vary. In addition, the reader is referred to Chaps. 6, 7, 9, and 10 for detailed descriptions of each element.

A computer system may have more than one central processor (Fig. 11-1), but at a minimum, it must have one central processor and one or more peripheral devices. The central processor may use one of the many types of internal memory, and the arithmetic and control units may be organized in a variety of ways. The design of the input-output area is heavily dependent on the peripheral equipment. Most peripheral devices are organized to handle data in groups of bits called *characters*, and in many cases, this makes them incompatible with the fixed-word format of the central processor. In addition, there is a speed-compatibility problem between the devices and the central processor. The peripheral devices are orders of magnitude slower than the main computer and vary substantially in speed from one device to another. The input-output element of a computer provides the interface between the slow peripheral devices and the rest of the computer and allows the computer to utilize its very high processing speed more efficiently. At the same time, it translates data from a form the programmer can use to a form the computer can use.

Input-Output Units. The high-speed, random-access internal memory of the central processor has a limited amount of storage capacity. The designer would like to have an extremely large internal storage, but this is uneconomical due to the cost per bit of storage for fast internal memories. Thus, the system designer and programmer often use slower, external-storage devices for storing subroutines, math libraries, and other data pertinent to the solution of the problems under consideration. An external device must be capable of being addressed by the central processor through the input-output transfer bus of the central processor. Although the central processor may demand and receive data from a peripheral storage medium, it does not directly control the operation of the device. The intervening logic between the device and the processor is usually referred to as the *device controller*.

As an example of how a controller functions, consider a computer system which includes a central processor and a magnetic-tape unit. The programmer may have a large number of subroutines, for performing complex mathematical operations, stored on a magnetic-tape unit which is on-line to the computer. Each of the subroutines is stored as records (blocks of data) on the tape and is referenced by the main programs stored in the internal memory. While processing a program, an operation may have to be performed requiring a subroutine which is stored on the magnetic tape. Thus, under program control, a command is transferred onto the input-output bus which states "Sequentially transfer to the main memory starting with location ABC the contents of record XYZ." At this point, the device controller takes over. It stores the record address XYZ in a register and starts the device on a search operation for that particular record. When the record is located on the tape, the controller sends a signal to the computer to signify that it is ready to start transferring data, and subsequently data are entered into the computer as described in Sec. 10-5. The data are transferred from the magnetic tape to the computer by the device controller, which supplies timing signals to the computer in synchronization with the timing pulses received from the tape. This element actually serves as the middleman between the main computer and the device by providing the logic necessary to interface them. Controllers are used for virtually all types of peripheral devices.

Many peripheral devices such as magnetic tape, paper tape, and typewriters are organized to store characters rather than words. This makes them incompatible with computers designed around fixed-word formats. Such computers require word-forming buffers as an interface between the character-oriented devices and the fixed-word-length processor. These word-forming buffers may be part of the input-output unit, but they are usually a portion of the device controller, where the timing signals required for the conversion operation are readily available. An example of the conversion and transfer process from character-oriented tape to fixed-word storage is illustrated in Fig. 10-5. This example shows the buffer operation as it might be performed in the input-output unit of the central processor. Independent of the physical location of the logic, each 6-bit character is stored sequentially in a portion of a buffer register to form a computer word. A reverse conversion process utilizing a buffer register is required to go from fixed-word format to character organization.

Another function frequently designed into the input-output unit is that of allowing external lines to interrupt a program which is being processed. Peripheral devices can interface with the central processor when both devices are ready; they can be fully buffered by an independent input-output processor, or they can be allowed to interrupt the program when they are ready to accept or receive data. To have the computer remain idle until the slower-speed peripheral device is ready is very inefficient. On the other hand, it is not feasible to activate the peripheral device only when the central processor is ready. The inertia of a magnetic-tape system is too great to permit starting and stopping for each character. Therefore, a program-interrupt system is usually set up to allow several input-output operations to proceed while computation is being performed. Whenever the peripheral device is ready, computation is suspended and the input-output transfer is executed. A computer with interrupt logic monitors the external lines for control signals, which occur asynchronously with respect to the internal timing of the computer. When a line becomes active, the current program is momentarily stopped and the data on the active interrupt channel are processed. The external lines may be from peripheral devices or from real-time input lines which demand immediate processing. In the case of a peripheral-device interface, the interrupt feature can be designed to allow the computer to process a program while waiting for the slower device to transmit or receive the next piece of data. There are a number of automatic and programmable ways in which interrupts can be designed.   One method is to complete the execution of the instruction in the program at the time an INTERRUPT signal is received.   The contents of the program counter, which contains the address of the next instruction in the program, is stored in a preassigned location, and the computer jumps to a subroutine to process the data on the channel which caused the interrupt.   Upon completion of this subroutine, the stored instruction address is read and the program, which was interrupted, continues.   A priority is generally assigned to multiple external interrupt lines so the computer can determine the order in which multiple INTERRUPT signals should be obeyed.

Almost all computers, scientific and business, have an input-output bus. These buses enable a central processor to interface with many peripheral devices.   A computer system may have a central processor which is connected to magnetic tapes, line printers, card readers, and other peripheral devices.   With a single bus organization, only one device can transfer data into the bus at one time although techniques can be used to time-share the bus sequentially between multiple slow-responding devices. With multiple channels, a number of peripheral devices can be addressed simultaneously.   Each device connected to the central processor has a unique address to allow the computer to select any device by providing proper control signals.   The operation of the input-output bus is similar to that of the transfer bus in the control unit discussed in Chap. 9.

The design of the input-output areas is influenced by the number and types of peripheral devices, the relationship of the computer word format to the particular characters of each peripheral device, the device controlling and word-forming properties, the characteristics of the priority interrupt logic, and other system requirements.

Memory Unit.   The memory is used to store data and instructions until needed by the computer.   It is desirable to be able to store very large amounts of data and obtain these data at speeds comparable to the speed of the arithmetic section.   Random-access high-speed memories, however, are more expensive per bit of storage than slower-speed sequential-access memories, and different memories may be used in a computer to provide a variety of storage capacities with different access times.

The memory is organized around the word format of the particular computer.   There is a significant difference in memory organization between a fixed-word-length and a variable-word-length computer.   In both cases, the word is a physical location in memory which is addressable by proper selection of X and Y lines.   However, the number of bits so addressed and the logic required to properly address data may vary significantly in the two cases.   Memory design and cost are also dependent on the word length of the computer. The memory of a 32-bit computer will cost much more than that of a 16-bit computer for the same number of words of storage.

Most memories have been designed so that every word of memory can be directly addressed by the operator. A number of addressing schemes are possible to accomplish this. The computer word can specify any absolute address or can reference any address within a given area. When it is desired to specify a memory address in another area, more than one instruction word may be required. This is analogous to telephone direct dialing, where more digits are required to make a long-distance call than to place a local one.

It is desirable for the programmer to protect himself from accidentally destroying a subroutine he has written. It is possible to allow certain segments of the memory *to be read only* under normal operation. In cases where more than one program is written in the memory, it may be desirable to protect the program of one user from accidental or deliberate reading or modification by another user. With memory-protect features, certain sections of the memory are not accessible unless a particular code word or subprogram is recognized. When the word is written, the computer translates it and provides special program-control signals. In this way, the privacy of data can be guaranteed, and there is less likelihood of accidental program modification.

Multiprogramming is a system in which several batch-processed or time-shared programs are stored in a computer. Only one program is acted on at any time by any section of the computer, but when the program is complete or the computer is waiting for more information, it automatically switches to the next program. Different parts of the computer can be acting on different programs at the same time. For example, while the results of the last program are being transferred on the output bus, another program is being executed in the central processor, and a third program may be read into the memory. In multiprogramming, the memory must be divided into distinct segments so that the execution of one program cannot interfere with the activities of another.

A *multiprocessing* system uses two or more central processors to handle a total programming load. The central processors, which may be working independently or as duplicate computers, have access to one or more shared memory elements in order to reference common programs and to handle peak memory requirements. Usually, the two computers can also share the same peripheral units. A multiprocessing system is highly reliable since, if one computer develops a malfunction, it can automatically be removed from the processing path and the other computer can handle the entire load, although at a slower rate.

A large computer system may use multiprogramming, multiprocessing, and time sharing, or any one feature may be designed into the computer. Each will have an effect on memory organization.

Arithmetic Unit. The design of the arithmetic element is influenced by the considerations described in Chap. 6. In general, the arithmetic element contains an adder or accumulator and a number of registers with transfer paths between them. Subtraction can be performed by means of one of the methods of complement addition or, in a few cases, by special subtractors. Either serial or parallel logic can be used to implement this process. In some computers, portions of the memory are used in place of arithmetic registers, with control signals supplied by programming means.

A major decision in the design of the arithmetic unit involves how many arithmetic operations to provide as hardware (and, therefore, as part of the machine's instruction complement) and how many to provide as software. A DIVIDE instruction built into the machine would result in proper control signals applied to the arithmetic unit so that one number could be divided by another directly. A DIVIDE operation implemented by a software routine involves a series of instructions to the memory and control units which result in a series of addition, shifting, and comparison steps. One possible routine is suggested in Sec. 6-14. In this routine, the computer acts as if it has a DIVIDE instruction. Implementation of arithmetic operations by software results in lower hardware costs, but the operations take much longer to perform since at least one extra memory cycle is required to perform any instruction.

Other system considerations in the design of the arithmetic section include the word length and format, whether a fixed point or a floating point is required, and the general speed and performance requirements of the computer.

Control Unit. The control unit contains the clock generator, counters, registers, and logic which provide the sequentially timed command signals that are distributed throughout the central processor. These signals execute the instructions the computer is designated to perform. The process by which command signals are generated and the detailed operation of some of the logic circuits in a control unit are covered in Chap. 9.

A typical instruction-execution sequence, performed in a two-cycle operation of instruction time and execute time, is as follows:

1. A fetch cycle is initiated, and an instruction word is read from the memory location specified by the program counter.

2. The computer normally will go into an execute cycle by addressing one or more memory locations to obtain the data and by performing the

operation specified by the instruction on these data.   In a single-address machine, the execution cycle may involve obtaining the data in memory location XYZ and adding it to the number in the accumulator.

In some cases, an indirect-address bit is specified in the instruction word.   The address portion of the instruction becomes the address of the next instruction to be executed, and the current instruction is not executed.

In other cases, an index operation may be specified.   This results in modification of the data address by adding the contents of an index register to the address specified in the instruction to obtain the effective address of the data.   These data are then read from the memory, and the operation specified in the instruction is performed.

The program counter is then increased by 1, and another cycle is initiated by fetching the next sequential instruction unless the sequence was broken by either indexing or indirect addressing.

The instruction-execution sequence as defined by the previous steps requires two readings of the contents of specific memory locations.   One access is required to obtain the instruction word, and another to obtain the data specified by the address of the instruction.   With a few instructions, no operand is specified and only one memory access is required.   In some cases, three or more memory access times are necessary if indirect addressing is specified.   The time required to perform a specific instruction is the sum of the fetch time, which is required to obtain the instruction word specified by the program counter from the memory, and the execute time, which is required to retrieve the operand from memory and execute the operation code specified by the instruction.   While the fetch time, sometimes referred to as the *memory-cycle time*, is fixed for any computer, the execute time varies considerably depending on the specific operation being performed.

In order to minimize processing time, many computers utilize the concept of overlapping fetch.   This technique allows the fetch operation to start before the previous execute operation is complete.   The program counter is incremented as soon as the fetch operation is initiated.   Thus the program counter always stores the address of the next instruction. When the instruction-execute sequence arrives at the point where the computer starts to execute the operand portion of the instruction, the next instruction fetch can be enabled.   In this way, the control unit continuously retrieves the next instruction while the previous instruction is being executed.

In many high-speed computers, the concept of overlapping fetch is taken one step further by utilizing an instruction look-ahead.   With instruction look-ahead, the control section not only retrieves the next instruction while the arithmetic unit is processing the previous operation but also retrieves the next operand. Thus the control section has the next operation code ready to process by the time the arithmetic unit finishes the previous operation.

The *instruction complement*, or *command repertoire*, refers to the operations which a computer can implement. The larger the instruction complement, the more rapidly can problems be executed; but the cost of the computer also increases as the instruction complement increases. The computer designer must decide which instructions are needed and how best to implement them.

A number of classes of instructions are normally provided in each computer. These include:

1. Arithmetic instructions, such as add, multiply, divide
2. Load and store instructions for transferring data between the memory and various registers
3. Logic instructions, such as logic AND, OR, exclusive OR
4. Shift instructions for moving data within and between registers
5. Jump instructions for jumping to specified memory locations or for branching in one of two or more directions based on certain conditions being fulfilled
6. Input-output instructions for performing input-output operations
7. Control instructions for supplying start, stop, and other basic commands

In addition, the computer may be designed to accept floating-point and decimal arithmetic instructions, special instructions for the index registers, and other desired commands.

Each instruction is represented by a different combination of bits in the operation-code portion of the instruction word. The control section of the computer is designed to decode the operation code and to generate the timing signals necessary to implement each instruction. In the design phase, decisions are made as to what the command repertoire of a computer should be. Since the efficiency of a computer is heavily dependent on its instruction complement, it is desirable to have a large number of instructions. This, however, increases the cost of the system, and at some point, a compromise is reached between the instruction complement and the cost. The trade-off usually involves which instructions to implement with software. Instructions implemented with software result in a lower hardware cost but increase the computer time required to perform these instructions. In addition, the storage of algorithms, which specify the programmed steps required to perform given computations, may require a significant number of memory locations.

11-3 *Organization of a Computer*

A major portion of this text discusses the logical implementation of the multiple functions performed within a computer. Other sections of the text deal with the operational aspects of a computer. This section will tie the two together by presenting the organizational block diagram of a computer along with a description of how information flows between the blocks.

Figure 11-2 is a block diagram of a single-address fixed-word-format machine which is principally oriented toward real-time applications. A variable-format organization differs from a fixed-word format in that most information is handled as characters (groups of 6 to 9 bits). Although the two formats may differ in organization, the mechanism by which instructions are executed inside the computer can be similar. Figure 11-2 is one example of many possible ways in which a computer can be organized. This computer is organized around special-purpose registers, with a transfer bus between registers. No two computers offered in the market have identical organizations or characteristics, and some may differ significantly in detail from Fig. 11-2.

The single-address word length in this organization is 24 bits: 2 index bits, 1 bit for indirect addressing, 6 bits for the operation code, and 15 bits for the memory address. Information is processed in a parallel fashion, with data transfers between blocks occurring simultaneously. Thus, when the contents of the A register are transferred to the adder by activation of command line ATA, all 24 bits are transferred simultaneously. The key to system timing is the control logic, which receives its instructions from the operation-code register. All the input signals to gates are identified by specific three-letter codes, e.g., ATA, ZTT, and SAL, which represent "A register to adder," "Z register to transfer bus," and "Shift A register left." These command signals are generated in the control unit. Refer to Figs. 9-1 and 9-2 for examples of command-signal generation. These control signals are distributed throughout the computer and provide the means for executing various operations.

The following paragraphs give a short functional description of the principal blocks in the system. The *transfer bus* is a 24-bit gating structure which serves as the data-transfer medium for the system. Information is transferred by the simultaneous gating of paths to and from the bus. Refer to Sec. 9-4 for a description of the operational aspects of the bus. The *A register* is a 24-bit register which is the primary arithmetic and logic register of the central processor. Data from the arithmetic-unit bus are gated into this register by command line AUA. The output from the A register is gated to the transfer bus by ATT. Outputs are also gated to the adder by command signals ATA and CAA. ATA gates the

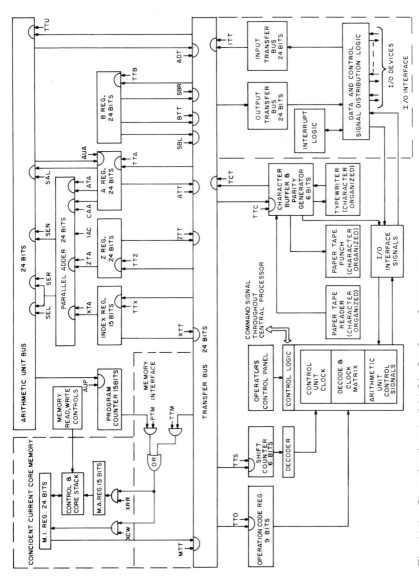

Fig. 11-2 Organization 2 of 24-bit fixed-word computer.

265

assertion outputs of the A register to the adder for addition, and CAA gates the complement outputs of the A register to the adder for performing complement subtraction. During a left-shift operation, SAL gates the A register 1 bit to the left on the arithmetic-unit bus. The 24-bit *B register* is an extension of the A register for multiplication, division, and certain shifting operations where more than 24 bits are required. The 24-bit *Z register* receives data from the memory by way of the transfer bus. After an instruction is read out of the memory during a fetch operation, the Z register contains the memory-address portion of the instruction in its least-significant 15 bits. After data are read out of the memory, the Z register contains the 24-bit data word.

The *index register* is 15 bits long and can be used to modify the memory address to obtain a new effective address. The computer organization can be expanded to have three index registers, with 2 bits in the instruction word reserved for index-register selection. Index registers allow the programmer to perform jump instructions by adding a certain number stored in an index register to the memory address of an instruction word. The 9-bit *operation-code register* contains the coded instruction which the computer is currently executing. The 15-bit *program counter* is a binary counter which contains the memory address (location) of the next instruction to be performed. In normal operation, its contents are incremented by 1 each time a new command is fetched from memory. In cases when a jump instruction is being executed, the program counter is loaded with the address of the memory location to which the program is to jump.

The 6-bit *shift counter* is a down counter which is used during instructions that require shifting. At the beginning of a shift operation, the desired number of shifts is transferred into the register by control line TTS. The shift counter allows shift operations to occur as long as the count is not 0. Each time a shift occurs, the counter is reduced by 1. This continues until the desired number of shift operations is completed and the shift counter contains all 0s.

The *adder* is a logic structure which can produce the algebraic sum of the A and Z registers. During indexing, the adder produces the sum of the index register and the 15 least-significant bits of the Z register. During arithmetic operations, such as subtract, divide, and multiply, the A register is gated to the adder in either its true or 1s-complement form. The results from the adder are always transferred to the A register via control lines SEN and AUA. The adder is also used to perform logic operations, e.g., forming the exclusive OR of two numbers. In this case, the IAC signal inhibits carries from being propagated in the adder.

The following sequence of steps describes how a typical instruction is executed within the general block diagram of Fig. 11-2.

1. During the execution time of the previous instruction, the command lines PTM and XRR are activated. PTM transfers the contents of the program counter to the memory address register (M.A. REG), and XRR initiates a READ cycle in the memory element. This operation places the instruction word specified by the program counter in the memory information register (M.I. REG). XCW is activated when it is desired to write information into the memory.

2. When the previous instruction is complete, command lines MTT, TTZ, and TTO are activated. This places the 9-bit operation code in the operation-code register and the operand address in the Z register..

3. If an index or indirect address is not specified, the control lines ZTT, TTM, and XRR are activated. This fetches the operand specified by the operand address in the Z register and places it in the memory information register.

4. At the same time, the operation code is decoded and a sequence of command lines is activated. For example, if the operation code specifies "Transfer the contents of the memory location specified by the operand address to the A register," the command lines MTT and TTA will be activated, placing the contents of the memory information register into the A register. Note that this simple instruction requires two memory-fetch cycles to complete and that relatively few command signals are generated as a result of decoding the operation code. An instruction such as ADD requires the activation of more command lines, while other operations such as MULTIPLY would require even more. Usually, the execution time is increased by the number of commands required to execute the instruction. Depending on the organization, the execution time of a typical MULTIPLY instruction may take four or five times as long as an ADD instruction.

The control logic, clock, decode and clock matrix, and arithmetic-control signals generate the sequentially timed control signals, as described in Chap. 9. The input-output area shown in Fig. 11-2 is organized as described in Chap. 10 and Sec. 11-2. Other command lines shown in the figure are used to transfer data from one register to another or to shift data within a register.

The reader is reminded again that the example is one of a fixed-word-length computer and that a variable-length machine would have a different organization. In a variable-length computer, the memory and arithmetic units are organized around characters. The control section supplies more command lines for processing each instruction, and the input-output section will probably have more capabilities built into it. On the other hand, a variable-length computer has a smaller arithmetic unit and may not require as much internal-memory capacity.

11-4   *Time-sharing Systems*

A computer can be used by a single operator, who enters information into the computer through one of its input devices and receives information through one of the output devices.   There is, however, a substantial difference—between one million and one billion to one—in the response times of the computer central processor and of the operator.   This means that with only one operator, the computer would spend most of its time waiting for input information.   In addition, the operator might desire access to a very powerful computer with a large instruction complement, a large memory, a good library of programming routines, and a variety of peripheral equipment.   Such a computer system is very expensive. In order to use a large computer more efficiently and to divide the cost of the computer among more users, most computers are operated in a batch-processing mode.

Batch processing refers to a method of problem solution in which programs are prepared independently by a number of users.   The programs are then coded and prepared in off-line equipment.   A number of programs are then sequentially written on tape or other media for entry into a central computer.   The computer operates on each program, one at a time, until the entire batch of programs has been processed.   In cases where the program is well defined and is free from error, batch processing offers a very efficient method of operation and makes the computer less dependent on human response time.   The computer can work out the payroll for the week, analyze the company's sales for the year, and then review the inventory status of all manufacturing material.   Programs from a number of operators can be run without human intervention, and a large computer center can be run almost continuously.   The efficiency of a computer center is frequently indicated by the number of hours per week the computer is operational.   Batch processing has disadvantages when programs contain errors or when there is need for a closer relationship between the user and the computer.   When the program is written, the user must frequently wait his turn until time is available on the computer.   A program, after being written and coded, may be supplied to a central group of operators for key punching, transfer of the program to tape, and running on the computer.   When the program has been run and results obtained, the user may discover errors in his program.   He must then debug the program and repeat the sequence.   Often, due to the delay in running the program, it may take hours or even days to correct very simple programming errors.   It is desirable to allow the programmer to interact more closely with the computer in real time and still retain many of the economies of batch processing.

Time-sharing systems have been developed which provide this advantage. In a time-sharing system, the computer's time is divided among many users; each has a small increment of time repeated at frequent intervals. This allows many people to work with the computer simultaneously as if they alone were using it. It also allows many operators to cooperate with one another in the development of common programs. During his selected time, the user has the full attention of the computer and all or a portion of his program can be executed. The computer then switches to the next channel, executes a portion of its program, and continues until all active channels have been serviced; the computer then returns to the first user. In this respect, a time-sharing computer is similar to a switching network or multiplexer which switches between many inputs and divides a total available time among many users. The time a given input is activated is called the *process time*. The time in switching from one input to another and in getting ready to execute the program by transferring data and instructions into the memory is called the *swap time*. Because of the high speed of a computer, only a very short process time, a few thousandths of a second, can be assigned to each channel. By minimizing the swap time and by having a moderate number of inputs, each user can essentially have immediate access to the computer. As the number of active channels increases, or as the swap times becomes long, the computer eventually reaches an overload condition and must refuse other users. The number of users can be increased by decreasing the swap time or by providing a shorter process time for any one user. A time-sharing computer might be designed so that it has 100 input terminals, any 25 of which can be used at one time. When more than this number requests processing time, the computer prints a message stating that access to the computer is not available.

Most computers can be modified for time-sharing application. The design of a computer specifically for time sharing, however, affects the computer organization, particularly in the memory, input-output, and internal-control areas. A time-shared computer must be extremely reliable, and this usually results in duplicate system hardware. A variety of time-sharing systems have been developed. They vary in the number and types of input terminals, the order and priority with which these input terminals are serviced, and the programming language or languages that they can use. Programming languages will be discussed in the next chapter.

A time-sharing computer can service a variety of input terminals, including typewriters, light pens, or any of the peripheral devices described in Chap. 10. In addition, a console terminal may use a small general-purpose computer to convert data from one code to another, buffer messages to and from the typewriter, display station, or other peripheral device, and serve as a message concentrator.   Data can be sent from the terminal by means of direct wiring, data phones, teletype links, or other means.   If only one input terminal is activated, information flow into the computer is identical to that described previously.   When more than one terminal is used, however, the time on each channel, the time and method of switching from one channel to another, and the sequence and priority of accepting inquiries must be established.   Each inquiry station could be serviced for an equal period of time on a round robin basis. When the maximum acceptable number of stations are on line, the computer can refuse to accept inputs from other stations until one of the initial stations is turned off.   More sophisticated priority systems can be set up based on the time each channel has been serviced, its relative activity, the type or importance of each program, or other criteria.

In general, the computer will activate an input channel for a given period of time, performing computations, making decisions, or supplying input-output control signals, and then will shift to the next input terminal. The time allocated to each program is critical; too short a processing time for a given channel leads to frequent swaps and is inefficient.   If a program runs too long without interruption, only a limited number of terminals can be serviced.

For the computer to follow a series of instructions, the instructions and the data upon which the instructions are to be performed must be available in the memory.   Therefore, it is essential to have a very large memory in a time-sharing system in order to store the programs of all input stations and to provide a common library of subroutines.   Ideally, all data should be available in fast-access core memory.   From an economic point of view, it is impossible to provide sufficient core storage for all data, and a hierarchy of memories is provided.   These memories might include cores, disks, drums, and tapes, in order of decreasing speed and cost per bit of storage.   The backup storage holds the programs not needed at the time, while the main memory holds all or part of the program under execution, the common subroutines, and a supervisory program.   The efficiency of a time-sharing system is very dependent on which data are stored in which memory.   Programs and data are continuously being transferred from one memory to another in order to have the right material in the right place at the right time.   The decision of where to put what data in order to minimize the average swap time is very important.   The most frequently used data should be stored in the fastest-access memory, while information which is only occasionally referenced can be provided in slower-speed tape storage.   At the time it is likely to be needed, however, data should be transferred to a faster-access memory.

Programs are frequently divided into segments so that a subroutine or subprogram common to many programs need only be written once in the memory and then referenced by identifying the segment by a unique name. Programs are also divided into standard-size pieces, or pages, and only those pages required by a running program are brought into the main memory. In this way, pages from a number of programs can be stored in the main memory simultaneously.

An operator must have full access to his program in order to add to it or modify it. At the same time, he will usually have his own library of common programs and subprograms which he may reference during the writing of his program. His library will be added to from time to time, but a program in the library will not often be modified. The user may also wish to reference a common library of subprograms developed by the computer designers or by other operators. Here the program may be read but should not be modified by any one user. Finally, the time-sharing system must be set up in such a way that it is impossible for one program to read, erase, or modify the contents of another program. This is normally accomplished by requiring the operator to supply coded command words in order to initiate his program and use general programs.

The function of the supervisory program, also called the *executive program* or *monitor*, is to act as a general office manager for the time-sharing system, allocating time between the users and performing general scheduling. The supervisory program assigns all memory locations and codes these locations. The user references the code name, and the supervisory program translates this code into the current absolute address of this program. As the program is relocated from one memory to another or within the same memory, the supervisory program keeps track of its location. The supervisor also calls for subroutines where required, loads new programs, provides the control signals for input-output functions, and in general, handles routine clerical operations. One of the clerical operations it performs is to keep a record of the accumulated running time of each user on the central processor. The supervisory program also can keep track of the programs in the file and supply this information to any operator. When two programs require simultaneous use of the same peripheral device, the supervisory program resolves the conflict and provides the appropriate commands. Commands of each user are automatically translated into correct machine instructions. The supervisory program keeps track of the programming language used by each operator and, when required, calls in the proper compiler and library of subroutines. The next chapter will introduce some of the basic concepts of programming.

Figure 11-3 is a diagram of one time-sharing system. The file which is shown in the diagram as one drum might include a disk file and a number of drums to provide greater storage. The user's console might also include graphic-display terminals. Outputs from any station can be

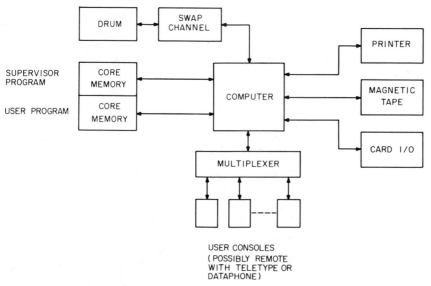

SUPERVISOR
PROGRAM

USER PROGRAM

Fig. 11-3   Time-sharing system.

supplied directly to the programmer or can be supplied in any desired format.

EXERCISES

11-1. Describe the differences between:

    (*a*) A special-purpose and a general-purpose computer in terms of cost and applications

    (*b*) A scientific and a business computer

    (*c*) Real-time and non-real-time computers

11-2. Review the specifications of a particular computer and describe it in terms of the criteria of Exercise 11-1.

11-3. Describe batch processing and time sharing.

11-4. What functions are performed by a device controller?

11-5. Define multiprogramming and multiprocessing.

11-6. Describe the primary function of each block in Fig. 11-2.

11-7. Obtain a list of the instruction complement of a particular computer and categorize the instructions into the classes outlined in Sec. 11-2.

11-8. Draw a more detailed block diagram of the transfer bus shown in Fig. 11-2 using AND and OR gates.

11-9. How would information be transferred from the A register to the memory? Which command lines are activated and in what sequence?   Refer to Fig. 11-2.

11-10. Draw a timing chart for the addition of two numbers within the organization of Fig. 11-2. Use the following instructions: "Transfer one number to the A register," "Add the second number to the contents of the A register," and "Transfer the sum to a location in memory." Show the relative timing of the activated command lines for each of the three instructions.

11-11. In Fig. 11-2, how is information read into the memory from a peripheral device?

11-12. Review the organization of any other computer.

11-13. What are the advantages of a time-sharing system?

11-14. If the computer shown in Fig. 11-2 were to be modified for time-sharing application, what are some of the modifications which would be made in its organization?

11-15. What is the purpose of a supervisory program in a time-shared system?

TWELVE

Introduction to Programming

12-1 *Introduction*

The first 11 chapters were concerned with the elements within a computer, i.e., what a computer is and how it works. This chapter introduces some of the basic concepts of program planning, or programming, and discusses how the computer can be used to solve a specific problem. The word "program" refers to the sequence of instructions which the computer must execute in order to solve a problem. The word "software" is used to describe the computer programs or programming aids, e.g., compilers and assembly systems, supplied with a particular computer which allow the programmer to implement his program with maximum efficiency. The basic concepts of programming can be covered here in only the most elementary manner. For detailed programming instruction, the reader is referred to the books on programming listed in the Bibliography as well as to the information available from the manufacturer of the specific computer of interest. As a rule, programming can best be learned by doing. If at all possible, the reader is urged to write a few programs and run them on a computer in order to begin to develop an understanding of the applications and capabilities of a computer.

A computer, assembled from the elements previously described, has many capabilities. It can add, subtract, multiply, divide, accept and print out data, and perform many other functions. In order to implement the various operations, a large number of control signals must be generated. The time required to add two numbers may be a few millionths of a second. If the ADD signal were given by an operator pressing an ADD button, almost all the time would be spent in waiting for the command and very little time in following the instructions. For this reason, the entire set of instructions for a given program is stored in the computer memory. In a stored-program computer, instructions have the same access time as data. At all times, the computer must have specific instructions regarding its next operation. The number of instructions that a computer can follow, as shown in the command repertoire, is limited, and all problems must be reduced into elementary commands understandable by the computer. In other words, the computer must be furnished with a complete program made up of instructions which are recognized by the machine so that each and every step to be performed is defined and available as needed in the problem solution.

The programmer must understand the problem, work out a logical step-by-step approach to the solution of the problem, and then define each step in a language understandable to the computer. This process is usually expanded to include the following eight steps: (1) generally present the problem; (2) analyze the problem, determining what information is available, what answer is needed, and what degree of accuracy is required in the result; (3) form a general approach to the solution; (4) define a precise step-by-step approach to the solution, frequently with the aid of a flow chart; (5) code the precise steps to be followed in a language understandable to the computer; (6) write the instructions on cards, tape, or other media for entry into the computer; (7) enter all the instructions into the computer so that each command generates specific control signals in the proper order, e.g., generate control signal X at time T; and where necessary (8) design a test method to discover errors made in the programming process. Usually, specific coding into machine language is performed by the computer itself, thus allowing the programmer to write instructions in advanced programming languages. Key elements in the procedure are the original statement of the problem, the formulation of a step-by-step procedure to solve the problem, and the coding of this procedure into computer instructions.

12-2 *Problem Definition and Analysis*

All computers are used to solve problems. The word "problem" includes scientific, engineering, marketing, manufacturing, financial, and management areas in which calculations must be performed or information processed, analyzed, reduced, or compared. It is worthwhile, therefore, to review how problems are solved by a human being.

Not all steps used in a problem solution are well understood. However, a number of aspects can be defined. An initial definition or analysis of a problem might include problem restatement in order to establish exactly what is trying to be accomplished, what data are available, and what is trying to be solved and also perhaps to develop some general operational considerations. The next step might include the development of a plan of action and the accumulation of pertinent facts. The problem solution can involve the use of one's memory for retrieving information, the transfer and manipulation of data, the performance of calculations, decision making, and the preparation and changing of instructions based on the validity of the results. Many other steps can be involved, and many problem solutions cannot be defined in terms of these steps, as anyone will agree who has watched woman's intuition reach the correct conclusions long before facts or logic justified it. Two types of problem solutions should therefore be defined.

Problem solutions can be described in terms of algorithmic and heuristic solutions. The computer is extremely effective in solving those problems in which explicit procedures or algorithms can be written. An *algorithm* is a series of simple operations which can be applied to a problem to produce a solution. The word "heuristic" means serving to discover, learn, or invent and describes those approaches which require intuition, judgment, goal setting, and extreme flexibility. The heuristic aspects of problem solving are handled by the programmer prior to the entry of the problem into the computer. The computer handles those portions of the problem which can be described in terms of specific procedures or algorithms. A computer can duplicate man's ability to solve a problem by following a preset series of instructions, by using a memory, by performing arithmetic operations, by transferring information, and by making comparisons and decisions based on previously programmed criteria. Thus it is important to understand where a human being follows a well-defined procedure in solving a problem and where the approach is more intuitive or creative.

It is interesting to review some of the steps followed in solving a specific problem, e.g., in answering the question: "How much will I be paid next week?" An initial step is to determine whether the question refers to gross pay or take-home pay. This is an example of problem restatement or redefinition and might result in a new question: "What will be my take-home pay next week?" In solving this problem, a number of questions must be answered:

1. Am I paid by the hour, or do I receive a base salary? What is my rate? How many hours did I work? What is the overtime policy?

2. What are the Federal and state income tax rates? How many dependents have I claimed?

3. What is the social security deduction? Have I already contributed the full amount for this year, or will an amount be deducted this pay period?

4. What other deductions can I expect? Insurance? Charity? Retirement program? Savings?

Based on the answers to these and related questions, the problem could be solved. In solving the problem, it could be determined that the net pay is related to the hours worked, the hourly rate, and the number of deductions.

An algorithm might be written as follows:

$$P = (H)(R) + \tfrac{1}{2}R(H - 40) - F_3 - S_1 - I_1 - I_2 - C - S_2$$

where   P = net take-home pay and is the problem solution
            H = hours worked
            R = hourly rate
$\tfrac{1}{2}R(H - 40)$ = premium pay for overtime
This would give the gross amount.   To determine the net take-home pay,
the following deductions must be determined: F_3 = Federal tax deduction
for a person in my salary range with three dependents; S_1 = social
security deduction; I_1 = deduction for life insurance and is related to
salary; I_2 = deduction for medical insurance and is related to the number
of dependents; C = weekly deduction for money pledged to charity;
S_2 = weekly deduction for savings program.   By subtracting these and
any other known deductions, the net pay is calculated.

If it is possible to describe the problem solution to this level of detail,
i.e., in a series of explicit mathematical and logical operations, then it
is possible to solve the problem within a computer.   As a rule, a problem
should be analyzed for a general solution.   In this way, the program
could be used for similar types of problems.   A general solution might be
defined, and the information required for the specific solution presented,
either as part of the problem or as background information.   For example,
in determining the entire payroll of a company, information about pay and
tax rates, social security, and other deductions would be placed in storage
prior to the initiation of any specific solution and might not be changed
for months.   On the other hand, the hours worked per employee would
be supplied as an input to the problem each pay period.

It is important to emphasize that there can be substantial differences
between the relative difficulties of a number of problems as seen by a
human being and as seen by a human being using a computer.   A computer can solve a problem if it can be expressed in terms of specific mathematical or logical procedures.   The ease with which the computer solves
a problem is dependent on the simplicity of these rules.   The following
four problems illustrate this point:

1. Given 20 numbers, find the largest.
2. Given the same 20 numbers, add them.
3. Square the integers 1, 2, 3, . . . , 1,000 and add the results.
4. Translate five lines of French poetry into English.

Most people could solve problem 1 in their heads.   Problem 2 is more
difficult and would require pencil and paper.   Problem 3 is so difficult that
few would even attempt it.   The time required to solve problem 4 is
dependent on one's background, but many could solve it within a few
minutes.   The computer would rate these problems differently.   The

first two problems are solved easily, but problem 2 is simpler than problem 1 since fewer instructions and operational steps are required to perform addition than to perform comparison.   Problem 3 can be solved easily by the computer.   While the calculations are cumbersome, the rules for performing these calculations are straightforward, and the problem could be solved in a few thousandths of a second.   Problem 4, on the other hand, is almost unsolvable.   The rules for language translation are quite involved and are not easily written as procedures.   Thus a problem which can easily be stated in English may be extremely difficult to express in detailed computer instructions.

12-3 *Flow Charts*

In determining the method to be used in solving a problem, it is necessary to break the solution procedure into a number of fundamental steps and show the relationship between these steps.   The steps must be specified exactly since the computer will follow instructions exactly.   If there are any gaps or ambiguities in the instructions, the computer will be unable to resolve these differences and therefore will not solve the problem.   Logical steps to be used in approaching a problem can be written mathematically or in tabular form.   A more common approach is by the use of special block diagrams called *flow charts*.

A flow chart is a schematic representation of the logical steps necessary to solve a particular problem.   A number of blocks are drawn representing the various operations.   The flow of information and relative interdependence of these blocks are shown.   One advantage of the use of a flow chart is that a picture assists the programmer in organizing and clarifying his thoughts about a complex problem and forces him to break a problem into logical, workable segments.   By means of a pictorial display, the basic elements of the method of solution are made much more understandable to anyone who has to participate in the work or review it.   A good flow chart brings to light areas of the problem which need further clarification and analysis and aids in the discovery of labor- and time-saving alternate solutions.

There are many different levels of detail possible for a flow chart. Usually, an initial system flow chart is drawn to break down a complex problem into relatively large logic blocks.   A system flow chart may be universal, involving no reference to the computer on which the problem will eventually be solved.   After the system flow chart is completed and is verified, flow charts in much greater detail are drawn for the individual blocks on the system chart.   The level of detail is dependent on the programmer and the problem.   The more detailed and specific to a computer the flow chart is, the easier the coding operation becomes.   Coding into the language of a specific computer occurs after the drawing of the flow chart.

Basically, a flow chart is simply a collection of boxes, lines, arrows, and comments, which taken together, indicate the logical flow to the solution of a problem. Many notations are therefore possible. It is desirable, however, to have a consistent system of symbols and consistent methods of writing comments. The degree of flow-chart standardization which should be established varies with the needs of an organization and the number of individuals who must read each other's flow charts. It is essential that flow charts always be as readable as possible in order to minimize errors. Drawing flow charts is an individualistic process. No two programmers may come up with exactly the same flow chart for a given complex problem, although both may be correct in their analysis and solution of the problem.

Figure 12-1 shows one notation used widely in flow-chart preparation. Each box has one line entering it and one or more lines leaving it. Arrows are used to indicate direction of information flow. A rectangle is used to represent a box in which an operation is performed. A diamond is used to represent a box in which a decision is made; it always has two or more lines leaving it with the conditions specified. An oval or a hexagon is also frequently used to indicate a decision box. A decision box is referred to as a *branch point* since the program can branch in two or more directions. A circle is used to represent a terminal box, i.e., one in which a STOP or START command is given. Other symbols are shown for a card input-output and a printed output. Many other symbols can be defined. An ellipse is frequently used to denote general input-output operations. Normally, all connections are shown by connecting points with straight lines. However, remote connections are used when the flow chart takes

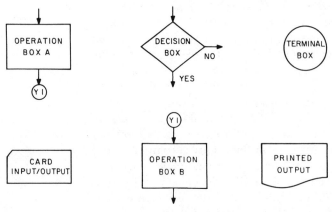

Fig. 12-1   Flow-chart notation.

two or more pages to complete and in situations where direct connections needlessly complicate the drawing. The remote connection Y1 in Fig. 12-1 indicates that the output of operation box A is connected to the input of operation box B.

The meaning of any special symbol should be clearly defined, preferably on the flow chart itself at the place where the symbol is used for the first time. It is desirable that wherever possible, clear English words be used on flow charts rather than symbols. There are a number of acceptable symbols, however, which are common and have well-understood meanings. Some of the most commonly used abbreviations are:

:   comparison (the nature of which is indicated separately)
=   equal to
$\neq$ not equal to
>   greater than
<   less than
$\geq$ greater than or equal to
$\leq$ less than or equal to

The use of these symbols and the development of three flow charts will be shown in the next section.

12-4   *Flow-charting Examples*

There usually are a number of possible ways of solving a particular problem on a computer. Two approaches may be equally desirable, or a best solution may be selected based on some criterion such as ease of programming, actual computing time, the number of bits of memory required by the program, the ease of isolating errors in the program, or overall elapsed time including coding. Two programmers may prepare different flow charts for the same problem solution. The following examples are merely indicative of possible ways of approaching the problem definition and organization by means of a flow chart and are not the only, or necessarily best, solutions.

A-1. *Problem Statement:* 100 positive numbers, stored in memory locations 1000 to 1099, are to be compared, and the largest number is to be stored in the B register.

A-2. *Flow Chart:* See Fig. 12-2.

A-3. *Description of Flow Chart:* The approach to be taken in solving this problem is to compare the first two numbers and store the larger. Then each number is successively compared against the stored number, and whenever a larger number is reached, it becomes the stored number. After the last number is compared, the stored number is the largest. At the beginning of the problem, the B register is reset to 0 and the memory

address register which stores the data address is set to 1000.   A second
address J is set to 1.   J will count the number of times the operation is
performed.   The number in J is compared against 100.   Since it is less,
the data in memory location 1000 are read into the A register.   The
number in the A register is then compared against the number in the
B register.   Since the B register was reset at the beginning of the problem, the number in A is larger and, therefore, is read into the B register.

Next, the data address is increased by 1, and the count in J is increased
by 1.   The data in the corresponding memory location 1001 are read into

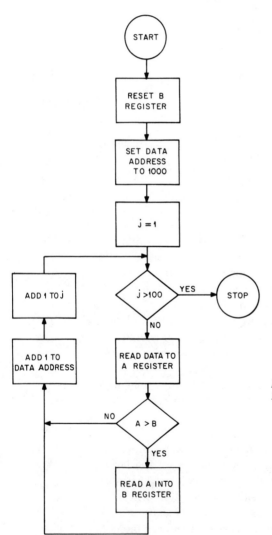

*Fig. 12-2 Flow chart for comparing
100 numbers.*

the A register. This new number is compared against the number in
the B register. If it is larger, it is read into the B register. If it is
smaller, then the B register is left alone. This process is continued, with
each number in memory locations 1002 to 1099 being successively compared against the number in the B register. When any one is larger, the
number in the B register is changed. When J equals 101, the comparison
J > 100 results in a "yes" answer and the problem is stopped. The
number stored in the B register is now the largest of the 100 numbers.

A-4. *General Comments:* It would be possible to define this problem in
the following manner: Read memory location 1000 into A register, compare A with B and either store A or not; read memory location 1001 into
A register, compare A with B and either store A or not; etc. To repeat
these instructions 100 times would provide the same answer but would
take many more steps than required by the flow chart of Fig. 12-2. In
Fig. 12-2, a section of the program is executed repeatedly as J is increased
from 1 to 100. A process of repetitive instructions is called *looping*,
which is the repeated performance of a group of instructions a given
number of times or until certain conditions are fulfilled. In this case,
the loop will be repeated exactly 100 times.

This flow chart is also illustrative of the use of an address which is
incremented by 1 with each cycle. Data are taken out of successive
memory-address locations.

Every flow chart must be checked to guarantee that all possibilities are
included. For example, without the reset-B-register operation, it is
possible that the number in the B register at the solution might have
been in the register at the start of the problem and might have been larger
than any number in memory locations 1000 to 1099. In a similar manner,
if both positive and negative numbers are stored in the memory, the flow
chart must show whether the absolute values are to be compared or
whether a positive number is automatically larger than a negative number.

B-1. *Problem Statement:* The numbers 2 to 1,000 are to be examined.
All numbers which are prime, that is, only divisible by themselves and
unity, are to be printed out.

B-2. *Flow Chart:* See Fig. 12-3.

B-3. *Description of Flow Chart:* The approach to this problem is to
examine each number, *n*, by dividing it by all integers between *n* − 1
and 2. If any division results in 0 remainder, *n* is not a prime number.

The program starts at the top of Fig. 12-3. A 2 is placed in the A
register, and it is then printed out as a prime number. Next, a 1 is
added to the number in the A register, making it 3. This number is
compared against 1,000. Since it is not equal, it is then moved to the
B register. A 3 now appears in both the A and B registers. The B
number is then reduced by 1 to become 2, and 3 is divided by 2. The

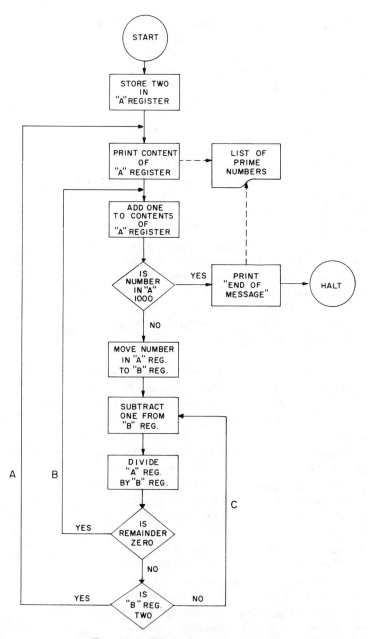

*Fig. 12-3   Flow chart for printing a table of
prime numbers between 2 and 1000.*

remainder is compared against 0. Since the remainder is not 0, the number in the B register is compared against 2. Since it is 2, the number in the A register is printed out as a prime number.

Next, the A register is increased to 4. The 4 is written in the B register and is then reduced to 3. The 4 is divided by 3. The remainder is not 0, so the B number is then reduced to 2, and 4 is divided by 2. Since the remainder is 0, 4 is not a prime number.

The A register is then increased to 5. When 5 is divided by 4, 3, and 2, the remainder is never 0. This means that 5 is a prime number. This procedure is continued until 1,000 is reached. At that time, the program is automatically stopped and an END-OF-MESSAGE signal is printed. The list of prime numbers under 1,000 is available, through a storage process, as a printout.

B-4. *General Comments:* If, during the division process, the number in the A register were destroyed, it would be necessary to store the number in A in another register or in the memory and then transfer the data back at the completion of the division process. The flow chart, as shown, assumes that neither the A register nor the B register is affected during the division process.

In this problem, three loops, or repetitive paths, are shown and are labeled A, B, and C. The number of times that loop A is repeated is equal to the number of prime numbers below 1,000. The number of times loop C is repeated varies, depending on which number is being examined. In many cases, the number of cycles in the loop is determined prior to entry in the loop. In other cases, as here, the number of times in the loop is determined as part of the solution. To write out each command individually would take many thousand different commands. By the use of loops, the problem can be flow-charted in 13 operations.

This problem would be quite difficult to solve manually. It would be even more difficult to guarantee that the solution was correct. However, using a computer, the problem is extremely simple. The rules are straightforward, and the problem can be solved in a very short time.

C-1. *Problem Statement:* A computer is used to store the inventory status of material in a stock room. Six computer words are assigned for each item:

Word 1—item identification
Word 2—item name
Word 3—standard unit price
Word 4—current quantity in stock
Word 5—minimum inventory-control point
Word 6—date of last action

It is desired to print out a list of all material which should be reordered.

C-2. *Flow Chart:* See Fig. 12-4.

C-3. *Description of Flow Chart:* In this problem, the six words representing the status of each item of material are stored on magnetic tape. Data are normally stored on tape in blocks. In this example, three items, or 18 words, are stored in a block. Data will be read into the computer one block at a time, and the three items will be examined. The data are stored at the beginning of the tape, and a special number, 99999, inserted following the last data word, is used to indicate the end of the data. If

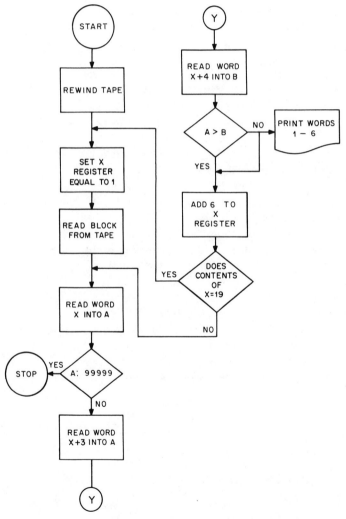

Fig. 12-4   Material-ordering flow chart.

the data were stored in the middle of a tape, a special number would be required to indicate the beginning of the data.

The general approach to the solution is to look at each group of six words and print out the item if word 4 (the current number in stock) is less than word 5 (the minimum number before additional material should be ordered).

At the beginning of the problem, the tape is rewound. This sets up the first data block. The X register is then set to 1. This is the address of the first memory location in which data will be stored. Next, a block of data is read from tape into the memory, starting at the first memory location called out in the X register. In this example, 18 words will be read from the tape into successive memory locations at one time. These 18 successive memory locations are referred to in the flow chart as the tape block.

The first word is compared against 99999. Since the two numbers are not equal, the problem is allowed to continue. Word 4 of the first item is read into the A register, and word 5 is read into the B register. These two registers are compared, and if word 4 is not greater than word 5, the complete status of that part is printed out.

Next, the program jumps six memory locations by use of the X register in order to obtain the next six items. By this means, each item would be examined successively. Each item whose current quantity in stock (word 4) is less than the minimum inventory-control point (word 5) is printed out. When the contents of the X register is equal to 19, the end of buffer (last memory address which had data read into it), a new block of data is read from the tape and the X register is set to the first memory address. Eventually, the symbol 99999 is recognized, signifying that all data have been examined and the problem is complete.

C-4. *General Comments:* This flow chart illustrates the use of a special register to jump memory locations. In this case, the program specifies the identical command structure for many loops, with the data location increased by 6 on each loop. Thus it is possible to examine a very large inventory with this relatively simple command structure.

The flow chart also illustrates one method of getting information into the computer from a peripheral device and some of the requirements in the input-output area.

Although this problem is elementary, it indicates some of the applications of a computer. The primary function of a computer is to serve as a mechanism for information processing and retrieval. The requirements for information vary depending on the user. Purchasing is primarily interested in those items which should be reordered, i.e., when word 4 is less than word 5. Another word might be assigned to indicate the maximum inventory-control point. This would allow the quantity to be ordered to be easily determined by the computer by subtracting the quantity in stock from the maximum inventory-control point. Finance is principally interested in the total cost of inventory and might require a listing of the 100 largest inventory items. This would require that word 3 (unit price) be multiplied by word 4 (number in stock) and the 100 largest products be printed. Another group might require a runoff showing the cost and names of all inactive material, e.g., all items which have not been used in the last year. This could be obtained by examining word 6 of each item. A manufacturing-control person would want to know the current status of a particular item (i.e., given a part number, how many are available) and, in some cases, might want to reserve a number of these items. Thus it can be seen that a common system can be set up to satisfy the diverse requirements of many.

12-5 *Coding*

Once a general approach to a problem solution has been determined, the problem still must be coded into a precise series of instructions in a language understandable to the computer before it is entered into the computer. The computer will only solve a program presented in a step-by-step series of instructions which specify each operation. The only language which the computer can understand is its machine language, i.e., a series of 1s and 0s in the particular word format of the machine. The machine language may be different for every computer type and will depend on the instruction-word format and the organization of the computer. The flow chart must therefore be translated into these basic instructions, which are then transferred onto punched cards, paper tape, typewriter, or other media for entry into the computer. These instructions can be written as a series of binary numbers by the programmer. However, to simplify the coding process, a number of advanced languages have been developed which allow commands to be written in a more general form. These languages are then translated by the computer into machine language. The next two sections will discuss the coding process and these advanced languages.

It is important to remember that a program sequence is preestablished and self-sustaining. If a program of 10 steps is written, the computer will read the first instruction and act on it. Then it will read the second instruction and act on it. Then it will read the third instruction and act on it. Unless interrupted, the computer will follow instructions in sequence. The program can jump instructions based on programmed decisions. Thus, if the fifth instruction is to compare X with Y, the computer can be ordered to jump to the seventh instruction if $X > Y$ and to continue to the sixth instruction if $X \leq Y$. The process of jumping instructions based on certain conditions being fulfilled is called a *conditional jump*. By the use of loops and other techniques, the computer will generate many hundreds of control signals, although the program only specifies a few instructions. However, the computer follows instructions exactly, and the programmer must provide sufficiently detailed and explicit commands to solve the problem.

The computer can only follow those instructions which are included in its command repertoire. A computer can be designed with a large number of instructions or with a limited number. The programmer's task is made easier as the number of commands which the computer can recognize increases. However, the complexity and expense of the computer also increase. Some computers have been designed without a direct instruction for division, while other, more expensive machines have been designed with direct commands for square root. The choice between how much to implement with logic (hardware) and how much to provide via programming (software) is one of the most important decisions in the design of a computer. For most computers, the minimum instructions will include a number of arithmetic, logic, control, decision-making, and input-output commands.

The concept of routines and subroutines should also be introduced at this point. A *routine* is a set of instructions coded and arranged in the proper sequence to direct the computer to perform a desired series of operations. A *subroutine* is a frequently used series of instructions which are available as a unit to perform a specific operation or type of operations. Certain functions, e.g., sine X, square root X, and e^X, are often required. Rather than writing a set of instructions each time one of these operations is required, the functions are available as ready-made building blocks. When needed, these subprograms or subroutines, which are stored in the memory or in external storage, can be addressed by a single command in the main program. The series of instructions stored in the subroutine will then operate on the data stored in the main program. After the completion of the subroutine, the instruction is transferred back to the main program. A subroutine can be stored in the memory and used many times in the course of a program to accomplish certain operations. A number of these subroutines will be stored in a library and made available for all programs.

The specific commands required to solve a problem must be entered into the computer in the word format of the machine. Each command must include, as a minimum, an operation code and one or more memory addresses. The individual commands will vary, depending on the size and format of the instruction word of the machine; the specific commands that must be written are influenced by whether the computer has a single-address or multiple-address instruction word, what its specific command repertoire is, and whether data should be entered in the floating-point or fixed-point system. Each command word will be interpreted by the machine as a specific instruction. Based on the instruction, appropriate gating and control signals will be generated within the computer to perform this instruction.

These instructions normally would be stored in the computer in sequential memory locations. In solving the problem, the computer would read the instructions in sequence and act on them. By means of jump instructions, subroutines, indirect addressing, and indexing, the program will go to other, nonsequential memory locations. By use of the memory to store instructions and data, the program can be solved in a minimum of processing time. Whenever possible, data and instructions stored in slower-speed storage media should be transferred to the main memory prior to any requirement for them, in order to minimize the computer time spent in waiting for additional information. The programmer should therefore be aware of the data in the hierarchy of memories as he codes his program. Traditionally, programs have been prepared and stored onto tapes or other peripheral storage media remote from the central processor. The computer would then sequentially solve the programs entered from the peripheral devices. This batch processing is dependent, for optimum performance, on the immediate availability of data and instructions for each program. More recent computer organizations have allowed many programs to share the computer simultaneously and thus have alleviated the problem of idle computational time spent waiting for data from one of the programs.

With any machine-language coding, all commands must be written in terms of individual binary, octal, or decimal words. This requires the programmer to understand the organization of the computer and the actual command formats and to know at all times the memory address of each command and each piece of data. Thus the command to add the contents of memory location 300 to the A register must be written in an instruction format understandable to the machine. In Fig. 8-1, a 20-bit instruction word was illustrated for a single-address machine. This is not a typical single-address-word size or format since no bits are provided for indexing, indirect addressing, or other logic expansion. It will serve, however, to illustrate the problems of coding directly in machine language. The previous command might be written as 10000000000100101100, where the first 6 bits are operation code for the arithmetic instruction ADD and the last 14 bits are the binary code for memory address 300. Each command in the program would be written as a separate 20-bit word, with the first 6 bits specifying the operation code and the last 14 bits specifying the memory address. With a large instruction word and a multiple-address machine, a longer binary word would be written for each instruction.   To write a program, each command would have to be written as a separate word, perhaps 16 to 60 bits long, in the specific word format of the computer.

It can be seen that to program in such a manner would be a very tedious operation.   In the first place, at all times the programmer would have to be aware of the contents of many memory locations and know which addresses were available for instructions.   In the second place, it would be difficult to memorize the codes for all instructions, and much cross-checking would be required.   The program would be quite likely to contain errors since the programmer might make mistakes in writing many long binary words.   Finally, it would be extremely difficult for the programmer to check and correct errors in his program since the numbers were not readily identified with particular instructions.   In order to ease the problem of the programmer, a number of higher-order languages and programming aids have been developed which perform much of the routine coding operation and, in some cases, eliminate the requirement for the user to have a detailed knowledge of the individual computer.   Coding in machine-dependent languages will be discussed in this section; the next section will discuss more advanced languages.

A machine-language program is the only type of program that can be executed by a computer.   Programming, on the other hand, is greatly simplified when instructions can be written in mnemonic or symbolic codes.   The use of a symbolic assembler language allows this.   An assembler language normally possesses a one-to-one correspondence with machine language except that the commands are written as symbolic codes and not as binary numbers.   An assembly program, or assembler, translates the symbolic codes of the programmer into the binary codes of the particular machine in such a way that there is a direct relationship between assembly instructions and machine instructions.   Thus an assembly language is designed specifically for a particular computer. The computer manufacturer provides as a part of his software package a mechanism for translating from the assembly language to the language of the machine.   As an example, the mnemonic operation code ADD could correspond to the machine instruction 100000.   Both commands will be translated by the machine into an ADD command and will result in the generation of appropriate control and gating signals.   Similarly, STA might be translated as "Store the contents of the A register," resulting in the appropriate commands being generated.

Associated with the concept of advanced languages is the idea of relative memory addressing, or *relative coding*.   In many programs, it is difficult to assign all memory locations since the number and relationship of all memory locations may not be known prior to the completion of the program writing or the programmer may not be aware of what memory locations are available.   During the writing of a program, the programmer may discover that a new memory address may have to be added. This could necessitate rewriting all instructions. In order to avoid this, relative coding can be used. In this scheme, symbolic addresses are specified either directly or relative to one another, and the computer assigns absolute addresses prior to the initiation of the problem solution. In most cases, memory addresses are written as mnemonics.

A program written in an assembly language is called a *source program*. Instructions are translated into the machine-language program, called the *object program*, by the assembler. The assembly program consists of a series of machine-language routines which convert the source program to the object program. In the source program, instructions, data, and memory addresses are referred to by symbolic names. These symbols are stored in the computer memory in a table. By referring to the table, symbols can be looked up and replaced with operation codes and absolute addresses in the machine language. These instructions are then assembled one at a time by the assembler.

In coding using an assembly language, the programmer uses mnemonic instructions such as ADD (perform addition), STA (store the contents of the A register in memory location XXX), BCD (binary-coded-decimal-to-binary conversion), SKG (skip next instruction if A is greater than the contents of a specified memory address). Instead of writing each memory address, the programmer can identify addresses by a decimal or a mnemonic code. In some cases, an assembler is designed around a two-pass operation. On the first pass through the instructions, the assembler determines the number of memory locations that must be reserved, allocates the correct number of memory addresses, and prepares a table of locations. On the second pass, it translates the mnemonic operation code to binary machine language, substitutes binary memory address for decimal or mnemonic addresses by using the table prepared on the first pass, and translates all constants and numbers to the internal binary machine format.

It is worthwhile at this point to code one problem using an assembly language. Since the organization of AND notation used in an assembly language are dependent on the specific computer, no general rules can be written. However, using the notation of the assembly language of one computer is illustrative of the application of assembly languages in coding. The computer of this example is a single-address machine, so only one memory address will be specified in each instruction.

The problem to be coded is the one illustrated in the flow chart of Fig. 12-2. The contents of 100 successive memory locations are to be examined, and the largest of these positive numbers is to be stored in the B register. The computer will use a location in memory as the B register shown in the flow chart. Two other locations will be used to store the address of data and the current value of J. The following seven instructions, recognized by the computer, must be defined in order to code the program. Memory location Y refers to the address specified in the remainder of the instruction.

Notation	Command and meaning
CRA	Clear the A register; reset it to 0.
HLT	Halt. Computer will stop until a START command is received.
IRX	Increment and load. The content of memory location Y is incremented by 1, and the resulting sum is stored in memory location Y.
JMP	Jump to memory location Y and take next instruction from there.
LDA	Load A. Store the contents of memory location Y in the A register. The data in Y remain unchanged.
SKG	Skip if greater. Compare the contents of the A register with the contents of memory location Y. If $A > Y$, skip the next instruction. If $A < Y$, proceed to the next sequential instruction.
STA	Store A. Store the contents of the A register in memory location Y. The contents of A remain unchanged.

Using these seven instructions, the flow chart could be coded as shown in Table 12-1. Each instruction must include a command, and most will

TABLE 12-1

No.	Command	Memory location	Comment
	CRA		Reset A.
	STA	B	Store A in memory location B. This resets B.
	LDA	K1	Load constant K1 in A register. K1 will be defined later as 1000.
	STA	DATA	Store A in memory location DATA. This makes the initial DATA address equal to 1000.
	LDA	K2	Load constant K2 in A register. K2 will be defined later as 1.
	STA	J	Store A in memory location J. This makes $J = 1$.
L	SKG	K3	Compare contents of A register with K3. K3 will be defined later as 100. $J > 100$?
	JMP	N1	If "No," jump to instruction N1.
	HLT		If "Yes," halt.
N1	LDA	DATA	Read contents of DATA address into A register.
	SKG	B	Compare contents of A register with contents of memory location B. $A > B$?
	JMP	N2	If "No," jump to instruction N2.
	STA	B	If "Yes," read the contents of the A register into memory location B.
N2	IRX	DATA	Modify DATA address by increasing the address by 1.
	IRX	J	Modify the number in J by increasing it by 1.
	JMP	L	Jump to instruction L.

include a memory location. All memory locations must be defined at the end of the coding in order to determine the number of memory locations to be reserved. Not every instruction must be numbered. However, those called out in a jump instruction must be identified. The notation used in identifying memory locations and itemizing steps is completely arbitrary and is defined by the programmer. Thus the use of K1, K2, and K3 to identify constants stored in the memory, the use of N1, N2, and L to identify jump addresses, and the use of the word "DATA" to identify 100 memory locations are for the convenience of the programmer. None of the comments would be written in an actual program, and they are used here only for illustrative purposes.

Six memory locations were specified in the program and must be defined in order that the computer can assign proper addresses. Three of these, K1, K2, and K3, are constants and must be identified. Three, J, DATA, and B, are locations which will be used to store data. In addition, L, N1, and N2 are specified in jump instructions and are defined in the coding. One convention used is to write below the instructions a definition of memory locations. The notation DEC represents a decimal constant, while the notation M is used to identify a memory location. The comments are given for illustrative purposes and would not be written in an actual program.

Location	Type	Comment
B	M 1	B will require one memory location.
K1	DEC 1000	K1 is the decimal constant 1000.
DATA	M 100	DATA will require 100 memory locations.
K2	DEC 1	K2 is the decimal constant 1.
J	M 1	J will require one memory location.
K3	DEC 100	K3 is the decimal constant 100.

This completes the coding of the program. The computer, using the assembly system, would then translate these instructions into the machine language. Each instruction would be translated by the computer into the equivalent instruction in machine language. Each mnemonic memory location would have an absolute address assigned, and each address would be translated to its corresponding address. For example, the command STA may be written, in machine language, as 00000010-1000101011101010. The first 3 bits refer to indirect addressing and indexing and are 0s. The next 6 bits refer to the operation code and are binary 000 101, octal 05, the equivalent computer instruction word for the command STA. The last 15 bits refer to the octal memory address (decimal 2,794) into which the contents of A are to be stored. It can be seen that STA is much easier to work with than the long binary word.

This method of coding is by no means the simplest method of solving the problem. Using a greater variety of instructions, indexing, and indirect addressing would allow this problem to be coded in less than half the number of instructions. The larger the computer instruction repertoire, the easier the programming becomes. A multiple-address instruction word would also allow fewer instructions. It is beyond the scope of this book, however, to go into coding in more detail, and the reader is referred to instruction manuals on assembler languages available from the manufacturer of the computer of interest.

12-6 *Problem-oriented Languages*

Machine-language programs and assemblers are machine-oriented and are therefore dependent on an understanding of the organization of the specific computer. Commands must be given in terms of the computer instruction repertoire and specific organization. The coding process can be involved, and the amount of time required for writing and checking the instructions can be large. To simplify the coding process, a number of business and scientific problem-oriented languages have been developed which eliminate the necessity for the user to have any knowledge of the computer internal organization. These problem-oriented languages were developed to be similar to the language of a particular technical or business field and to allow a program to be written and solved on a wide variety of computers.

A computer, however, only recognizes instructions in its own machine language. Thus a translation is required from the problem-oriented language to the machine language. This is performed by the computer using a routine called a *compiler*, which translates the language of the source program into the specific language of the object program prior to initiation of the program. A compiler is a translating, generating, and assembly system. In an assembler, there is normally a one-to-one relationship between the symbolic codes and the machine instructions. In a compiler, a single instruction statement, e.g., a one-word instruction for square root, can be translated into an entire sequence of operations in the machine language. The mechanism for translating a particular problem-oriented language to the specific machine language is provided by the computer manufacturer as a portion of his software. The program in symbolic form is entered into the computer together with the compiler program. The program is then converted to the machine language. Once the program is converted, a permanent record is kept so that the program will not have to be translated the next time it is used. Thus a specific machine will be defined as being compatible with Fortran IV, Algol, Cobol, PL1, or other language, and the appropriate translating mechanism will be supplied as part of the software package supplied with the computer.

Before introducing specific languages, a review of the purpose of programming is in order.   The computer is used to solve problems.   For the computer to solve a problem, a specific series of instructions on how to solve the problem must be provided to the computer.   By the use of flow charts and other aids, a problem can be defined.   The procedure must then be coded into specific machine instructions.   It is possible to do this only once for a given class of problem, store this solution in a library, and then refer to this approach when required.   Common problems like sine X, square root X, or a quadratic equation involving X can be solved by a general procedure, and the procedure can be referenced many times as the need to solve for the value of X arises.   It is also possible to use any code to refer to this subprogram.   For example, the solution for the square root of X can be referenced by the expressions: "Take the square root of," SQRT, $\sqrt{}$, ZY, or other notation, providing that the code is consistent and that those using the language agree to the method of coding.

Universal languages differ in their purpose, in possible commands, in methods used to express these commands, and in the ease of translation into a specific machine language.   Some languages, called *procedural languages*, are similar to machine languages in that the entire procedure to be followed must be specified by the programmer although not to the level of detail required in a machine language.   A procedural language, e.g., Fortran, is universal and can be used to solve a wide variety of problems.   Other, nonprocedural languages are specific to a particular field and may use one word to represent an entire problem solution.   In this case, a mathematical model of the solution is built into the machine, and the problem is referenced as needed.   A nonprocedural language may be desired when the frequency of similar calculations is sufficient to justify the work involved in developing the language and the translating mechanism for the language.   A separate language can be developed for civil engineering, banking, atomic physics, or any other specific field.

Fortran (formula translation), Algol (algorithmic-oriented language), Cobol (common-oriented business language), and PL1 (programming language 1) are some of the principal procedure-oriented languages. Although any language can be used to write any program, Fortran and Algol were designed principally for the scientific user, while Cobol was designed for the business user.   A review of the basic rules of Fortran and Cobol will show some of the purposes of these languages.

With a language, terminology and conventions must be established. While the setting of these conventions is arbitrary, once established, they must be followed exactly.   The language should be as natural as possible in order to minimize the possibilities of errors.   Since Fortran and Cobol were developed for different applications, the method of expressing

identical operations is quite different.   This can be seen in Table 12-2.
Fortran was developed principally for the scientific user.   Therefore,
it is quite similar to mathematical equations.   Cobol was developed for
business applications, and its language is close to English, although a
particular style of English.

TABLE 12-2

Operation	Fortran	Cobol
Addition	+	Plus
Subtraction	−	Minus
Multiplication	*	Times
Division	/	Divided by

Thus the mathematical expression $Y = AX + B$ would be written in
Fortran as

A * X + B

and in Cobol as

Move A to Y
Multiply Y by X
Add B to Y

Other, business-oriented problems may be much easier to express using
Cobol than using Fortran.

The program of Fig. 12-2 could be written in Fortran as shown in the
following tabulation.   The numbers 10 and 20 are arbitrarily assigned to
identify specific jump instructions.   The explanation is only given for
illustrative purposes and would not normally be part of the program.
0 is used for the number, and Ø for the letter.

Command	Explanation
Dimension Data (100)	Data will have 100 values (100 memory locations will be required).
B = 0	Reset B.
DØ 20, I = 1, 100	Perform step 20 100 times, i.e., as I goes from 1 to 100.
If (Data (I) − B) 20, 20, 10	Subtract B from contents of location I. If difference is negative (B > I), go to step 20. If difference is 0, go to step 20. If positive (I > B), go to step 10.
10 B = Data (I)	Replace B with value at I.
20 Continue	Continue problem.
Stop	Halt after I > 100.

Fortran introduces a number of conventions which must be remembered. Once they are learned, however, a program can be written in simple terms and then programmed on any computer compatible with Fortran.

Figure 12-5 shows a block diagram of the operation of a compiler system. The programmer writes a source program in the problem-oriented language and prepares the information for entry into the computer. In this example, the information is prepared on cards. The cards are then read into the computer along with the compiler program. In this example, the compiler program is stored on tape. By following the rules written in the compiler program, the computer translates each source instruction into one or more object instructions. In some cases, the source program may refer to subroutines stored in the library, and one or more library tapes may be referenced. A working tape is also shown in the figure. In many cases, additional temporary memory storage may be required during the translation, and external bulk storage may be used by the computer to handle memory overflow.

The computer can be used to solve the problem after translation without any record of the coding process. In many cases, however, a permanent record of the program in machine language is desired in order to allow the program to be rerun. A tape can be used to provide permanent storage of the object program. At the same time, a printout is provided which lists the source program, the object code, and any clerical errors made by the programmer. Clerical errors, which include terms not defined, redundant terms, and general inconsistencies, are printed out for ease in isolating and removing all programming errors.

At the completion of the compiling procedure, the program can be executed immediately or stored off-line for future execution on another computer. The reader is referred to the books on programming languages listed in the Bibliography for more information on the subject of universal languages.

12-7   *Conclusion*

In writing programs and processing problems on a computer, a number of steps are involved. In the first place, the problem must be analyzed and adequately defined. The analysis must include a review of what the problem is, what information is available, and what range and significance are desired in the answer. The approach to problem solution should next be determined, and a flow chart drawn. Initially, the flow chart may be general, with each block representing a logical part of the problem. The blocks will then be expanded and analyzed in detail. Some of these building blocks may be filled by subprograms or subroutines. The more

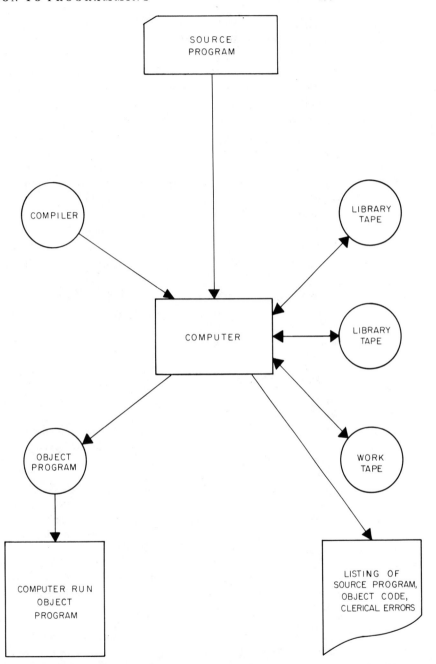

Fig. 12-5 Compiler system.

available building blocks, subprograms, that can be used, the easier the programming becomes.

The program must next be coded. The method of coding depends on the language used. Almost universally, however, the coding is performed using an advanced language. Once coded, the source program is prepared on cards, paper tape, magnetic tape, or a typewriter for entry into the computer. Next, the source program must be translated into an object program, i.e., into machine language, before the computer can follow the instructions. This is done by the computer, with the source program and an assembler or compiler program.

The object program thus produced, together with whatever library subroutines are required, is entered into the computer, and the program is executed. The results are analyzed, and where required, specific programming errors are isolated and debugged.

Any problem can be solved on a computer which can be defined in terms of commands specific to the machine. In many cases, a programmer eliminates much of the routine work of programming by developing subroutines and building blocks and by using advanced languages. The structure of these languages is continually being upgraded so that the language used to communicate with the computer becomes more natural and easier to use.

EXERCISES

12-1. Define the difference between an algorithmic and a heuristic problem solution. Give an example of each.

12-2. Write the steps required to solve a quadratic equation.

12-3. Redraw Fig. 12-4 for the condition where a seventh word is used to list the maximum inventory-control point. A printout of items to be ordered and their quantities is required.

12-4. Draw a flow chart for Problem C-1 to list the 100 largest-inventory items.

12-5. Draw a flow chart to show how change would automatically be made from a $10 bill for the sale of any item priced under $10.

12-6. An array of 100 numbers, both positive and negative, is to be summed in the following manner: All negative numbers are to be summed as the parameter X; all positive numbers are to be summed as the parameter Y. The absolute values of X and Y are then to be compared, and the larger value printed out. Draw a flow chart to show this.

12-7. What is a subroutine?

12-8. Define looping. Why are loops important?

12-9. What are the disadvantages of absolute addressing?

12-10. Assume that the assembler language described in Sec. 12-5 has the following two additional commands: SKL (skip next instruction if A is less than the data in memory location Y) and CRM (reset memory location Y). Redo Table 12-1.

12-11. Redo Table 12-1 for a double-address machine.

12-12. In the example of Sec. 12-5, why must memory locations be specified? Why must they later be defined?

12-13. What is a problem-oriented language? Why have different languages been developed?

12-14. What is the difference between an assembler and a compiler?

12-15. Obtain detailed information on a specific computer. Code Exercise 12-6 directly in machine language, in an assembly language, and into a problem-oriented language.

APPENDIX

Symbols for Demonstration Modules

Module type and symbol	Logic function	Purpose
Level switch (S)		Provides a source of logic 1s and 0s obtained by manual operation of four switches. The signals are used to initiate logic operations in the demonstrations.
AND gate (AN)	$A \cdot B \cdot C \cdot D = 1$	Implements the function A AND B AND C AND D. All input signals must be logic 1s to provide a logic-1 output.

Module type and symbol	Logic function	Purpose
OR gate (OR)	$A + B + C + D = 1$	Implements the function A OR B OR C OR D. Any input or combination of inputs at logic 1 provides a logic-1 output.
NAND gate (ND)	$\overline{A \cdot B \cdot C \cdot D} = 1$	Implements the function NOT (A AND B AND C AND D). Any input or combination of inputs at logic 0 causes a logic-1 output. All inputs must be logic 1 to cause a logic-0 output.
NOR gate (NR)	$\overline{A + B + C + D} = 1$	Implements the function NOT (A OR B OR C OR D). Any logic-1 input causes a logic-0 output. All inputs must be logic 0 to cause a logic-1 output.
Single-pulse generator (SPG)		Provides a pulse to trigger inputs to flip-flop modules (FF, SR) each time a button is pushed. Module comprises two independent generators, each with its own push button and output.

304

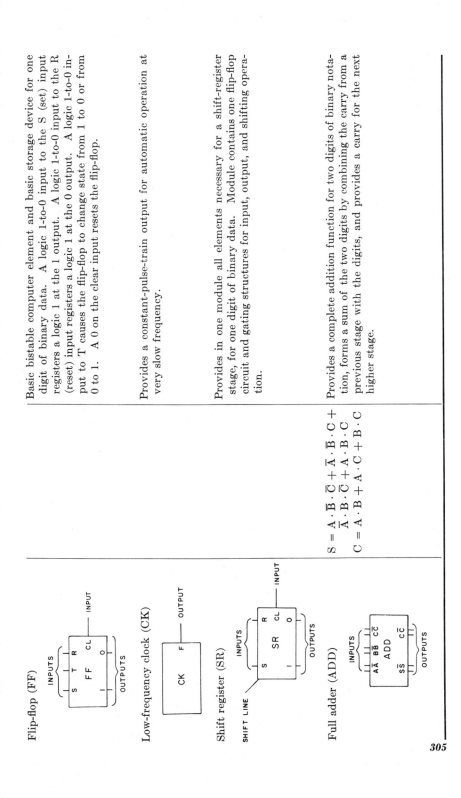

Flip-flop (FF)

Basic bistable computer element and basic storage device for one digit of binary data. A logic 1-to-0 input to the S (set) input registers a logic 1 at the 1 output. A logic 1-to-0 input to the R (reset) input registers a logic 1 at the 0 output. A logic 1-to-0 input to T causes the flip-flop to change state from 1 to 0 or from 0 to 1. A 0 on the clear input resets the flip-flop.

Low-frequency clock (CK)

Provides a constant-pulse-train output for automatic operation at very slow frequency.

Shift register (SR)

Provides in one module all elements necessary for a shift-register stage, for one digit of binary data. Module contains one flip-flop circuit and gating structures for input, output, and shifting operation.

Full adder (ADD)

Provides a complete addition function for two digits of binary notation, forms a sum of the two digits by combining the carry from a previous stage with the digits, and provides a carry for the next higher stage.

$$S = A \cdot B \cdot \overline{C} + \overline{A} \cdot \overline{B} \cdot C + \overline{A} \cdot B \cdot \overline{C} + A \cdot \overline{B} \cdot C$$
$$C = A \cdot B + A \cdot C + B \cdot C$$

Glossary

Absolute address. An address that is permanently assigned by the computer designer to a storage location. Also called a *machine address*.

Absolute value. The value of a number without an algebraic sign; the magnitude.

Access time. (1) The amount of time between a request for the content of a location in the memory and the availability of the data (READ operation). (2) The time between a command to store data in a memory location and the completion of the storage (WRITE operation).

Accumulator. A register in the arithmetic unit in which are formed the results of sums and other arithmetic and logic operations.

Accuracy. Freedom from error. Accuracy is contrasted with precision; e.g., a four-place table correctly computed is accurate, a six-place table containing an error is more precise but is not accurate.

Adder (full adder). A device whose output is the sum of its inputs. An output sum and carry are produced by adding two digits together with the carry output from the next least significant digit.

Address. A specific location in the memory where data or instructions are stored. A name, label, or number is used to refer to the memory location.

Address modification. The changing of the address portion of a computer word, before the instruction is performed, by the use of index registers, indirect addressing, and other techniques.

Address register. A register in which the memory address is stored. (See **Memory address register.**)

Algol (algorithmic-oriented language). A procedure-oriented language.

Algorithm. A rule of procedure, generally mathematical in nature, for finding the solution to a particular problem by a series of well-defined rules.

Alphanumeric. Pertaining to a group of characters which represent the letters of the alphabet, the numbers 0 to 9, and other special symbols by a 6-bit code.

Analog. (1) Pertaining to data in the form of continuously variable physical quantities. (2) A physical representation or analogy of quantities in a problem, e.g., voltage representing temperature.

Analog computer. A computer which operates on the principle of creating a physical analogy of a mathematical problem and solving the problem using this analogy.

AND. Logic operation that produces a 1 (true) indication when all inputs are 1 (true). If any input is 0 (false), the output (F) is 0. The equation is $A \cdot B \cdot C \cdot D = F$.

Arithmetic unit. The portion of the computer that performs the arithmetic operations.

Assembler. A program which prepares a machine-language (object) program from a symbolic-language (source) program by substituting absolute operation

codes for symbolic operation codes and absolute addresses for symbolic
addresses.

Associative memory.   A memory in which storage locations are addressed by
their contents rather than by their locations.

Asynchronous computer operation.   A computer operation which is principally
controlled by the sequential completion of functions within the computer and
not by clock timing.

Automatic programming (coding).   Machine-assisted preparation of machine-
language routines.

Base.   The base of a number system; a quantity whose successive integral powers
are the multipliers of the sequence of digits that represent a number, i.e.,
binary 2, decimal 10, octal 8.   Same as **Radix**.

Batch processing.   The processing of a number of programs during a continuous
computer run.

BCD (binary-coded decimal).   Pertaining to a special code for decimal notation
using binary symbols.

BCD counter.   An arrangement of counting stages to provide a decimal count
using binary stages.

Binary counter.   An arrangement of counting stages to count in binary notation.

Binary notation.   A number system using the radix 2, in which two symbols are
used, 1 and 0.

Binary point.   In a binary system, the point which separates the integer portion
of the number system from the fractional portion.

Binary-system complements.   (1) The 1s complement of a binary number is
found by changing each 1 to 0 and each 0 to 1, i.e., by subtracting the number
from all 1s.   (2) The 2s complement of a binary number is found by changing
each 1 to 0 and each 0 to 1 and adding 1 to the least significant digit.

Binary-to-decimal conversion.   The process whereby a binary number is converted to a decimal number.

Bistable.   Having two and only two stable conditions.

Bit.   The basic binary unit for registering and handling information data.   A bit
(from *binary digit*) is either a 1 or a 0.

Block diagram.   A pictorial view of a system, computer, or program in which
selected portions are represented by functional boxes and interconnected lines.

Boolean algebra.   A system for expressing and manipulating logic expressions by
means of a few basic operations.

Borrow.   In subtraction, the number taken from the next higher order when the
subtrahend and input borrow together are larger than the minuend.

Branch.   A point in a series of instructions in which one of two or more paths is
chosen depending on certain criteria being met.

Buffer.   A storage device used to compensate for differences in rate of flow of
data; usually an input-output storage element which matches the central
processor with slower external devices such as magnetic tape and cards.

Bus.   A common transfer path between sources and destinations.

Byte.   A sequence of adjacent binary locations operated upon as a unit; a group
of bits shorter than a word.

Carry.   In addition, the number that must be added to the next higher-order
digits when the sum of the two or more digits in the same column equals or
exceeds the radix of the number system used.

Central processor.   That portion of a computer that consists of control, storage,
and arithmetic units.   It is used to interpret and excute instructions.

Channel. (1) A path along which signals can be sent. (2) One or more of the parallel tracks on a magnetic tape, drum, or disk used for storage of data.

Character. An elementary mark that is used to represent data, e.g., the numerals 0 to 9, the letters of the alphabet, and special symbols.

Clear. To set a register of flip-flop configurations to the 0 state (entering 0s in all stages); to set core registers or memory elements to the 0 state.

Clock. Basic timing mechanism for a system; usually a circuit providing a chain of continuous pulses at a defined repetition rate.

Clock frequency. The repetition rate of a computer timing unit.

Cobol (common business-oriented language). A business data-processing language.

Code. (1) Arrangement of basic symbols to convey a system of notation. (2) A set of rules used to convert data from one representation to another. (3) The machine-language representation of a character.

Column. A vertical arrangement of characters or bits, pertaining to the binary representation of data on punched cards.

Command. A control signal; an instruction in machine language.

Comparator. An arrangement of logic operators that determine the relation of two sets of data or numbers. The logic decisions are either equality, nonequality, greater than, or less than.

Compiler. A program which prepares a machine-language program from a procedure-oriented source language. This generally involves determining the meaning of each coded instruction, generating the required subroutines, transforming subroutines into specific instructions, and performing the function of an assembler.

Complement. A number that is derived from another number by subtraction in accordance with very special rules. Examples include the 9s-, 1s-, 10s-, and 2s-complement systems.

Computer code. A machine code for a specific computer.

Computer instruction. A machine instruction for a specific computer.

Computer word. A sequence of bits or characters treated as a unit and capable of being stored in one memory address.

Conditional jump. A jump that occurs if specific criteria are met.

Console. Equipment used by the operator to communicate with and monitor the condition of the computer. It contains manual controls and system-condition panels.

Control unit. The portion of the central processor which effects the retrieval of instructions in the proper sequence, interprets the coded instructions, and initiates the proper control signals to execute these instructions.

Core memory. A storage device consisting of magnetic cores arranged so that each core stores a binary digit. A core is made of magnetic material capable of assuming and remaining in one of two conditions of magnetization.

Counter. An arrangement of elements (usually flip-flops) that count the number of occurrences of an event or signal.

Data. Numeric, alphabetic, or analog information.

Data word. A computer word containing only data to be operated upon.

Debug. To detect, identify, and correct malfunctions in the operation of computer equipment and in the computer program.

Decimal. Pertaining to a number system with a radix of 10.

Decimal-system complements. (1) The 9s complement of a decimal number is found by subtracting each digit in the number from 9. (2) The 10s complement of a decimal number is found by subtracting the number from the nearest power of 10 that is more than the number itself. A short method is to take the 9s complement of the number and add 1 to the least significant digit.

Decimal-to-binary conversion. The process whereby a decimal number is converted to a binary number.

Decoding. The process of converting an input code to another form or another code.

Delay. The finite time required for an element or circuit to respond to an input and provide an output.

Destructive readout. A process of reading data in a memory which causes the information sampled to be erased.

Diagnostic routine. A routine or special program designed to check out computer operations. These programs usually isolate and indicate malfunctioning areas of computers and designate the specific errors.

Digit. A symbol or character in a number system used to represent an integer smaller than the radix. The decimal system has ten, 0 to 9. The binary system has two, 0 and 1.

Digital. Pertaining to the representation of a quantity using digits or discrete steps.

Digital computer. A calculating device that operates on discrete data by performing arithmetic and logic operations.

Direct address. An address that specifies the location of an operand.

Disk storage. A form of magnetic storage in which data are stored by selective magnetization of small areas on tracks located on the surface of a flat circular plate.

Display tube. A tube, usually a cathode-ray tube, used to display data.

Double precision. Pertaining to the use of two computer words to represent a number.

Doubling and dabbling. A simple method for converting a binary number to a decimal number.

Dump. To transfer all or a specific portion of the system memory content into another section of the memory or into an external storage.

Effective address. The address that is derived by applying any specified indexing or indirect-addressing rules to the specified address.

Encode. To transform data from one form to another by applying the rules of a code.

End-around carry. A carry from the most significant digit to the least significant digit. Used in complement arithmetic.

Error. A difference between the computed, measured, or observed quantity and its proper value.

Excess-3 code. A code using binary notation and formed by adding binary 11 (decimal 3) to each number in the 8-4-2-1 code.

Exclusive OR. A logic operator with two inputs which produces a 1 output when one input is a logic 1 and the other is a logic 0. When both inputs are 1 or both inputs are 0, the output is a 0.

Execute. To perform a complete instruction, not including a fetch cycle.

Fetch. (1) To transfer instructions from memory to a register. (2) The portion of the control cycle in which the location of the next instruction is determined and the instruction is obtained and placed in the control register.

Field. A character or group of characters which is treated as a whole and signifies a particular category of data, e.g., a name or a wage rate.

Fixed point. A predetermined position of the radix point in the representation of numbers requiring fractional notation.

Fixed-point calculation. A method of calculation in which operations take place with a constant location of the point in each number.

Flip-flop. A circuit capable of assuming either one of two stable states.

Floating point. Pertaining to a number system in which the position of the radix point does not remain fixed.

Flow chart. A graphical representation showing the interconnected logical steps required for the definition, analysis, or solution of a problem.

Fortran (formula translation). A procedure-oriented language.

Gate. A circuit with one output and many inputs, designed so that the output is a logic 1 only under certain conditions of inputs.

General-purpose computer. A stored-program machine capable of a variable computing program; characterized by great flexibility and capability for solving a wide variety of problems.

Gray code. A binary code in which sequential numbers are represented by binary numbers, each of which differs from the preceding number in only one order.

Half adder. A logic element which adds two input digits and produces a sum and a carry.

Hardware. The electrical, mechanical, and magnetic components on a system. Contrast with software.

Index register. A register whose content is added to or subtracted from the operand address to determine the next instruction memory location. The computer instruction word contains a special section for designating the use of index register(s) in the program.

Indirect addressing. Designating an address that is the location of a command word, e.g., designating a return address at the conclusion of a subroutine to get back into the main program.

Information retrieval. The methods and procedures for recovering specific information from stored data.

Inhibit signal. A signal that disables a gate or disables a WRITE command into a memory cell.

Input-output. Pertaining to the devices and logic used to bring data into and out of the computer.

Instruction. A set of characters or digits which defines an operation and one or more memory locations used to store data. The instruction is decoded in the control element, which generates appropriate control signals to execute the instruction.

Instruction-execution time. The time required by the computer to execute a specific instruction.

Instruction register. A register that stores the instruction to be executed; same as *Operation-code register.*

Instruction repertoire. The set of operations that can be represented in a given operation code and performed by the computer.

Inverter. An element or circuit that provides as an output a signal that is the inverse of the input; e.g., a logic-1 input to an inverter produces a 0 output.

Jump. A departure from the normal sequence of executing instructions in a computer.

Language. A set of representations, conventions, and rules used to convey information.

Least significant digit. The lowest-order digit of a number. The least significant digit (LSD) is at the extreme right of a number or word.

Library subroutine. A standard routine that is on file in a library of programs for use at any time. The library contains routines and subroutines to solve common problems and parts of problems.

Logic design. A design which uses functional units and logic building blocks to organize an integrated whole. When implemented by hardware, the resulting organization performs the function specified.

Logic element. A gate or group of gates which performs a specified logic function.

Loop. A sequence of instructions that is executed repeatedly until certain conditions are fulfilled.

Machine language. The organization of bits within the computer which is used to represent data and instructions; the specific word format(s) used within the computer.

Macro instruction. An instruction in a source language that is equivalent to a specified sequence of machine instructions.

Magnetic core. A bistable ring-shaped ferromagnetic material which, when connected to windings (twists of wire around the ring) through which current is flowing, can be used to store binary data.

Magnetic disk. A magnetically coated flat circular plate with small areas magnetized around its surface. Used for storage of binary data.

Magnetic drum. A magnetically coated cylinder with small areas magnetized around its surface. Used for storage of binary data.

Magnetic tape. A tape with a magnetic surface on which data can be stored by selective magnetization of portions of the surface.

Memory. A device into which information can be entered, in which it can be held, and from which it can be extracted at a later time. Same as **Storage.**

Memory address register. That register of the computer that receives the memory-address bits from either input or arithmetic units and supplies the location where data should be read or written in the memory.

Memory information register. A register which stores the information to be written into the memory and the information which has been read out of the memory. Usually, the length of the register is equal to the number of bits in the computer word.

Memory size. The total number of bits which can be stored within the memory.

Mnemonic. Assisting the memory. Mnemonic sets of letters are used by the programmer to indicate a given instruction or operation.

Module. In computers, a physically independent package that includes one or more clearly defined circuits to implement logic functions, e.g., a gate, flip-flop, adder, or register.

Most significant digit. The highest-order digit of a number. The most significant digit (MSD) is at the extreme left of a number or word.

Multiaccess computer. A computer which can accept data from more than one independent input simultaneously.

Multiaddress. Pertaining to an instruction that has more than one address specified.

NAND. Logic operator that performs the inverse of the AND function. With a NAND gate, if four inputs (A, B, C, D) are 1, the output (F) is 0. If any or all are 0, then F is 1. The equation is $F = \overline{A \cdot B \cdot C \cdot D}$.

Negate. To perform the logic operation NOT.

Nondestructive read. A read process that does not erase the data in the source.

NOR. Logic operator that performs the inverse of the OR function. In a NOR function, if any input (A, B, C, D) is 1, the output (F) is 0. All inputs must be 0 to have F = 1. The equation is $F = \overline{A + B + C + D}$.

NOT. Logic operator that states that if A = 1, then $\overline{A}$ = 0; an inverter.

Object language. A language that is the output of a translation process; usually a machine language.

Octal. Pertaining to a number system with the base 8.

Off-line. Pertaining to peripheral equipment not under the direct control of the central processor.

Operand. A quantity which is operated on.

Operation code. The part of the command code of an instruction which specifies a certain operation or act.

Operation-code register. The register which stores the current instruction the computer is executing.

OR. Logic disjunction. In an OR function, if any input is a 1, the output (F) is a 1. The equation is $F = A + B + C + D$.

Order. The positional notation of digits in a number that represents powers of the radix.

Overflow. A condition that sometimes results when the result of a computation produces an answer that exceeds the storage capacity of a register.

Parallel mode. A mode of computer operation in which two or more different operations occur simultaneously; the opposite of serial mode.

Parity bit. A binary digit appended to an array of bits to make the sum of all the bits always odd or always even. Used for checking the validity of data.

Peripheral equipment. Input-output devices external to the central processor and usually operating off-line.

Precision. The degree of discrimination with which a quantity is stated; the number of significant digits in a number. (See *Accuracy.*)

Printer. An output device which prints or typewrites characters.

Problem-oriented language. A programming language designed for the convenient expression of procedures used in the solution of a class of problems.

Program. A plan for solving a problem; a sequence of instructions that guides a computer in its problem-solving computation.

Program counter. The counter or register in the control section which contains the address of the next sequential instruction to be performed.

Punched card. A card punched with a pattern of holes to represent data.

Radix. Same as *Base.*

Random access. A method of storage in which the time necessary to access any memory location is constant and independent of the relative locations of the last addressed location and the next location to be addressed.

Range. The difference between the maximum and minimum values that a quantity can assume.

Read. To sense and transfer information contained in system memory to another storage or to the operating register of the computer.

Register. A device capable of storing and manipulating a specified amount of data.

Relative address. A memory address indicated by an incremental change from the last address rather than by an absolute location.

Reset. To place a register to a prescribed state, usually 0.

Ring counter. A circular counter that counts by shifting a pulse through each stage, with only one stage a 1 at any time.

Routine. A set of instructions coded and arranged in proper sequence to cause a computer to perform a desired operation or series of operations.

Scale. To change a quantity by a factor in order to bring its value within prescribed limits.

Serial. Pertaining to the sequential processing of data. In serial mode, computer operations follow one another sequentially; i.e., the completion of one operation controls the start of the next.

Set. To place a register or flip-flop into the 1 state.

Shift. To move data from one storage cell to another, usually in a register.

Shift register. A register wired so that a single shift pulse, when applied, can shift the number in the register one stage to the left or right.

Single-address machine. A computer whose instruction word specifies a single memory address.

Software. The collection of programs and routines associated with a particular computer, e.g., compilers, assemblers, library routines. Software techniques are developed for the most efficient use of computer hardware.

Source language. The language in which a program is usually written.

Storage. A device which can receive data and hold them until interrogated. Same as *Memory.*

Stored capacity. The number of bits of data that can be contained in a storage device.

Stored-program computer. A computer that can store, reference, execute, and modify its instructions.

Subroutine. A routine that is part of another routine; a section of a program which can be used repetitively.

Symbolic coding. Coding that uses instructions expressed in symbols for the convenience of the programmer.

Tape transport. A device containing a tape drive, together with reading-writing heads, associated controls, and mechanical structure.

Time sharing. Using a computer for two or more interleaved programs.

Timing. Clearly defined incremental signals that control computer operations.

Toggle. The complementing input to a flip-flop which causes it to change state every time a pulse is applied; a flip-flop.

Translate. To convert one type of language (special codes, other machine languages, etc.) to another suitable for operations within the computer.

Trap. An unprogrammed conditional jump to a known memory location, with the location from which the jump occurred recorded automatically.

Truth table. A tabular evaluation of a logic expression that shows all possible combinations of the variables and the resultant output of each combination.

Up-down counter. Counter stages with logic arrangement to control counting in both ascending and descending order.

Venn diagram. A pictorial representation in which quantities or logic expressions are represented by closed regions.

Word. The group of digits that is handled as a unit by the computer. *Word length* refers to the number of bits within the word. *Word organization* refers to the arrangement of bits within the word.

Write. To deliver information to the system memory from a register of the computer.

Logic Circuits

There are many gate configurations that will implement an equivalent logic expression, as discussed in Chap. 3. This section will describe a few considerations for choosing logic circuits and will give typical examples of circuits which implement the various types of gates.

A number of factors influence the design of logic elements used in a particular computer. Some of these are the logic requirements of the elements, including number of inputs, logic function, and output-drive capability; the operating temperature; the rules which specify the interconnection of the elements; the speed of operation; packaging; and cost criteria. The circuit elements could employ vacuum tubes, transistors, or one of the microelectronic approaches. Tubes were used as the switching element in the first generation of computers designed in the mid-1950s, while transistors were used through the early 1960s. Most computers under development today are using either film circuitry or integrated circuits in which the transistors are packaged within or very close to the other circuit elements. As higher speeds are desired in machines, one of the approaches is to interconnect larger amounts of logic in a microelectronic format. Thus a large number of gates can be contained in a piece of silicon less than 0.1 inch square.

A computer can be designed around one basic gating element (such as a NAND gate) or with a combination of the basic gating elements. The following examples show a typical circuit for each of the logic gates. The choice of the voltage levels to represent a logic 0 and logic 1 is somewhat arbitrary and is usually determined on the basis of circuit considerations. Usually a negative or positive voltage is used, along with 0 volts, to represent the two logic levels. Integrated circuits normally require a positive voltage for V_{cc} to obtain maximum circuit performance, while discrete circuits may have either a positive or negative V_{cc}. With discrete circuits, the voltages are determined by the type of switching transistors used. If P-N-P transistors are used, a negative voltage represents the OFF condition of the transistor. With N-P-N transistors, a positive voltage is normally used. Most of the examples given are for positive-voltage logic. A 1 is defined as a positive voltage, while 0 is defined as 0 volts.

Following is an example of each of the logic gates. The resistor values are determined from the choice of voltage levels, circuit requirements, and device parameters.

Schematic	Logic	Circuit operation
Diode AND-OR logic	$F = A \cdot B + X \cdot Y$ An amplifier is usually required at F to provide gain and to restore logic levels.	If either A or B is a logic 0 (0 volts), the current flowing through R_1 goes through D_1 or D_2. If both A and B are a 1 (V_{cc}), the current flows through D_3 to F. If X and Y are both logic 1, this will also cause current to flow to F.
Logic inverter-amplifier	This circuit is used with diode AND-OR logic gates.	If current flows from F, the transistor is turned on and $\bar{F}$ is at 0 volts (logic 0). If no current flows from F (input = logic 0), the transistor is turned off and $\bar{F}$ is a logic 1 (V_{cc}).

Schematic	Logic	Circuit operation
Two-input NAND gate* 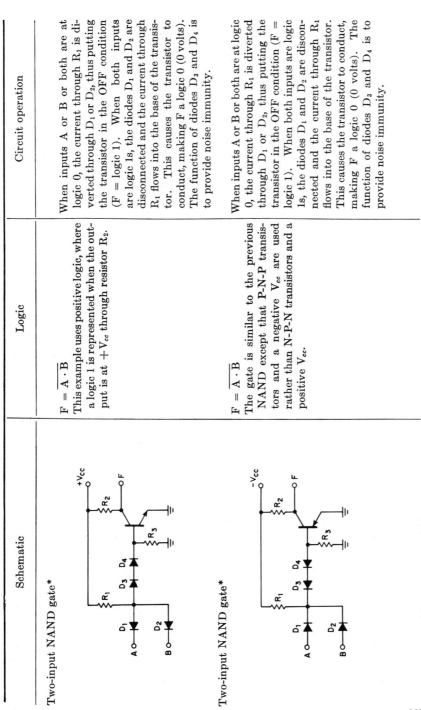	$F = \overline{A \cdot B}$ This example uses positive logic, where a logic 1 is represented when the output is at $+V_{cc}$ through resistor R_2.	When inputs A or B or both are at logic 0, the current through R_1 is diverted through D_1 or D_2, thus putting the transistor in the OFF condition (F = logic 1). When both inputs are logic 1s, the diodes D_1 and D_2 are disconnected and the current through R_1 flows into the base of the transistor. This causes the transistor to conduct, making F a logic 0 (0 volts). The function of diodes D_3 and D_4 is to provide noise immunity.
Two-input NAND gate*	$F = \overline{A \cdot B}$ The gate is similar to the previous NAND except that P-N-P transistors and a negative V_{cc} are used rather than N-P-N transistors and a positive V_{cc}.	When inputs A or B or both are at logic 0, the current through R_1 is diverted through D_1 or D_2, thus putting the transistor in the OFF condition (F = logic 1). When both inputs are logic 1s, the diodes D_1 and D_2 are disconnected and the current through R_1 flows into the base of the transistor. This causes the transistor to conduct, making F a logic 0 (0 volts). The function of diodes D_3 and D_4 is to provide noise immunity.

317

Schematic	Logic	Circuit operation
Three-input NOR gate 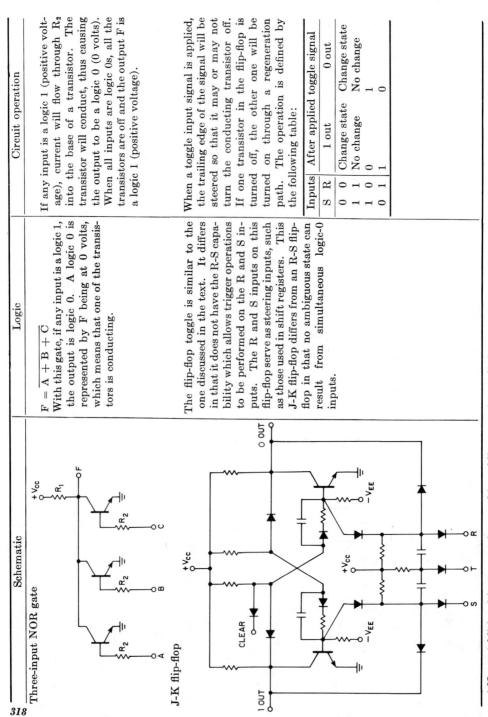	$F = \overline{A + B + C}$ With this gate, if any input is a logic 1, the output is logic 0. A logic 0 is represented by F being at 0 volts, which means that one of the transistors is conducting.	If any input is a logic 1 (positive voltage), current will flow through R_2 into the base of a transistor. The transistor will conduct, thus causing the output to be a logic 0 (0 volts). When all inputs are logic 0s, all the transistors are off and the output F is a logic 1 (positive voltage).
J-K flip-flop	The flip-flop toggle is similar to the one discussed in the text. It differs in that it does not have the R–S capability which allows trigger operations to be performed on the R and S inputs. The R and S inputs on this flip-flop serve as steering inputs, such as those used in shift registers. This J-K flip-flop differs from an R–S flip-flop in that no ambiguous state can result from simultaneous logic-0 inputs.	When a toggle input signal is applied, the trailing edge of the signal will be steered so that it may or may not turn the conducting transistor off. If one transistor in the flip-flop is turned off, the other one will be turned on through a regeneration path. The operation is defined by the following table:

Inputs		After applied toggle signal	
S	R	1 out	0 out
0	0	Change state	Change state
1	1	No change	No change
1	0	0	1
0	1	1	0

* Note: Additional inputs can be gated by adding more input diodes.

There are many ways of designing integrated circuits. The following circuits are representative examples of integrated-circuit gating elements.

Schematic	Logic

Diode-transistor-logic
(DTL)NAND gate

$F = \overline{A \cdot B \cdot C}$

The function of the additional transistor Q_1 is to provide additional logic gain so that F can drive many input loads.

Transistor-transistor-logic
(TTL) NAND gate

$F = \overline{A \cdot B \cdot C}$

The multiemitter transistor in this circuit is used to gate the inputs. If an input is a logic 0, the current through R_1 will flow through the base of Q_1 to that emitter input.

Resistor-transistor-logic
(RTL) NOR gate

$F = \overline{A + B + C}$

Any positive input causes the associated transistor to turn on (F = logic 0).

Schematic	Logic
Current-mode-logic (CML) NOR gate	$F = \overline{A + B + C}$ The current through R_2 flows through one transistor, depending on input conditions. If any input is a logic 1, the output F = logic 0.

Bibliography

American Standards Association Sectional Committee X3 for Computers and Information Processing, "American Standard Vocabulary for Information Processing."

Bartee, T. C.: "Digital Computer Fundamentals," McGraw-Hill Book Company, New York, 1960.

Benrey, R.: "Understanding Digital Computers," John F. Rider, Publisher, Inc., New York, 1964.

Buchholz, W.: "Planning a Computer System," McGraw-Hill Book Company, New York, 1962.

Caldwell, Samuel H.: "Switching Circuits and Logic Design," John Wiley & Sons, Inc., New York, 1959.

Chu, Yaohan: "Digital Computer Design Fundamentals," McGraw-Hill Book Company, New York, 1962.

Crabbe, Ramo, and Wooldridge (eds.): "Handbook of Automation Computation and Control," John Wiley & Sons, Inc., New York, 1959.

Flores, Ivan: "Computer Logic," Prentice-Hall, Inc., Englewood Cliffs, N.J., 1960.

———: "The Logic of Computer Arithmetic," Prentice-Hall, Inc., Englewood Cliffs, N.J., 1963.

Hoagland, A.: "Storing Computer Data," *Intern. Science Technol.*, January, 1965.

Humphrey, Watts S., Jr.: "Switching Circuits," McGraw-Hill Book Company, New York, 1958.

Husky, H. D., and G. A. Korn: "Computer Handbook," McGraw-Hill Book Company, New York, 1961.

Ledley, Robert Steven: "Programming and Utilizing Digital Computers," McGraw-Hill Book Company, New York, 1962.

McCracken, D. D.: "Digital Computer Programming," John Wiley & Sons, Inc., New York, 1964.

Phister, M.: "Logical Design of Digital Computers," John Wiley & Sons, Inc., New York, 1958.

Rajchman, J.: Memories in Present and Future Generation of Computers, *IEEE Spectrum*, November, 1965.

Renwick, W.: "Digital Storage Systems," John Wiley & Sons, Inc., New York, 1964.

Richards, R. K.: "Arithmetic Operations in Digital Computers," D. Van Nostrand Company, Inc., Princeton, N.J., 1957.

Whiteman, Irvin R.: New Computer Languages, *Intern. Science Technol.*, April, 1966.

Index

Index